Signal!

A History of Signalling in the Royal Navy

Captain Barrie Kent, Royal Navy

Of what avail the loaded tube,
The cannon or the shell;
If flags or W/T default
The Fleet will go to hell.

c. World War One

Hyden House

Published by
Hyden House Limited
Little Hyden Lane
Clanfield
Hampshire
PO8 0RU
England
Tel: (0705) 596500
Fax: (0705) 595834

Designed by
Tim Harland, Christopher Kent, Barrie Kent

Typesetting by
Tim Harland

Maps and diagrams by
Christopher Kent

Cover illustration and design by
Christopher Kent

Printed by
Woolnough Bookbinding Limited
Irthlingborough, Northamptonshire

British Library Cataloguing in Publication Data
Kent, Barrie
Signal!:History of Signalling in the Royal Navy
I. Title
359.8

ISBN 1 85623 006 6

Contents

Part II - Signal Anthology

Part III - The Colours of the Fleet

Acknowledgements

I am grateful to all those who have sent me contributions, or referred me to documents and sources; I have not been able to use them all but they have invariably been of interest and have provided useful background material.

I have received help from many people and organisations, and would particularly like to thank Nicola Scadding and the staff at the Royal Naval Museum; the staff of the naval section of the Portsmouth Central Library; Roderick Suddaby and Paul Kemp, Imperial War Museum; Dr Roger Morriss and Joan Dormer, National Maritime Museum; Fred Lake at the MOD Library (who had an uncanny knack of guessing what I would want to see), and John Claro of the Naval Historical Branch; Brian Head of the Submarine Museum; Dr Chris Woolgar of the Hartley Library, Southampton University (the Broadlands Archives), and Captain Gordon Wilson for his papers on Admiral Mountbatten; the Public Record Office; the Churchill Archive Centre, Churchill College, Cambridge; Captain John Wells for advice on how to get started on writing a book; Professor John Coales FRS, and Commander Derek Howse for information on the Experimental Department; Dr Andrew Gordon for access to his research on Jutland; Commander Bruce Nicolls, President of the Flag Institute, and Commander Malcolm Farrow for advice on matters 'vexillogical'; Admiral Sir Rae McKaig and Captain Patrick Harland who have spent much time reading drafts and offering valuable comments; Patrick also for help with proof-reading and indexing.

Much practical assistance has been given by the Chief Naval Signal Officers, Brian Perowne and then Tony Caswell, and members of their staff, particularly Lieutenant Commanders John Lennon and Martin Butcher who read every word of the draft and put me right on many historical facts. The Captains of the Signal School, Tony Morrow and Paul Sutermeister, and their staffs, provided much assistance - Warrant Officer 'Tiny' Little, 'Keeper of the Archives', in particular put up with many requests for help. I am especially grateful to CSS for permission to use material, including photographs and drawings, which first appeared in *The Communicator*.

My thanks to Lady Cunninghame Graham for permission to quote from *Random Naval Recollections*, and her husband's papers in the Churchill Archives Centre; Commander John Somerville for his father's papers, also in the CAC; Captain Dicky Courage and Commander John Buckeridge for access to their papers, Commander Saunders Watson for the memoirs of his father, Captain Leslie Saunders;

Commander MD Joel for those of his uncle and Mr Nander Robertson for his father's memoirs *Renegade Signalman RN*.

I am grateful to many authors, publishers and copyright holders for permission to quote from their works; details will be found in the Bibliography; also to the many individuals and organisations who have provided photographs and given me permission to use them.

The enthusiasm and practical advice given by my publisher, Tim Harland (son of Patrick), has been instrumental in getting this book off the ground. The artwork, many of the drawings and diagrams, and the dust cover have been designed by my son Christopher. Not least, I am grateful to my wife, Peggy, herself an ex-WRNS Signal Officer, for her forebearance, help and encouragement over the past three years, during which she has had to keep me fed, do the gardening, and forego many other activities. Her knowledge of signals was about as rusty as mine, but we are now both more fully qualified than we ever were in the Service!

Finally, my thanks to Admiral of the Fleet Sir Edward Ashmore who persuaded me to undertake this task and who has given me much encouragement and advice; I am grateful to him also for writing the Foreword.

B H K

Foreword

By Admiral of the Fleet Sir Edward Ashmore, GCB, DSC

Naval history and developments in strategy and tactics reflect the prevailing state of the art of communications. At times victory or disaster hung literally by a thread of bunting, seen or unseen. At others a deluge of information alerted an enemy or obscured an aim. Captain Barrie Kent's book, timed to coincide with the move of the Signal School (now part of the School of Maritime Operations) to HMS *Collingwood* is, therefore, of more than specialised interest. It illustrates and records our signals' story while conveying much of the spirit of a branch of the profession which has never doubted its vital contribution to the whole.

This account portrays above all the people who made this history and outlines the nature of the Fleet they served and the techniques they mastered ashore, afloat and in the air. The close link with research and engineering development, stemming from the early co-location of signal officer and scientist in the old Signal School at Portsmouth, is stressed. It is not the least of the lessons to be remembered today when the enormous capacity available for communications demands efficient and discriminating system management at every level.

The officers, warrant officers and ratings of the signals tradition, men and women alike, may take pride in their forebears. Alert of eye and ear, conscious of their immense responsibility on watch, whether in war or peace, in harbour or at sea, the ratings of the communications branch yielded pride of place to no one. With such support, the officers, whose duties kept them in the close councils of the command, could afford to temper professionalism with the tact, humour and resilience required of personal staff, and to keep a weather eye lifting on the wider world. Life for them all was seldom dull, often arduous and frequently great fun.

Change is ever the fate and fortune of the Navy and the values in this book remain among the surest guides to the proper conduct of the future Fleet. The Navy will not be failed in the effective exercise of maritime power by deficiencies in communications, electronic warfare and intelligence if the lessons of such a past are heeded and built upon.

I congratulate Barrie Kent on his work, its scope and message. I hope it will be widely read and commend it warmly.

Edward Ashmore

Introduction

I was originally asked to write a history of the Communications Branch, but soon found that this was inextricably bound up with the development of signalling methods, and it seemed sensible, and perhaps of more general interest, to extend the scope of the book. Much has been written about individual aspects of signalling, but this is an attempt to cover the story right through from the time when the first signal books appeared in the latter part of the seventeenth century to the highly automated communication systems in use today.

The history of the Branch is not neglected, since the activities of its members permeate and illuminate the story. The book is written primarily for past and present Communicators, hence the mention of many names and some 'in-house' references and anecdotes. But I have tried to avoid too much technical detail or jargon, and hope that it may be of some interest to the general reader. We are all, in one way or another, senders and recipients of messages, and have an interest in their timely and accurate despatch and receipt, which is really what this book is all about.

Spelling can be a problem; pendant/pennant and cypher/cipher are examples. In general I have used the spelling of the time, particularly when quoting from documents. Kilocycles and megacycles have turned into kilohertz and megahertz; for convenience I have used the modern abbreviations, kHz and MHz. Readers will no doubt spot other anomalies.

I have dealt in some detail with various actions and events in the two world wars, and since, because of the interesting eye-witness accounts and anecdotes about the signal aspects, which needed to be put into context. Jutland, it seems, will forever be a subject of discussion and controversy, and the signal aspects are of crucial importance; I thought therefore that it merited a chapter of its own.

Many of the documents and correspondence which I came across wouldn't fit easily into the historical narrative, but merited inclusion, and this led to the idea of a 'Signal Anthology'.

The history of flags and ensigns, and other aspects of the 'visible' side of signalling, is a subject of general interest, hence the final chapter, 'The Colours of the Fleet'. This, and the information in the Appendices, may be of use as references.

Barrie Kent
Petersfield, Hampshire
June, 1993

Chapter One

The Early Days of Naval Signalling

'Opportunity is of great advantage in all things, but especially in war; and among the several things which have been invented to enable men to seize it, nothing can be more conducive to that end than signals.'

Polybius, 204 BC

William the Conqueror's
'Flag of Command'

Until the middle of the 17th century signalling between ships in the English fleet was restricted to a few simple visual signals, sometimes backed up with the firing of a gun to draw attention to them. The first recorded use of a flag in the English seas is in the Bayeux Tapestry - a blue bordered white banner superimposed with a gold cross is shown, and thought to be used as a 'flag of command' to denote the ship carrying William the Conqueror. The flag of command is mentioned again at the Battle of Dover Straits in 1217 when Hubert de Burgh put an end to the threatened French invasion, a boarding party having cut down the banner of Eustace the Monk from his ship, which caused the rest of the French fleet to flee.

The 'Black Book of the Admiralty' is the earliest surviving book of instructions containing some mention of signals. It dates from the middle of the 14th century, probably about 1338, and is in essence a code of Maritime Law. It was described in 1664 by Dr Exton, who had edited a new translation, as containing:

> *'... ancient statutes of the Admiralty to be observed both upon the ports and havens, the high seas, and beyond the seas, which are engrossed upon vellum in the said book, and written in an ancient hand, in the ancient French language.'*

The 'Black Book' was lost for many years, but in 1874 Sir Travers Twiss, QC, recorded that the book had 'recently come to light, being discovered at the bottom of a chest which was supposed to contain private papers belonging to the late Registrar of the Admiralty Court, and which had been transferred from his private office to the cellars of the existing Registry.'

The section referring to signals reads, in part:

'If the King is in his own person in the fleet, then there ought to be in his ship three great lanthornes, one whereof ought to be higher than the other two, and those two others shall be hanged even.

'The admiral ought every night that the fleet is at sea to carry two great lanthornes at the two parts of the masthead of the ship wherein he is, to the end he may be known to be admiral. And if he hath an under-admiral (or rear-admiral), he may let each of them carry one lanthorne and no more at the top of his mast for seeing and knowing the fleet, and to the end that the ships of the fleet may not be separated for want of light.

'Tis to be noted that at some convenient time when the admiral pleaseth to call the captains and the masters of the fleet together, to consult with them, he shall hang up in the middle of the mast of the ship a flag of council so that it may be known and perceived in all parts of the fleet either in ports or out at sea and then immediately the captains and masters of the ships are bound without delay to come with their boats well manned on board the admiral's ship, there to hear and do what the admiral's council shall have ordered ...'

PENDANTS AND WHEFTS.

PLACE.	SIGNIFICATION.
Mizen peak.	That the ship's company are at prayers.
Ensign staff.	That a man has fallen overboard.
Over Affirmative Flag.	The man is saved.
Over Negative Flag.	The man is not saved.

WHEFTS.

Wh. Fore top-gallant-mast head.

To speak with the Admiral.

This is to be repeated by intermediate ships discovering it, until observed by the Admiral; after which it is to be continued only by the ship in which it was first hoisted.

N. B. The wheft to be made with any flag, stopped only at the head, the fly loose. Whenever it is certain that the wheft may be seen, it may be hoisted instead of Signal 2. 1. B.

Main top-gallant-mast head, or ensign staff.

For the boats of the ship which hoists it to return on board. May be shewn, according to the distance, any where but at the fore top-mast head.

PENDANT

Page from 1816 signal book

One other signal is included: if the banner normally flown from the aftercastle is shifted 'aloft', it notifies the presence of the enemy.

Signals could also be made by altering the positions of sails, and a wheft (a flag or ensign tied in the middle) was a signal of distress. But normally communication between ships was by shouting through a 'speaking trumpet' and it was the usual routine for ships to close the admiral before dark to receive his 'night intentions', or to send someone over in a boat.

The Flag of Council is the only signal mentioned in the 'Orders to be Observed at the Seas in the Queen's Majesties' Ships', dated March 1558, used by the ships which fought the Spanish Armada. In Elizabeth I's reign the instructions issued to Raleigh, Howard and Essex for their attack on Cadiz in 1596 included the instruction:

'It shall not be lawful for any second ship to follow chase unless the Admiral of the Squadron shall hang out two flags one above the other. If three ships are to give chase three flags ... the Admiral shall halt the chase by hanging out the Flag of Council ...'

The flags in the 1673 book included a red and white striped one, the signal to 'chase', which is sometimes suggested as the origin of the US flag. However a flag rather more similar to the stars and stripes was flown by ships of the East India Company; this had similar stripes and a St George's Cross, later replaced by the Union flag, in the canton where the stars now appear. The present flag of the State of Hawaii is somewhat similar.

Progress was made during the Dutch war of 1652, three flags (red, white and blue) and a pendant being used to convey orders from the new Fighting Instructions, e.g. a red flag at the fore top-masthead and two guns meant 'Engage the Enemy'. There was still no way of passing administrative messages, other than, for example, a cask at the yard-arm signifying a want of water, a hatchet when in need of wood, or a table cloth as an invitation to dinner!

The first 'signal book' proper appeared in 1673, with a coloured drawing of each flag or pendant (now up to fifteen), the meaning and place where hoisted being shown alongside. The significance of a flag signal varied according to its position on the masts or rigging, some eighteen different positions being available in the larger ships.

In the absence of printed books, officers frequently made their own manuscript 'pocket' signal books; some beautifully inscribed and illustrated ones still survive. The first printed signal book appeared between 1714 and 1717, a private venture by one Jonathan Greenwood. Each signal was represented by the drawing of a ship with the flag or flags shown in the appropriate position, and the meaning underneath; Greenwood liked to boast that he had 'disposed matters in such a manner that any instruction may be found out in half a minute'. The next printed book, again a private venture, was published about 1748 by John Millan - '2/6 plain and 4/- coloured'. In this case the flags were set out along the top of the page, with the meanings below according to their different positions, and with references to the articles in the various sailing and fighting instructions.

From 1750 onwards more Instructions were issued and more and more flags were needed to cope with them. Admiral Anson (later created Baron Anson of Soberton), issued 'Additional Instructions' to increase the number of signals available, and for the first time arrangements were made for 'sailing on a line of bearing'; these instructions also laid down that 'a fit and proper person is to keep an eye upon the Admiral and watch for signals'. By 1782, at the Battle of the Saintes, Admiral Rodney was using nearly fifty flags.

Some rationalisation was attempted by Admiral Lord Howe in 1776, reducing the number of flags, and introducing the system of having one book of signals, and a second book to explain their use where necessary. A revised version was issued in 1782, the titles of the two books then being 'Signal Book for the Ships of War', and 'Instructions for the Conduct of Ships of War, explanatory of, and relative to the Signals contained in the Signal Book' (the same system in principle as is used today). Howe's system was tried out the same year when he hoisted his flag in the *Victory* and took the 'Grand Fleet' to effect the relief of Gibraltar.

A couple of years earlier Kempenfelt had been Captain of Admiral Geary's flagship in the Channel Fleet; he and Howe had discussed their ideas, and Kempenfelt frequently exercised the signals in the fleet in order to try to devise improvements, both in the signal books and in the design of flags. In the course of one of his

Admiral of the Fleet Earl Howe, 1726-1799, from a painting by John Singleton Copley

exercises there was a certain amount of confusion; eventually Geary could stand it no longer and laying his hand gently on Kempenfelt's shoulder, he said 'Now my dear Kempy, do, for God's sake, oblige me by throwing your signals overboard, and make that which we all understand: "Bring the enemy to close action!"'. [1]

Kempenfelt read anything to do with communications that he could lay his hands on, from both sides of the Channel, as the French were ahead of the British in the field of flag signalling, and he came across the numerary system first suggested by Mahé de la Bourdonnais. In 1780, having been promoted to Rear Admiral, he devised a new code with ten flags for the numerals, and two substitutes, but this was turned down as being 'too complicated', and he had to revert to a revised version of Howe's system. But as he said in a letter of March 1781 to Sir Charles Middleton (later Lord Barham), Admiral of the Red and MP for Rochester, this plan was not entirely satisfactory: 'That which I would have adopted I could not get any of the Admirals or Officers of note to approve and countenance. I therefore followed in great measure Lord Howe's mode, he being a popular character'.

Kempenfelt unfortunately did not survive to develop his ideas, being lost in the *Royal George* in 1782, and it was left to Lord Howe, who was First Lord of the Admiralty from 1783 to 1788, to complete the reforms. By the time he took command of the Channel Fleet, he had another version ready to try out, and this book of 1790 did adopt the numerary system first suggested by Kempenfelt, a rather obvious arrangement which had taken a surprisingly long time to emerge. As well as the numerals, about a dozen other flags and pendants were introduced, such as the Affirmative and the Preparative, and also Substitutes which had been proposed by Kempenfelt; thus two, three or four flag groups could be used, without carrying several sets of flags.

At this time there was no centralised system for issuing books of instructions; these were usually drawn up by the admiral commanding a fleet or squadron, and this was one reason for individual officers producing their own 'pocket' versions of the code currently being used.

At night, guns, rockets and lanterns were used, the latter hung singly or in groups in different parts of the ship. In the 1790 signal book, for example, 'two lanterns vertical, a rocket and four guns' meant 'Bear up and sail large'.

With some modifications Howe's code lasted for several years, a revised version being issued in 1794 and a simplified and expanded one in 1799. Writing to Howe, whom he addressed as 'The first and greatest Sea-Officer the world has ever produced' to acknowledge his congratulations on the victory of the Nile, Nelson said:

> 'By attacking the enemy's van and centre, the wind blowing directly along their Line, I was enabled to throw what force I pleased on a few ships. This plan my friends conceived by the signals (for which we are principally, if not entirely indebted to your Lordship) and we always kept a superior force to the enemy'.

[1] Quoted in Sir John Barrow's *'Life of Richard Earle Howe KG'*, 1838

Rear Admiral Richard Kempenfelt, 1718-1782

On 6 October 1841 a 'spy-glass' was brought up from the wreck of the Royal George and returned to its owner, Admiral Sir Philip Durham. He had been the signal-lieutenant of the ship, and had the 'spy-glass' in his hand when the ship began to sink. He was one of those able to reach a perch in the rigging from which he was rescued.

Portrait of Sir Home Riggs Popham, 1762-1820, from an engraving by M Brown

The 1799 book contained some 340 signals, and became generally used throughout the Navy, though there was scope for Admirals commanding each fleet or Squadron to add a few of their own; they also issued a tabular 'pendant board' which allocated each ship in the fleet a two-pendant identity, used to address individual ships. By the time of Trafalgar the 1799 book already had some eighty manuscript additions, and amendments were also made for other reasons; for example in 1803 a 'private' manuscript copy of the 1799 code was obtained by the French from the captured frigate *Redbridge*, whose Captain had failed to throw it overboard. The loss was discovered when a British frigate, scouting off Toulon, was sighted by the captured *Redbridge* which made a signal, using the British code, instructing the scouting ship to 'anchor'. The Captain of the frigate reported what had happened, and in November 1803, after some discussion as to the best way to restore some security to the code, the Admiralty issued a circular letter re-arranging the numeral flags. This new version of the code was adopted in the Mediterranean in January 1804 and thus became the one in force at Trafalgar.

Before this, Sir Home Popham, Captain of the *Romney* in the Baltic, had been experimenting with a word vocabulary when he found himself having to relay messages from the Ambassador in Copenhagen to Admiral Dickson off Elsinore. 'Its utility', he wrote, 'was in that instance so obvious ... that (I) conceived it might be brought into more extensive practice ...' He had the first version, which contained about 1,000 words, printed privately; in 1803 he produced an expanded version with a further thousand or so less important words, and another thousand sentences, which was issued to the fleet. Groups from this vocabulary code were signalled by the numeral flags from the current naval signal book, but were distinguished by the use of the Telegraph flag, and this was the method used to transmit Nelson's famous signal (see plate I).

In the Introduction to the 1803 edition of his Vocabulary Code, Popham wrote:

> *'The general port signals may also be expeditiously communicated from the C-in-C's ship, by which the wear and tear of boats will be materially saved, and the necessity of their bearing up for Portsmouth harbour in bad weather obviated ... boats frequently get very much damaged, and the crews desert, or get ill by lying in their boats with their wet clothes on.'*

Popham continued to develop his vocabulary code, but ran up against the limitations of ten numeral flags if the individual hoists were not to become unduly long. A maximum of three flags was considered desirable, so he added some letters, A to O, thus allowing for some 11,000 three-flag signals, and many more if four flags were used. This new version was issued to the fleet in 1813. A further revision took place in 1816 and this time it was issued by the Admiralty as an official Vocabulary Signal Book.

The great advantage of Popham's vocabulary code was that a 'conversation' could be carried on. Henry Blackwood, Captain of the frigate *Euryalus*, in a letter to his wife written a couple of days before Trafalgar, after they had sighted the French and Spanish fleets on the move out of Cadiz, wrote:

> ' ... *though our fleet was at sixteen leagues off, I have let Lord N. know of their coming out ... At this moment we are within four miles of the Enemy, and talking to Lord Nelson by means of Sir H Popham's signals, though so distant, but repeated along by the rest of the frigates of this Squadron.*'

Another revision took place in 1827, when the Admiralty signal book was recast in three parts, the General Signal Book (manœuvring signals), Vocabulary Signal Book, and Night & Fog Signals.

It was soon realised that merchant ships could use a similar system, and in 1817 Captain Frederick Marryat produced his 'Code of Signals for the Merchant Service'. This was similar to Popham's vocabulary but with more appropriate words and sentences and also many place names. Initially it used ten numeral flags and some special flags and pendants, such as a Rendezvous or Geographic flag, Telegraph flag, and Distinguishing Pendants which were also used as substitutes. These were all carefully designed so as to be different to the naval ones. No signal was to use more than four flags, and to achieve this some groups were used more than once, in different 'tables', the table in use being signified by one of the distinguishing pendants.

Marryat's code provided distinguishing signals for individual ships, both merchant and naval, each ship being given a three or four figure number; in the case of merchant ships this was hoisted with the white, or first distinguishing pendant, superior, while the Union flag superior was used for naval ships. As the number of merchant ships increased, additional numbers had to be provided using the second distinguishing pendant, and eventually the third and fourth.

In 1855 the Board of Trade decided to regulate matters and set up a committee: 'To enquire into and report upon the subject of the Code of Signals to be used at sea.' This produced a revised code containing some 70,000 signals, adopting many of Marryat's flags but based on an alphabetical system. Initially it used only 18 letters, B to W, omitting vowels (so that objectionable words of three or four letters could not be signalled by rude sailors!). The new code

'What a beautiful day! Will you be tempted out of your ship? If you will, hoist the Assent and Victory's pendants.'

Nelson to Collingwood, 19 October 1805

Page from Signal Book showing signal No. 16

SIGNIFICATION.		Nº of signal
DISTRESS.	To assist ships in — — — — —	236
	To stay by ship in — — — — —	238
DIVINE SERVICE—See page 98		
ENEMY	In sight — — — — — —	11
	Their fleet if it has been seen— — — —	12
	To engage (page 17) and — — —	15
	To engage more closely — — —	16
	Gain the wind of — — — —	18
	To reconnoitre — — — —	19
	To lay them on board — — —	20
	Attack a particular body of, on the bearing pointed out	21
	Attack their convoy— — — —	22
	Destroy their convoy — — —	23
	To fire upon in passing — — —	24
	To attack their rear — — —	25
	To keep sight of — — — —	26
	Engage passing through their line — —	27
	To rake — — — — —	31
	To fire on their sternmost ships and tack or wear	32
	Engage their center — —	33
	Engage their van or weather division — —	34
	Engage their rear or lee division — —	35
	Engage on their starboard side — —	36
	Engage on their larboard side — —	37
	To signify if *ready to Engage* — —	40

John Pasco and the Trafalgar Signal

Rear Admiral John Pasco,
1774-1853

Pasco joined the *Victory* in April 1803. He was the senior Lieutenant, and would normally have become First Lieutenant of the flagship, but Nelson's practice was apparently to make the officer first on his list for promotion do the duty of Signal Officer.

In a letter written some years after the battle, Pasco described how the Trafalgar signal came to be made: 'His Lordship came to me on the poop, and after ordering certain signals to be made, about a quarter to noon, he said "Mr Pasco, I wish to say to the fleet 'England confides that every man will do his duty'", and he added, "You must be quick, for I have one more to make, which is for 'Close action'". I replied: "If your Lordship will permit me to substitute expects for confides, the signal will soon be completed, because the word expects is in the vocabulary, and confides must be spelt". His Lordship replied in haste, and with seeming satisfaction, "That will do, Pasco, make it directly"; when it had been answered by a few ships in the van, he ordered me to make the signal for 'Close action' and to keep it up; accordingly I hoisted No.16 at the top-gallant masthead and there it remained until shot away'.

There are some slight discrepancies in the letter, no doubt because of the time which had elapsed since the battle. It is clear from other ships' logs that the first groups of the famous signal were hoisted at 1156, the whole signal taking no more than about four minutes to transmit, and this was followed immediately by the signal 'Prepare to anchor at the close of day' (Nos 8 and 63). The general signal for 'Engage the enemy more closely' (16) was made at 1220.

As it turned out, although Pasco was the senior Lieutenant, in the promotions made after the action he only received a Commander's commission, while Mr Quilliam, the First Lieutenant, was advanced to Post rank. Pasco had been wounded by grape-shot for which he did, however, receive a grant from the Patriotic fund, and later an annual pension of £250.

Promotion was slow, but he attained Post rank in 1811, commanded various ships, and then in 1846 returned to take command of his old ship, the *Victory*, at Portsmouth. In 1847 he was promoted to Rear Admiral of the Blue; he retired the same year, and died in 1853.

*   *   *   *   *

Because of the time taken to distribute amendments to signal books, failure to correct them, and errors in making copies, there was sometimes a certain amount of confusion. Indeed there has been some doubt over the actual flags used with Nelson's signal. In 1908 W G Perrin, the Admiralty Librarian, concluded that the 'telegraph flag' hoisted in *Victory* every Trafalgar Day was incorrect, being red over white instead of white over red. Both versions can be seen in hand-coloured signal books of the time. In Popham's 1803 code it was described as 'red and white' and it seems certain that he intended it to be red uppermost. However in copies of the 1808 signal book it is depicted as white over red, and there is some evidence that this change occurred in 1805, possibly to avoid confusion with flag 4 (red and white squares, also sometimes shown with the colours reversed). Perrin concluded that white over red was most likely to be correct for the Telegraph flag, and that version has been used since 1908.

E 5

238	Each	1238	Either-wise
239	Early	1239	Eligible
240	East-erly-ward	1240	Else-where
241	East-Indies-an	1241	Embay-ed
243	Ease-y-ily	1243	Employ-ed-ing-er-ment
244	Effect-ed-ing	1244	Empty-iness
245	Embark-ation-ed-ing	1245	Enable-d-ing
246	Encamp-ed-ing-ment	1246	Encourage-d-ing-ment
247	End-ing-less	1247	Endanger-ed-ing
248	Endeavour-ed-ing	1248	Enough
249	Enemy-ies	1249	Entire-ly
250	Enforce-d-ing	1250	Error-oneous-ly
251	Engage-d-ing-ment	1251	Especial-ly
253	England-ish	1253	Esteem-imate-ion
254	Enjoin-ed-ing	1254	Evacuate-d-ing-ion
255	Entitle-d-ing	1255	Even
256	Enter-ry-ance	1256	Evolution-s
257	Erase-d-ing-ment	1257	Evidence-t-ly
258	Essential-ly	1258	Exact-ly-ness
259	Establish-ed-ing-ment	1259	Excellent-ce-cy-tly
260	Evening	1260	Exceed-ed-ing-ly, excess-ive-ly
261	Ever-y-thing-where	1261	Except-ed-ing-ion-able
263	Examine-ation-ed-ing	1263	Exclude-d-ing-sive-ion
264	Example	1264	Expend-ed-ing-ce
265	Exceed-ed-ing	1265	Explain-ed-ing-ation
266	Excuse-d-ing-able	1266	Explode-sion
267	Execute-d-ing-ion	1267	Extend-ed-ing-sive-ion
268	Exert-ed-ing-ion	1268	External-ly
269	Expect-ed-ing-ation	1269	Extinguish-tinct
270	Expedite-d-ing-ion-ous	1270	Extol-led-ing
271	Express-ed-ing-ion-ly	1271	Extreme
273	Extra-ordinary-ly	1273	Extricate-d-ing

D

E	238 to 278
	1238 to 1278
F	279 to 327
	1279 to 1327
	328 to 352
	1328 to 1352
I	354 to 386
	1354 to 1386
IJ	387 to 428
	1387 to 1428
K	429 to 436
	1429 to 1436
L	437 to 470
	1437 to 1470
M	471 to 524
	1471 to 1524
N	526 to 560
	526 to 1560
O	561 to 600
	1561 to 1600
P	
Q	1673 to 1688
R	688 to 755
	1688 to 1755
S	
T	
V	895
U	1910 to 1931
W	
X	1981 to 1991
Y	
Z	

Page 'E' from Popham's Vocabulary Code, showing three words from Nelson's signal - 'England' (253), 'Expects' (269) and 'Every' (261). The groups were signalled using the flags from the 1803 naval signal book, with the Telegraph flag superior. (See plate I)

Frederick Marryat, 1792-1848, from a watercolour by W Behnes, 1827

was published in 1857 in two parts, the first containing 'universal' signals, the second those for British use only. In due course it was adopted by most seafaring nations and, contrary to the original intention, translations were often made of the British as well as the International sections.

The 1857 code lasted for thirty years, despite the obvious limitation that it couldn't be used for spelling. In 1887 another committee was set up: 'To bring the International Signal Book up to date.' The flags were increased to cover the complete alphabet, the most important signals were allocated single or two flag hoists, and instructions for night flashing and semaphore were included. The new version came into force in 1901. The code was again revised in 1931, when ten numeral pendants and three substitutes were added. It was also divided into two volumes, one for visual signalling and the other for radio, and it was decided that radio callsigns should be the same as the signal letters of a ship.

Thus from 1857 onwards 'signalmen' in the Royal Navy had to cope with two separate sets of flags, only twelve of which were of the same design, and for a period only one had a meaning common to both the naval and merchant systems! The 'signalmen' were, until the early part of the 19th century, the Quartermasters and their Mates; in a 1st rate in 1800 there would be eight Quartermasters and six Quartermaster's Mates, thus in action several would be available for handling the flags. A man might be called 'signalman', but this merely referred to his occupation at the time; all training in signals was carried out 'on the job' at sea.

In 1816 the first official signal rating made his appearance, a Petty Officer 2nd class who was given the title 'Yeoman of Signals'; no 'specialist' junior rating appeared until the 1860s, when a number of Able Seamen were selected for transfer to an embryo Signal Branch.

*   *   *   *   *

With the development of electricity, and the telegraph, dot-dash types of code were invented, and this led to the idea of using flashing lanterns for military operations. Lieutenant Philip Colomb, who had been flag lieutenant to two admirals, and was an enthusiast in signalling and manœuvring matters, collaborated with Captain (later Colonel) Bolton of the East Suffolk's who 'had a natural flair for signalling, and specialised in night communications.' Bolton had developed a 'splendid portable lamp for limelight with compressed gases in a knapsack'. Colomb patented a 'Flashing Night Signal' system in about 1862, and in 1863 he and Bolton gave a series of lectures on signalling at the Royal United Services Institution, which attracted wide interest.

Colomb's flashing code was a simple one, covering ten numerals and twelve additional symbols, as he thought the complete alphabetical code used for telegraphy, which had been devised by Samuel Morse, would be too difficult for operators to remember under sea-

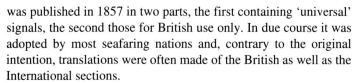

Vice Admiral Philip Colomb, 1831-1899

9

Samuel Morse

Samuel Morse, born in the United States in 1791, graduated at Yale and then went to England to study painting. He was a gifted painter, especially of portraits, and exhibited at the Royal Academy. After five years he returned to the US, and in 1826 became a founder member of the National Academy of Design, and Professor of Sculpture and Painting at New York University.

He had also studied chemistry and electricity, and when it became difficult to make a living as a painter, he turned to his hobby with the aim of achieving, in his own words: 'The instantaneous transmission of intelligence by electricity to any distance.' By 1838 he had developed his ideas to the point where he could demonstrate sending messages over an electric wire, and he petitioned Congress for funds to continue his work, but without success. He tried to patent his system in England but this was refused; the French granted a patent but then adopted his ideas without paying him! Having become friendly with Daguerre, he set about making one of the first cameras to be built in the United States.

Congress did eventually vote him $30,000 to build an experimental telegraph line between Washington and Baltimore, and in May 1844 the first message was transmitted. The alphabet which he had evolved to use over the telegraph became known as the Morse Code.

The Government was still not very interested, and further developments were left to private enterprise. Morse was later involved in experiments with submarine cables, stood unsuccessfully for both Mayor of New York and for Congress, and died in 1872. There is a statue of him in Central Park, New York.

going conditions: 'Signals by the electric telegraph are transmitted and received by operators seated in quiet rooms ... Naval and military signals are transmitted and received by operators exposed to the weather, in the midst of confusion, personal danger, and every variety of disturbing cause'. Colomb's system was adopted by the Navy in 1867, the Admiralty instructing 'all Officers of HM Ships to make themselves fully acquainted with the use of them - and that all Signalmen do the same'. The complete Morse code was eventually adopted for flashing purposes and included in the signal books in 1889.

Colomb thought up other devices, such as a venetian blind type shutter for training purposes which showed the light sky through it when the slats were horizontal or open, and looked dark when they were shut; and a large black collapsible drum, which could be extended or collapsed like long or short flashes, 'a curious ugly-looking black object ... which opens and shuts like a magnified Chinese lantern' as *The Times* reported. Needless to say signalling by 'shapes' did not take on.

Colomb, who became a Vice Admiral, was subsequently engaged in other signal reforms, including the production in 1874 of the *Manual of Fleet Evolutions*; this was needed to cope with the advent of steam ships which could manoeuvre in a more precise way than had hitherto been the case with sail. In 1878 he became a member of a

'It is the Admiral's direction that the Signal Officer is always on deck half an hour before daylight, in the morning; and he is to take care, when making signals, to have a man aloft to clear any of the flags which may get foul.'

'It is my orders that one of the two signal midshipmen visits the masthead every hour in the day, to look round with a glass for strange vessels; the officers of watches, and signal officer, are directed to see this order attended to ...'

From the Order Book of HMS *Bellerophon*, Admiral Hawker, October 1814 and July 1815

Committee set up to revise the General Signal Book and associated publications such as the 'Night and Fog Signal Book', and to tie these in with his own Manual of Fleet Evolutions. The President of the Committee was Rear Admiral C W Hope, with Captains Lord Walter Kerr and George Tryon, and Commanders Bruce and Romilly. The two latter had wide experience as flag lieutenants, Colomb was more of a theoretician, while Tryon was included to look after the practical aspects of manœuvering and steam tactics.

Several later developments of flashing lanterns, for day as well as night signalling, were proposed by a gunnery officer, Sir Percy Scott. These included a masthead light, and a lamp with shades or shutters pulled up and down by a wire. His proposals were sometimes based on Colomb's ideas, although Scott took much of the credit. Modified versions of some of these were eventually adopted by the Admiralty, and they in their turn didn't give Scott as much credit as was his due! Interestingly, the French sometimes refer to their equivalent of the 15" signal projector as 'Le Scott.'

Another visual signalling innovation was the fitting in ships of the mechanical semaphore. The use of posts with mechanical arms had been thought up by the French, and versions of the French system for use in naval signalling were proposed by both Popham and by Colonel Pasley, Royal Engineers, at about the same time. Popham's version had one arm on each of two posts, while Pasley (a nephew of Admiral Sir Thomas Pasley whose Flag Lieutenant had at one time been Philip Colomb), put two arms on one post. Popham's system was favoured by the Admiralty and was installed ashore in the early part of the nineteenth century, as described in the next chapter.

Popham had written to the Admiralty in 1816 suggesting that his system might be employed afloat:

'In considering the difficulty of displaying flags in a calm, it occurred to me that the powers of the new Telegraph

Semaphore might be so employed on the quarterdeck of a ship as, in great measure to obviate the use of flags ... and quite apart from anything else, upon the saving that must result from the diminished use of Buntin' ...'

When this idea was taken up, Popham's two masts were made to rotate and were fixed to trollies so that they could be lashed to any convenient bulkhead. Later the two arms were put at different heights on one post, together with a 'subsidiary' indicator arm to show in which direction the rotatable device was pointing, so that it could be read from either side. For a period a fourth arm was added for certain signals to do with evolutions. Finally, in about 1874, the two signalling arms were put together, and mechanical semaphores based on this version remained in use in larger ships in the fleet until finally withdrawn in 1943. It wasn't until about 1880 that someone thought of using the human arms to imitate the machine.

One final development of the mechanical system was introduced in 1895 when it was decided to fit big ships with a 'truck' semaphore at the masthead, so as to allow signalling to be conducted at longer ranges.

With sail giving way to steam, a new form of signalling, wireless, in the offing, and the Signal Branch in being, a new era was about to begin at sea. But first we need to look at the way things were developing on shore.

'The Signal Lieutenant is always to be on deck by daybreak, and he is to cause a most vigilant look out to be kept upon the admiral, night and day ...'

Captain's Orders,
HMS *Britannia*, 1827

'Captain Thompson of the Royal Navy, better known to the public as poet Thompson, who died some years ago in his command on the coast of Guinea, contrived, while a lieutenant, a set of alphabetical signals which, there is every reason to suppose, furnished the idea of the telegraphic signals now in use ... At that time a double intrigue subsisted in the fashionable world, between the late Duke of Cumberland and Lady Grosvenor on the one hand, and on the other between Captain Hervey and the notorious Miss Chudleigh, afterwards Duchess of Kingston. In the conduct of this joint intrigue, the alphabetical signals were eminently useful, as they enabled each of the gallants to further the views of the other ... for carrying on the amorous correspondence.

'That the telegraphic signals now employed in the navy originated in this way may be inferred from this circumstance, that Sir Home Popham, to whom the service is directly indebted for them, was a midshipman under Capt Thompson, when the latter acted as commodore on the coast of Guinea ...'

From the *'Naval Chronicle'*, 1812

Chapter Two

The Shutter and Semaphore Lines

*'They sent the Greenwich Time daily to Portsmouth
in about 45 seconds.'*

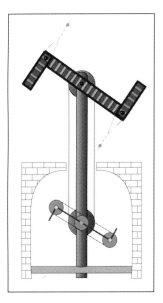

Abbé Chappe's beam
and arm system

ommunications from Their Lordships to admirals and ships
had for centuries been sent by hand - via Despatch vessels
to those at sea, and by 'stage' or horse to those in port at
home. It could be a slow process, weeks or even months to ships on
a foreign station, which meant that the man on the spot often had to
take major decisions, even perhaps on matters of peace or war. It also
meant that he had more freedom of action than is the case today - no
'big brother' giving instant advice or orders over the telephone via
the satellite link!

During the eighteenth century various people had given some
thought to the problem of long distance signalling, but it wasn't until
the Napoleonic wars that the Admiralty began to be interested. In fact
the French led the way with a telegraph system radiating from Paris
for communication with the Army, which had been devised by a
family of brothers called Chappe, led by Claude, an Abbé. The
French system comprised 'levered' semaphore arms on the ends of
a pivoted beam fixed to a mast on towers nine or ten miles apart. The
beam and the arms were manœuvred by ropes, giving enough
positions for the alphabet and numerals, but as can be imagined it was
not easy to achieve accurate angles with the three moveable parts,
and interpreting signals could be difficult.

On one occasion a British Army officer observed the French
moving troops in 'tune' with the movements of the sails of a
windmill. He mentioned this to the Reverend John Gamble, Chaplain
to the Duke of York, who was interested in mechanical inventions,
and when drawings of the Chappe brothers' system were captured,
Gamble set to work to devise something better, and his ideas reached
the Admiralty in 1795. At this time the Navy did have signal towers
around the coast, 48 of them from Sheerness to Lands End, but these
could only make a series of fixed signals by combinations of ball and

flags. Thus Gamble's ideas for an alphabetical system was seen to be a big step forward.

Gamble's proposed machine had five 'shutters' mounted vertically; they could be opened or closed separately giving 31 different signs. He was sent off with an experimental model for trials on Portsdown Hill, which proved that it could easily be read from the dockyard at Portsmouth. Arriving back at the Admiralty he was dismayed to find that, by a strange coincidence, another clergyman, the Reverend Lord George Murray (fourth son of the Duke of Atholl), had hit on the same idea and designed an even better shutter system. This had six shutters in two columns, giving 63 possibilities, which Their Lordships naturally preferred.

In September 1795 successful trials of Murray's system on Wimbledon Common led the Admiralty to arrange to erect fifteen stations between London and Deal, Chatham and Sheerness. Things moved fast, and they were complete by the end of January 1796. Each station cost £215, and contained two rooms for accommodation plus an 8 guinea clock, and two 12 guinea telescopes (supplied by Messrs Dollond). The system seems to have been a great success - messages from Dover via Deal were said to have reached London in seven minutes - and proposals for further lines began to take shape.

Murray became the Superintendent of the Kent lines for a short period, having been awarded £2,000 for his invention. Born in 1761, by 1787 he was Archdeacon of Man, and at the same time Rector of Hurston in Kent and Dean of Bocking, Essex. While holding these appointments he raised and trained a volunteer corps to help defend the South coast. One of his nine children became a Commander in the Navy. In 1801 he became Bishop of St Davids. He was only 42 when he died in 1803.

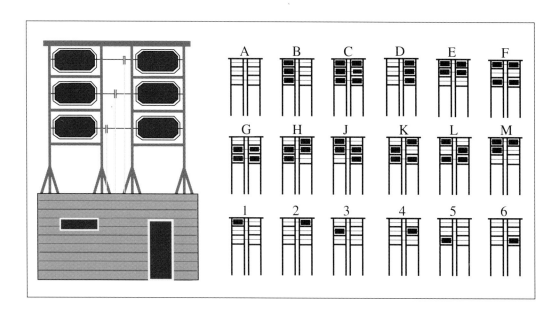

Examples of Murray's system - the 'Putney Code', 1796.

The Portsmouth line was the next to be completed, by August 1796, when the Port Admiral was instructed 'to use the telegraph on occasions of importance or when in want of immediate directions.' It consisted of ten stations (at £240.15s.0d each), one on the roof of the First Lord's house, the next on the Royal Hospital in Chelsea (less than two miles but visibility in London was often poor in those days), then Putney Heath (the 'Telegraph Inn' is nearby) where the rent was

5/- per annum payable to Lord Spencer; five more, then Portsdown Hill and finally to Southsea Common, west of Clarence Pier.

Signals reporting the movements of the Western Squadron in the Torbay and Plymouth area were reported along the coastal signal stations, and then telegraphed up the line from Portsmouth to the Admiralty. In 1805 it was decided to set up a line to Plymouth, and

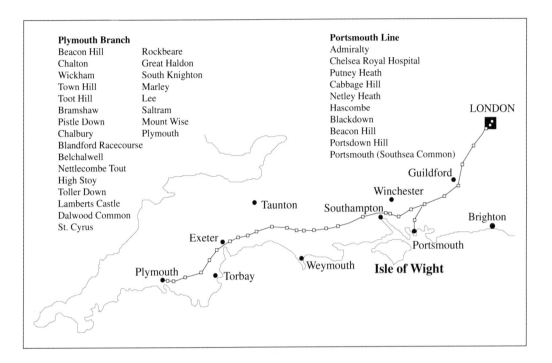

Plymouth Branch

Beacon Hill	Rockbeare
Chalton	Great Haldon
Wickham	South Knighton
Town Hill	Marley
Toot Hill	Lee
Bramshaw	Saltram
Pistle Down	Mount Wise
Chalbury	Plymouth
Blandford Racecourse	
Belchalwell	
Nettlecombe Tout	
High Stoy	
Toller Down	
Lamberts Castle	
Dalwood Common	
St. Cyrus	

Portsmouth Line

Admiralty
Chelsea Royal Hospital
Putney Heath
Cabbage Hill
Netley Heath
Hascombe
Blackdown
Beacon Hill
Portsdown Hill
Portsmouth (Southsea Common)

The London to Portsmouth and London to Plymouth Shutter Lines

this branched off from the Portsmouth line south of Haslemere. There were twenty two new stations, ending at Mount Wise, and this line was completed by July 1806. Soon after it opened it was recorded that the one o'clock time signal from Admiralty was made and acknowledged in three minutes - not bad for a round trip of four hundred miles. Finally in 1808 a line to Yarmouth was opened.

The Shutter lines were always considered a temporary war-time innovation and in 1814, when Napoleon was banished to the Island of Elba, post-war savings were the order of the day. The Port Admiral at Yarmouth was ordered to strike his flag on 21 May, and the Yarmouth line was closed, the eight stations being sold for the sum of £817. By the end of September the coastal signal stations and the other shutter lines had also been shut down.

A year later Napoleon escaped from Elba, and the coastal stations were hastily resurrected, though this time using a three-arm 'semaphore', based on another French system. The Portsmouth Shutter line was also re-opened. Hardly had this happened than Wellington defeated Napoleon at Waterloo, and the whole thing was once more in the melting pot. However the value of the lines for

The Hampshire Antiquary, Volume I, records that the Shutter station at Southsea Common 'was kept at work all day long and transmission of messages was as quick as the transit of a discharged cannon-ball', and 'They sent the Greenwich Time daily to Portsmouth in about 45 seconds.'

normal peace-time communications was now realised and the Admiralty decided to set up a 'permanent' system, but using semaphore rather than shutters.

As has been seen, improvements to the French semaphore system had been proposed by both Popham and Pasley. The latter first thought of the two-arm system in about 1804, and tried to get his ideas adopted by the Admiralty. He managed to get introduced to the First Lord in 1807 but Their Lordships told him they were 'perfectly satisfied with the (shutter) system in use - desiring neither a better nor a worse'. Pasley published his ideas for 'The First Polygrammatic Telegraph', but again to no avail.

Popham had modified his system for use on shore, with the two arms at different levels on one thirty foot post, and in 1815 the Admiralty decided to try this out on the line to Chatham, extending it to Sheerness by using two guardships, *Bulwark* and *Northumberland*, which were fitted with the sea version. Two extra seamen were allowed to be borne supernumerary in each ship to man these semaphores.

Meanwhile the Portsmouth shutter line had been closed, and for the next six years there was no telegraphic communication system between London and Portsmouth. However in 1817 the Admiralty did suggest to Admiral Thornborough at Portsmouth that a semaphore post should be erected on the Parade 'for the purpose of carrying on the communications with the ships under your orders by that mode instead of using flags, as at present, with a great expense of bunting ...', and in due course a Semaphore replaced the existing flagstaff.

In 1820 the experimental Chatham line was made 'permanent' and extended to Deal and Dover, and the Admiralty decided to restore the Portsmouth line using the new semaphore system. The old shutter sites mostly proved unsuitable, and new buildings were built, fifteen this time, the average distance apart being about five miles. After a series of delays (shortage of bricks, difficulties with land owners, and a contractor who had clearly taken on more than he could cope with), the line was finally opened in mid-1822. Each station was manned by a Lieutenant and an assistant or 'Handyman' (one or both were often pensioners - 'good with the glass'). The pay of the Lieutenant, including 3/- a day 'superintendence' money, was about £182 per annum; they were also allowed 6d per day coal allowance. The assistant probably earned about £1 a week, or something over £50 a year.

The Lieutenants in charge of stations had quite a hard time, not least through lack of support from the Admiralty. In 1821 Lieutenant Nops at Coombe Warren, Kingston Hill, asked if he could have the kitchen stone floor covered, while 'a bit of half worn canvas for the Semaphore room, likewise a stone floor, would obviate the cold'. 'No' said the Board, 'It would create a precedent.'

When Lieutenant Spiller took charge of the Semaphore line in 1822 he found that the Superintendent's house in Southwark entailed liability to pay £2.10s p.a. for pew rent at the parish church, and this

The building and operation of the Admiralty to Portsmouth shutter and semaphore systems are well described in 'The Semaphore' by ex-Yeoman of Signals Tom Holmes.

Keeping a clear line of sight, as well as a suitable background, could be a problem. In 1822 Thomas Goddard, the Surveyor, found that from Chatley Heath 'the lower arm only at Coopers Hill throws itself with the high part of the clump of trees upon Cockrow Hill ... which trees have considerably increased ... I have communicated with Lord King's tenant who is willing to lopp as much of the trees as may be necessary'. Later he wrote: 'His Lordship cannot be prevailed upon to remove what he is pleased to consider a great ornament'. In the end they had to raise the height of the Coopers Hill semaphore.

was already one year in arrears. The Board refused to contribute, despite having bought the rights to a pew at Cobham for £20 for the officer at Chatley Heath. The latter incidentally was very indignant when the churchwardens tried to make him 'sit among the upper servants of the surrounding gentry.' In 1828 when Lieutenant Jay took over at Southwark he found that his predecessor had not yet been

The Admiralty in Whitehall, showing the Semaphore on the roof

In Marryat's novel 'Peter Simple', an officer who has a row in the Admiralty hastens out into Whitehall and is relieved to find that it is too foggy for the telegraph to work; thus a message will not reach Portsmouth before he can drive there poste-haste.

buried, and he lodged temporarily at Deptford. His claim for lodging and coach hire was refused - he 'should have lived nearer.'

The system could be rapid and efficient in good visibility, but in London this was often very poor, and the Admiralty station was frequently unable to send or receive messages for reasons such as 'smoke', 'state of the atmosphere to the Eastward' or 'vapour rising from the lake in St James's Park.' At the Portsmouth end there were similar problems: 'Smoke from King's Terrace obscuring Portsdown.'

In 1822 surveying was started for sites for a Semaphore line to Plymouth, but it was not until 1826 that building commenced. The new line branched off from the Portsmouth line at Chatley Heath, eight miles north-east of Guildford, and a total of twenty eight new sites were chosen. Progress was slow, money being tight (these stations were costing about £1,000 each), and by 1831 only nine had been built, the last west of Romsey, and there work stopped. The reason was that the electric telegraph was becoming a practical possibility.

Wheatstone, like Samuel Morse, demonstrated the possibilities in 1838, by transmitting electrical signals between London and Birmingham. The Admiralty became interested, and by 1844 they had entered into a contract with Wheatstone and the London & South Western Railway Company to install and maintain an electric telegraph line between London and Gosport, using a two-wire single needle system. Wires were laid following the railway tracks to the Royal Clarence Victualling Yard, and then by submarine cable (one of the first) under the harbour to King's Stairs.

The semaphore traffic gradually declined until only the Greenwich Time Signal and a Portsmouth weather report were transmitted regularly. In 1847 the electric line was extended to the Semaphore Tower in the Dockyard, and at the end of the year the Semaphore system was finally closed down, though not without some misgivings by senior officers at Portsmouth, including John Pasco who was by then Captain of HMS *Victory*. *The Times* was not happy either, the issue of 31 December 1847 carrying some 'Naval Intelligence from Portsmouth' which said:

> *'We are all aware of the proneness to derangement of the electric mode of communication ... what, for instance, would be easier than for any evil disposed person to cut the wires in any obscure place on the line? Such mischief could not be perpetrated upon the Semaphore; there the Government had an exclusive, safe and speedy means of communicating their commands ...'*

This ignored the fact that the Semaphore could only operate by day in good visibility, and anyway evil persons could well have attacked the remote semaphore stations! The paper went on:

> *'It takes years to thoroughly comprehend the vocabulary of figures by which Government notifications are made. Many of the assistants to the Lieutenants have been upwards of a quarter of a century in acquiring and practising their duties. It will be no easy task to resuscitate the system ...'*

However, on 25 September 1850, *The Times* was completely won over, referring to

> *'the great advantage of electric over the old system ... despatches can be sent and received night and day ...'*

'As the transmission of messages by the Admiralty Wire of the Electric Telegraph is rapidly increasing, and it becomes desirable to ensure despatch and accuracy, my Lords desire that all expletive or unnecessary words be struck out, so that all messages be condensed into as few words as practicable, consistent with clearness.'

Admiralty, Whitehall,
3 January 1855

Chapter Three

The First Signal Schools

'Gongs, Drums, Flags and Banners are Signals to unify
the eyes and ears of the troops.'

Sun Tzu, *'The Principles of Conflict'*

U ntil the latter part of the 19th century Signalmen acquired the necessary skills 'on the job' at sea. But as sail gave way to steam, and manœuvring became more precise, it was realised that more formal training arrangements needed to be made. In 1882 the rate of 'Qualified Signalman' was introduced, to replace the previous non-substantive rate of the same name held by seamen employed on signal duties, and an Admiralty order ordained that these young signalmen should be drafted to the Channel Squadron as supernumeraries for training in signals.

In 1888 a 'Higher Standard Qualification' was added - this was to include instruction in electric telegraphy, electric light, and the heliograph. Up to 15% of Signal ratings could qualify for the higher standard, which entitled them to 3d a day extra pay, and this resulted in a great improvement in professional knowledge and in the status of the Signal Branch.

The rates of Chief Yeoman and Yeoman of Signals had existed for many years, and these were now joined by a new rate of Second Yeoman of Signals (Petty Officer 2nd class), and a new intermediate rate of Leading Signalman.

In October 1888 the Admiralty said that it was proposed to establish Schools of Signalling at one or two Home Ports, where these subjects were to be taught:

'My Lords ... have been in communication with Her Majesty's Postmaster General, and it has been arranged that four Chief Yeomen or Yeomen of Signals shall undergo a five months Post Office course to fit them for the duty of Signal Instructor.'

The term 'Yeoman' was originally used to refer to the Petty Officer rate, eg 'Yeoman of the Powder Room', Yeoman of the Sheets', etc. The term 'Yeoman of Signals' was introduced in the Royal Navy by Order in Council dated 25th November 1816. The Signal Branch was the only one to retain the title, rather than 'Petty Officer', the others having fallen into disuse many years ago.

A letter of 12 December 1888 announced:

> *'The Lords Commissioners of the Admiralty have decided there are to be two Schools of Signalling, one at Portsmouth on board the Duke of Wellington, the other at Devonport when the Barracks are properly organised.'* It went on to say that, at Portsmouth, the Gunnery Lieutenant of the *Duke of Wellington* was to take charge of the signalling instruction, having undergone the Post Office course.

The C-in-C instructed the Flag Captain, Captain Robert Woodward, who was in command of the *Duke of Wellington*, to report what facilities would be needed. In his report, Captain Woodward said:

> *'A suitable place can be found on board HMS Victory for the instruction room. The Victory is proposed on account of the incessant and unavoidable noise in the Duke of Wellington, occasioned by the various drills being carried out ... I beg to point out that the stay of Gunnery Lieutenants in the ship is very short, and during my command of eleven months I have already had three and am now without one. Therefore I would suggest that a suitable Warrant Officer have charge until a Lieutenant can be appointed solely to undertake this work.'*

He also suggested that the duration of the signal course should be one hundred days, with five hours instruction per day.

In January 1889 the Admiralty approved most of the suggestions contained in Captain Woodward's report and added that '...the course of instruction is to be commenced on board HMS *Victory* as soon as practicable. Mr John Newell, Torpedo Boatswain, of HMS *Vernon* will be appointed to superintend the signalling instruction'. But later that year it was decided that a limited number of Chief Yeomen of Signals were to be promoted to the rank of Boatswain; one of the successful candidates was Henry Eason, who relieved Newell in March 1890 and took charge of what he usually referred to as the Naval School of Telegraphy. Two more of the new Signal Boatswains were appointed to the *Vivid* in 1890, and *Pembroke* in 1891, and these appointments mark the establishment of Signal Schools at Devonport and Chatham, subsequent Navy Lists showing that these officers were in charge of signalling instruction.

A picture of life in the *Victory* was provided by Eason after he retired, as a result of a letter from the Signal School dated 1 February 1908, in which Charles Collins wrote:

> *'The Captain wishes you to send him a short crisp history of Signal School during your time there ... towards making an history book of the Signal School during your appointment. We hope to continue it up till today.*
>
> *'PS: Wireless telegraphy is obsolete, superseded by Poulsen's wireless telephony having accomplished 250 miles. I give W/T 2 years longer to die.'*

> *'One good Leading Signalman should be detailed for odd jobs repairing flags etc. He should be the biggest fraud on the staff for he will come in handy when returning flags etc. to the Dockyard.'*
>
> Rear Admiral Sir Christopher Cradock, *'Whispers from the Fleet'*

Henry Eason as a Signal Boatswain, in about 1900

Commander Charles Collins,
Commander in Charge of the
Signal School, 1915-1916

He was the first Signal Boatswain
to reach the rank of Commander.

This prediction was somewhat premature - W/T survived for many years, and although gradually displaced by Voice, radio teletype and data, it is still not completely dead over eighty years later.

Eason did indeed write a 'short crisp history' in reply, from which the following extracts are taken:

> *'At the latter end of the year 1889 HMS Victory was fitted up as a Naval School of Telegraphy. The instruments set up in the Admiral's after cabin were Sounders, Bells, Needles and Printers. Similar instruments had been set up at the Schools at Devonport and Chatham. On 6th March 1890 the first batch of eight Signal Boatswains were made, one of which was appointed to each of the Schools in charge of the instructions ...*

> *'Heliograph was also taught, classes being sent to the Semaphore Tower where communication was established between RMA Barracks at Eastney, RMLI Barracks at Forton, the Military on Southsea Common and Clarence Yard.'*

It was not long before *Victory* became a proper Signal School, sets of flags and signal books being supplied, and flag-hoisting drill being carried out with the fore and mizzen masts representing different ships. Signal ratings from ships paying off were sent to *Victory* instead of the Barracks, and volunteers from other branches were called for. The initial training course lasted two months, the first devoted to theory, and the second to practical signalling when other ships in harbour also took part. Much trouble was taken to make exercises realistic:

> *'Manœuvring signals were made and models worked, and everything such as turning flags etc. carried out the same as it would be in a fleet at sea. Gun signals were taught by firing friction tubes, and before each class passed out the Hero or the ship used as Excellent's tender fired a series of gun signals with saluting charges. This exercise was most instructive as many a signal rating had never heard a gun signal before. Fog-horns were also practised, men being posted round the deck each with a police whistle, and treated as a single ship, flagships and leaders being denoted, signals made as in a fog, being answered or repeated according to the instructions.*

> *'Flashing signals were carried out on the orlop deck of the Victory, and two large Semaphores were in position for instructional purposes, one being set up on the night-heads and the other on the poop, small hand flags being used for quick semaphoring. A few officers by special permission of the Admiralty were allowed to go through a course of telegraphy, a few other officers came and received instruction in Signal Books, Manœuvres, etc. The demand for these*

HMS *Victory* in about 1875, showing one of the small mechanical semaphores introduced a year or so earlier

The machine was literally worked manually, the operator holding the arms in the appropriate position. An even smaller version was produced for use in boats. The idea of using the human arms does not seem to have occurred to anyone until about 1885, when hand-held flags began to be used. Bigger mechanical semaphores were fitted with rather cumbersome sprocketts and chains made to a special Admiralty pattern. In 1941 the firm of Thomas Haywood realised that ordinary bicycle chains would be cheaper and just as effective, and several of the new sets were actually delivered to the Signal School at Chatham, and to HMS *Cabbala* for training V/S Wrens, in 1942, just a year before mechanical semaphores were finally withdrawn from ships to save top-weight.

> instructions increased so rapidly that it was found necessary
> to open a class for officers in the Naval College in the
> Dockyard, where an instructor was sent to conduct.'

In a letter dated 5 November 1895 the C-in-C recommended that the Signal School should be placed in charge of a Commander or senior Lieutenant specially selected for his knowledge of signal duties 'as in consequence of the largely increased numbers of signalmen, the School of Signalling on board HMS *Victory* has now grown so important'. The C-in-C also proposed that this officer should periodically inspect the Signal Schools at the other ports, so that there would be uniformity of training.

Commander Lionel Tufnell, first Superintendent of Signalling Schools. Tufnell subsequently rose to the rank of Admiral and, having retired, reappeared during the first world war serving as a Lieutenant Colonel with the British Expeditionary Force. He was the inventor of the Tufnell Box. (See photo page 97)

With a speed that suggested that this proposal had already been agreed informally, Commander Lionel Tufnell was appointed on 19 November to HMS *Victory* 'in charge of Signal Schools'. The letter of appointment went on to say that he was authorised to inspect and report, through the respective Commanders-in-Chief, upon the Signal Schools at Sheerness and Devonport.

Commander Tufnell thus became the first Superintendent of Signal Schools. He was relieved in 1898 by Commander Hugh Evan-Thomas, who was followed in 1900 by Allan Everett, then a Lieutenant but shortly to be promoted Commander; both subsequently became Admirals.

Everett, who commanded the Signal School again from 1906-08, was a great signal enthusiast, often carrying out experiments with new equipment, making proposals for amending signal books, and indeed writing many of the books himself. He made many formal submissions on the subject, and carried on an extensive correspondence with other enthusiasts. Equal Speed manoeuvres, new signal lamps, the use of W/T by scouting cruisers and competition for the top of the mast were all subjects on which he engaged in discussion. Some of this correspondence is reproduced in chapter 19.

Meanwhile, it had been decided that a permanent home ashore was required for the Signal School at Portsmouth. While waiting for this, training was transferred temporarily in 1904 to HMS *Hercules*, lying alongside in the dockyard. A shore establishment was finally achieved in 1906 when the whole School moved to K Block at the Royal Naval Barracks. As the school expanded, L Block was taken over and then parts of M and V, and finally a collection of temporary huts had to be erected alongside. This remained the home of the Signal School, and later also the Experimental Department, for the next thirty five years. The 1937 Naval Estimates included provision for a new Signal School in Portsmouth, but the war intervened and this was never built.

Signal!

Chapter Four

Wireless in the Fleet

*'When wireless telegraphy went to sea senior officers
afloat lost much of their freedom of action
- and none of them liked it.'*

Lord Hill-Norton, *'Sea Power'*

The British mathematician, James Clark Maxwell, predicted in about 1870 that electro-magnetic waves could be propagated in space, and that they would travel at the speed of light. But it was another decade before the German scientist Heinrich Hertz actually demonstrated this in his laboratory, and several more years elapsed before Sir William Crookes forecast their use for communication purposes.

The possibility of using these newly discovered Hertzian waves occurred to Lieutenant Henry Jackson, who had been in charge of 'Whitehead' torpedo instruction in HMS *Vernon* since 1885, and was looking for a method by which friendly torpedo boats could identify themselves at night. However at that time there was no known means of readily detecting these waves, and for the moment he had to put the idea on one side.

Promoted Commander in 1890, in January 1895 Jackson was appointed to command the torpedo training ship *Defiance* at Devonport. Later that year he read of the work on coherer detectors by Sir Jagadis Bose, which indicated that the problem might now be capable of solution. Jackson organised a number of experiments, which culminated early in 1896 when he succeeded in sending morse signals from one end of the ship to the other. The apparatus used was of a primitive nature - after detection by a coherer, which he made himself, the received signal operated a relay which in turn actuated an electric bell. The ringing of the bell without the agency of any external wiring heralded a new epoch - the radio age.

The importance of these results seems to have been lost on the Admiralty since no attempt was made to patent the system. The consequences can hardly be exaggerated, for in the following year an historic application was lodged at the Patent Office in the name of Guglielmo Marconi.

The early equipment with which Jackson experimented is described in HMS *Collingwood's* archives:

'Captain Jackson's Coil, under which lay his Condenser, was fed from a DC source, stepping this voltage up and charging the Condenser. The Condenser was then discharged through the oscillating spark balls when the key was closed and the transmission passed through the aerial and could be detected on his own iron filing coherer.

'The Coherer was a receiving device, using iron filings in a container which, in an RF field, magnetised, linking the filings and providing a conducting path. Due to hysteresis, the filings remained magnetised when RF ceased and so the conducting path had to be broken by continuously tapping the coherer with a tapping stick.

'Marconi's induction coil differed from Jackson's in that it had no oscillating balls, but instead used adjustable spark gap rods. This method, due to its advantage of a variable intensity spark (governing transmission distance) was generally accepted.'

Admiral Sir Henry Jackson, First Sea Lord 1915-17

Promoted Captain in 1896, Jackson continued his experiments and in August, by using a larger spark and a more efficient coherer, he received signals over several hundred yards. By this time Marconi had offered to demonstrate his system to the Italian government but they were not interested and, partly for family reasons (his mother was Irish) but also because he saw the greatest need likely to be at sea and the British had the largest Navy and merchant fleet, he moved to England. He was introduced to Jackson at a conference; each had been unaware of the other's work and they both had a great belief in the future of their inventions. Though they were in a sense rivals, they became friends, shared most secrets and neither abused the trust placed in the other.

Soon Jackson had obtained results over some 5,000 yards, between the *Defiance* and the gunboat *Scourge* underway in the Hamoaze, and later three miles between *Defiance* and Admiralty House, Plymouth. In 1897 Marconi achieved four and a half miles over land, and set up a station at Alum Bay in the Isle of Wight to work with local paddle steamers in which he installed trial sets. Before long he obtained ranges of over eighteen miles.

The Admiralty was now persuaded that further work would be of value and allocated funds for this purpose. Jackson unfortunately was unable to take much advantage of this, since in 1897 he was appointed Naval Attache in Paris. He gave what advice he could to his successor in *Defiance*, Captain Hamilton, and Lieutenant (T) William Nicholson, who continued the experiments but without very much success. Promoted Commander in 1898, Nicholson became, in effect, the first Experimental Commander of the W/T Department.

Marconi however had a band of trained assistants and continued

On 3rd August 1898 wireless communication was established between the Royal Yacht and Osborne House, Isle of Wight, so that Queen Victoria might communicate with the Prince of Wales who was suffering from the results of an accident to his knee. Constant and uninterrupted communication was maintained during the sixteen days the system was in use, about 150 messages being exchanged.

Quoted in *'Wireless over 30 years'*, by R N Vyvyan of the Marconi Co.

his work with increasing enthusiasm and ambition. Jackson realised that he would no longer be able to compete; he wrote to Marconi:

> *'I was naturally very disappointed at having to leave off my experiments when they were in a very interesting stage and at a time when probably my personal supervision was most required as, at the time, everyone seemed against the system except you and I.'*

Typically he was able to refer to this, which must have been a great disappointment, as 'one of the little things one has to put up with in our Service'. [1]

Jackson's one concern now was that the Navy should enjoy the advantages of wireless as soon as possible. Accordingly he devoted his energies to trying to persuade the Admiralty that Marconi's equipment was worth a trial. The Admiralty continued to be lukewarm, one of the counter-arguments advanced being based on a report by the Signal Committee against the use of wireless 'for fear that it would blow up a ship's magazine'. Perhaps this was not an unreasonable worry considering that so little was known of the new invention, but it further delayed any advance in developing it as a non-visual means of comunication for the Navy.

Jackson's persistence paid off in 1899 when the Admiralty agreed to let Marconi fit his equipment in four ships for that year's fleet manœuvres. Jackson commanded HMS *Juno* for the manœuvres and made sure she was one of the ships selected for the trials. These were astonishingly successful, ranges of 60 - 70 miles being obtained quite regularly; Admiral Domvile, commanding the victorious fleet, attributed his success largely to the use of wireless which, he said, with obvious wonderment, 'was equally efficient in all weathers'.

The Admiralty's doubts were now removed and a contract was placed with the Marconi Company for thirty two sets, though they were somewhat reluctant to pay the royalty of £100 per installation asked for by the company. Six of these sets were set up at shore stations - Dover, Culver Cliff, Portland, Rame Head, Scilly and Queenstown; with a range of some 50 miles by day and more by night, they gave overlapping coverage along the Channel. Indeed so enthusiastically did the Admiralty now take up wireless telegraphy that Jackson complained in a letter to Marconi that 'it was all being done so hurriedly that we suffer from a want of skilled operators'.

Whether or not Jackson would ever have seriously challenged Marconi in this field it is not possible to say. The Admiralty did seek expert advice to determine whether an action to dispute the validity of the Marconi patents would be likely to succeed. Sir Oliver Lodge was asked for his opinion and pointed out that on 1st June 1894, eighteen months before the Defiance demonstration, he himself had performed a very similar experiment, and implicitly accused Jackson and Marconi of copying his work. Jackson retorted:

> *'At the time I first commenced my experiments in 1895 I had not heard of Lodge's experiments and I had not read any of*

[1] Quoted in *'Jackson of the Defiance'* by Alan Rawles, Journal of the Institute of Electrical Engineers, December 1955

'My Lords Commissioners ... have been pleased to appoint Captain H B Jackson RN temporarily to HMS Vernon for services in connection with the Marconi system of signals. 'This appointment has been made with a view to Captain Jackson imparting to the officers of HMS Vernon the results of the experience gained by him during several years of experiments with this system of telegraphy, and also, for the purposes of working out the many small details required for ship fitting ... and establishing a course of instruction for the operators ...

Admiralty Letter of 26 October 1899 to C-in-C Portsmouth

Jackson was elected a Fellow of the Royal Society in 1901

his works nor any of those mentioned by him and though I
have since studied some of them and have learnt therefrom
much of the phenomena connected with wireless telegraphy,
I certainly have not learnt anything of any practical use
from any of them.'

Jackson also defended his erstwhile rival Marconi from the charge of plagiarism; describing Lodge's report as 'extremely egotistical and biased', he pointed out that Marconi had begun his work in an Italian village where 'Dr Lodge's work and name were less well known than he thinks possible'. Lodge admitted that he 'did not pursue the matter into telegraphic applications as he was unaware that there would be any demand for this kind of telegraphy'. Jackson had seen just such a demand, and as Marconi's first successful transmission did not take place until December 1895, and Jackson's early in 1896, they seem to have been neck and neck. If it had not been for the restrictions imposed by a naval career Jackson might well have challenged Marconi as the inventor of radio.

At this time wireless telegraphy was regarded as a matter for electrical rather than signal experts, so responsibility for its operation and maintenance was given to the Torpedo branch. Thus the development of wireless for fleet purposes was entrusted to the Torpedo School at Plymouth, HMS *Defiance*, moving to HMS *Vernon* at Portsmouth in 1901. In the same year Marconi achieved transatlantic communication, faint signals from a new station at Poldhu in Cornwall being picked up in Newfoundland.

The next year Marconi sailed in the liner *Philadelphia* to see how far messages transmitted by Poldhu could be detected in a ship. A receiving aerial was fixed to the mast, 170 feet high, and readable messages were received up to 700 miles by day, and 1550 miles at night; signals could be detected, though not read, up to 2,100 miles.

The Admiralty ordered a further 50 sets to equip all battleships and cruisers on the Home, Mediterranean and China stations. Only one ship could transmit at a time, and interference between ships was severe. It also began to be appreciated that transmissions could be intercepted by an enemy, or even jammed. Thus in the 1902 fleet manœuvres ships were told to use wireless only for urgent transmissions. One report on the exercises read: 'In most ships the Marconi room is between decks. An operator, often a young signalman, is shut up in this room alone. What he does there no one but himself knows; he is told to send a certain message and, regardless of other messages passing, he at once commences, thus stopping all signalling.' Another report commented: 'Apparently every ship was at the same moment calling up some other ship, and the only result was miles of tape run off the instrument which no one could make any sense of.' No doubt many ships disregarded the instructions about restricting the use of wireless and with only the 'inker and tape' type of receiver, the difficulties were considerable. One exasperated Admiral said that what was really wanted was more despatch vessels!

Jackson became First Sea Lord in 1915, after the resignation of Prince Louis of Battenberg. After the war he became the first President, and Signor Marconi Vice President, of the British Wireless Dinner Club, which was formed to bring together those officers who had played an active part in the operational use of wireless in the war. The first annual dinner was held at the Trocadero Restaurant in 1922.

The Admiralty continued with their own wireless experiments in the torpedo school, although they were probably infringing Marconi's patents. In July 1903 they signed an agreement with the Marconi Company by which, on payment of an annual fee, they were granted the use of all his patent rights for eleven years, and the use of the Poldhu transmitter for twenty minutes each day. In the same year HMS *Duncan* sailed from Portsmouth to Gibraltar and was able to receive Poldhu's transmission the whole way. By 1906 some additional time on Poldhu had been arranged, but the Admiralty also began to plan for its own high powered stations. To cover the North Sea, Channel and South Western approaches, transmitters giving a range of about 1,000 miles were to be installed at Cleethorpes, Horsea Island and Gibraltar.

The Poldhu transmitter was a 25 kw alternator driven spark set coupled to a very large umbrella shaped aerial working on about 366 metres.

Naval and commercial requirements now began to diverge. The Royal Navy decided to use aural reception and to train signalmen to read morse by ear, instead of using the 'inker and tape' method. Technical developments led to a number of improvements, such as a magnetic detector ('Maggie') to replace the coherer in the receiver, better selectivity, and a wavemeter to measure the wavelength accurately. A 'roof' aerial, slung between the masts of a ship, allowed lower frequencies to be used. 'Standard Wireless Installation 1905' was designed, to be fitted in all ships larger than destroyers, and powered from the ship's mains instead of batteries.

With other navies and merchant ships beginning to fit wireless sets, the problem of interference was becoming serious. The early sets operated on only one frequency but the ability to change frequency was being developed and three naval channels were established, known as 'Tunes' A, B and C. Confidence increased, and it was said that the probability of receiving a message when within 1,000 miles of Poldhu was distinctly good. Senior officers had become convinced that wireless communication offered great possibilities.

In the 1906 manœuvres Poldhu transmitted to both sides four times a day, all ships ceasing transmission five minutes beforehand. One report of the first phase of the exercise said: 'The working of W/T was most inefficient, not because it didn't work, but because of the enormous number of useless and obsolete messages transmitted' - a problem that the Signal Branch has faced throughout its history!

As a result of these exercises it was decided to give up 'Tunes' A and B which were also used by merchant ships, more flexibility in tuning transmitters and receivers now being possible. This was in line with the decisions of an International Radio Telegraphic Conference held in Berlin in 1906 at which frequencies were allocated for specific purposes, and procedures for using wireless were agreed. Two frequencies, 1,000 and 500 kHz, were allocated for commercial purposes, others for naval use. The Royal Navy established six 'Tunes', lettered P to U; P and Q were the commercial waves, the others being R (380 kHz), S (300), T (235) and U (198). Two further Tunes were allocated as more powerful sets, known as 'Service

Installation Mark II', became available for some larger ships. These could transmit on lower frequencies, so Tunes V (174 kHz) and W (152 kHz) were introduced.

It was now decided that destroyers should be fitted with wireless; the stated requirement was for a range of 50 miles, so the set designed by *Vernon* was of relatively low power. Also, because their 'roof' aerials were inevitably smaller, the destroyer set was designed to transmit on a higher frequency, 1,415 kHz, though all the other fleet frequencies could be received. Some 40 of the latest destroyers were fitted during 1907. The wireless office was a small box-like compartment situated between the bridge and the fore-funnel, a position in which it remained until just before the second world war.

In 1907 *Instructions for the Conduct of W/T Signalling* were issued by the Admiralty. A fleet in home waters was to keep in touch with the shore by listening to broadcast routines from Poldhu. 'Tunes' were allocated for sending messages to commercial or naval shore stations, and another was reserved for the flagship to keep in touch with scouting cruisers or other detached ships. Manœuvring was of course still conducted by V/S. As ships generally only had one wireless installation, a system of guardships was introduced. A destroyer's complement allowed for only one operator, so they were limited in their ability to keep watch, which was usually in specific circumstances, or when ordered.

The possibility of direct control of the fleet from the Admiralty had by now become apparent, and this led to the installation of high power (100 kilowatt) spark transmitters at Cleethorpes, Horsea Island and Gibraltar in 1909, and a fourth (150 kw) at Rinella, Malta in 1913, as well as low power 'local' stations at Gibraltar, Malta and Hong Kong. 'Fixed Services' were set up from Horsea to Gibraltar and Malta, and Horsea was also used for experimental purposes. The transmitters at Cleethorpes, Gibraltar and Malta were used for the main broadcasts to ships, and replaced Poldhu, at the same time extending the area over which transmissions from shore could be received. Five new medium power stations were set up at Aberdeen, Ipswich, Pembroke Dock, Malta and Gibraltar to be used for ship-shore purposes by ships within about 500 miles.

A wireless station was also set up at the Admiralty for direct communication with Cleethorpes and the three UK ship-shore stations. Thus was established the basis of the broadcast and ship-shore system used by the Royal Navy, and in due course by NATO navies, for the next 60-70 years.

The Wireless Telegraphy Branch

The new wireless equipment was manned initially by Signalmen who were given special training. At a conference of representatives of the Channel, Mediterranean and Atlantic Fleets in early 1906, it was concluded that a separate branch was a necessity, and that because of the urgent need to increase numbers, any system of

RN W/T Stations in Europe in 1909

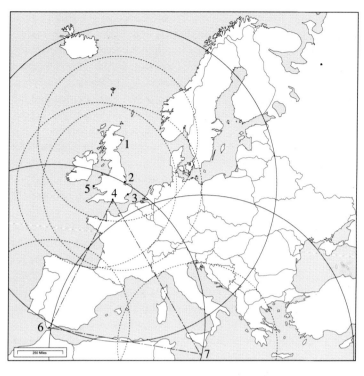

1. Aberdeen
2. Cleethorpes
3. Ipswich
4. Horsea Island
5. Pembroke Dock
6. North Front, Gibraltar
7. Rinella, Malta

———— Fixed Services between High-Power Stations

◯ Limits of High-Power Broadcasts

◌ Limits of Medium-Power Ship to Shore

Admiralty files on the introduction of the Telegraphist Branch can be found under PRO references ADM1-7920, 8128 and 8368/35.

training new entries would be too lengthy and volunteers from any branch of the service should be eligible. 'The requirements for a candidate will be a good education in reading and writing, a good character and intelligence.' Their report also recommended that the wireless operators should be under the control of the Torpedo Department, and that 'An expert officer in wireless telegraphy should be attached to each fleet ...'

Their Lordships agreed, and announced that '...pending settlement, it is very desirable to instruct and employ on wireless duties specially selected ratings other than Signal ratings ...' A Committee was set up which recommended that: 'A separate Wireless Telegraphy Branch should be established on board ship with its own operators who should be borne and employed exclusively for Wireless duties.' The minimum number of operators for a ship fitted with wireless was said to be four, and this resulted in a proposal that a total of 192 Higher Signal ratings should turn over to the new Branch. The Signal School pointed out that this '...would strike a heavy blow at the efficiency of V/S', but undertook to note those with a particular aptitude and to transfer as many as possible.

The new Branch was formally introduced in 1907. A gradual build up took place but the numbers required had been under-estimated, because more and more equipment was being fitted in the fleet, and additional 'tunes' were also being introduced. Thus there was a continuing shortage of W/T ratings, and to alleviate this some cross-training was continued. In July 1908 it was decided that the training of Signalmen should be extended so that they could 'render assistance in the Wireless room.' By this time it had also been concluded that in ships at sea: 'W/T operators should be in four watches, with two men in each watch, as two hours is considered to be as long as a man can remain in the silent cabinet without loss of efficiency.'

By the end of 1909 the numbers in the new Branch had risen to 16 Chiefs, 144 Petty Officers, 405 Telegraphists, and 192 Boy Tels, totalling 757. But this was by no means enough and in July 1910 an Admiralty Weekly Order reiterated the need to train young signalmen to take a share of the work in the wireless room; furthermore, 'so far as practicable ordinary deck hands are to be utilised in subsidiary W/T duties.' Despite the pressure on telegraphists, it was thought that an interchange of duties would help to assimilate the new branch, and ships were instructed 'to arrange for wireless ratings off watch to be employed for two or three hours a day on the bridge'! However the AWO added: 'To afford further relief, all signalling is to be reduced to the minimum.'

PO Tel Benson was one of the first to join the new Telegraphist Branch. He recalls a special inspection on board the training ship Impregnable to decide on the Badge. Two groups of three boys each were dressed for the occasion, one group with the signalman's crossed flags and the letters WT on either side, the others with the winged globe and streak of lightning. Voting seemed to be about 50-50 until a junior lieutenant pointed out that the crossed flags looked rather like flag E so that the badge read: WET! Everyone joined in the laughter, and the winged globe won the day.'

Operational Responsibilities

With the new branch still settling down it was not surprising that there was some confusion as to the respective responsibilities of the signalmen and the telegraphists. This was clarified in an Admiralty letter of 17 August 1910, which also set out the operational responsibilities of the Signal Branch as a whole in a way which has been of great benefit to the Royal Navy ever since.

> 'The control of all Signalling, whether visual or wireless, is to be vested in the Signal Lieutenant, Signal Boatswain or Senior Signal rating, who is to be held responsible for every signal during the whole of its route (except as regards the actual means used for its transmission by W/T).'

The letter went on to spell out these responsibilities in more detail:

> '...the receipt from and report to the Admiral or Captain of all signals, their transmission by the proper route, and knowing whether a signal has or has not been despatched ... The Signal Officer, or Senior Signal Rating is to have complete access to the wireless office, and is to be entitled at any time to give orders to the Telegraphists respecting the sequence in which signals are to be made.'

This was an important declaration, for it established the doctrine that the 'Signal Officer' was responsible for a signal from the moment it was originated to its safe and timely delivery, whatever technical means might be used over some part of its route. In this respect, the navy has always operated differently from the other services, where messages tend to be handed over to the 'engineering' branches for their routeing and transmission; in the navy an 'operational staff officer' now took overall responsibility for the fate of a message from Originator to Addressee. Furthermore, by virtue of his operational responsibilities, and direct access to the 'Command', he was able to make decisions on priorities, methods of transmission, the routeing and indeed the wording of messages, and to control the flow of traffic to the best advantage.

The practice in the navy for an admiral's flag lieutenant [2] to be a signal officer, usually combining this duty with that of Squadron Signal Communication Officer, meant that he was very well placed to take on this responsibility, which could be exercised with the full 'authority' of his master.

An incidental but important advantage arising from this system was that the signal officer was able to ensure that the precedence allocated to a message was related to its content, and not to the rank of the originator, as so often happened in the other services, particularly the army, which of course completely defeated the object of the precedence system.

The Admiralty letter referred to above also clarified the administrative arrangements for the new Branch:

> *'The Telegraphist ratings are to fall in with the Signal staff for Divisons, and generally are to be considered part of the latter as regards their disciplinary organisation. Except as above, the control of the Telegraphists, together with their exercises and training, are to remain as at present, with the W/T officer, Torpedo Lieutenant, or Senior Telegraphist as the case may be.'*

The need for the signal staff to have a general knowledge of W/T matters was now realised, and courses were adjusted to include instruction on wavelengths, message routeing and W/T procedures, ranges to be expected from the various wireless sets, and the general capabilities and limitations of W/T. The Signal Officer's long course was extended to include six weeks on the theory of electricity and five weeks practical wireless telegraphy, to be carried out at *Vernon*, with the normal fourteen weeks on V/S etc. at the Signal School. An allowance of 2/6d per day was authorised for a Lieutenant (S) when appointed for Signal duties 'whenever he does not mess with a Flag Officer.'

A couple of years later a conference was held to investigate whether the Signal and Telegraphist Branches should be amalgamated. The report, dated 31 January 1913, concluded that Signalmen and Telegraphists tended 'to be in opposite camps, the difficulty being largely a matter of sentiment.' It was decided that junior rates, up to but not including leading rate, should be 'interchangeable', the amalgamation being brought about gradually and not beginning until

[2] For the historical development of the Flag Lieutenant, see Chapter 24

the next year (1914). Events overtook this plan, and no change was made until after the war, by which time the Signal School had taken over responsibility for W/T from *Vernon*. The Telegraphists were then fully integrated into the Signal Branch, though still as a separate specialisation.

The Wireless Section at HMS *Vernon*

Meanwhile the wireless section at *Vernon* had continued its experimental work, as well as being responsible for training the officers and ratings who had to operate and maintain the W/T equipment in the fleet. In 1904 the first scientist, Henry Madge, joined the staff, being described as a 'civilian wireless expert.' By 1911 the section included three civilian scientists, C L Glen-Bott having joined in 1908 and W S Peake in 1911, plus several draftsmen, three naval officers and a Captain, Royal Marines, the latter being responsible for training seagoing telegraphists.

The responsibilities of the section, which was essentially naval with civilian experimental staff, included research and experiment, development for manufacture, and instruction. Virtually all the actual experimental work was carried out by Lieutenants (T), amongst them C E Kennedy-Purvis and J F Somerville. The section was housed in huts on the deck of HMS *Warrior*, then attached to *Vernon* and known as *Vernon III*; the old line of battleships *Donegal* and *Marlborough* were *Vernons I* and *II* respectively.

The three 'hulks' forming HMS *Vernon*, moored in Portchester Creek. Left to right: *Donegal*: 101 guns, 3,245 tons, launched 1858 *(Vernon I)*. *Warrior*: the first iron-clad battleship, 32 guns, 6,039 tons, launched 1859 *(Vernon III)*. *Marlborough*: 121 guns, 4,000 tons, launched 1855 *(Vernon II)*. *Donegal* was the first to be attached to *Vernon* in 1885. *Marlborough* became the main living ship in 1903, and *Warrior* joined in 1904 as the Wireless Telegraphy instruction ship and floating workshop. The move to a shore establishment, still named HMS *Vernon*, took place in 1923.

As wireless became more important to the fleet, the question of expanding the W/T section at *Vernon* was considered by yet another committee, this time chaired by Sir Henry Jackson, now a Vice Admiral and Chief of the War Staff. The Committee reported in August 1913, recommending another 'expert' to act as Supervisor of Research, plus an Electrical Engineer; B S Gossling, and G D Dewar were eventually persuaded to take up these posts, after a protracted correspondence with the Treasury on the proposed remuneration for these civilians, which was said to be far lower than was obtainable elsewhere.

The Committee also recommended setting up a small research laboratory, as 'Many of the trials of new apparatus and of new inventions are becoming more of the nature of laboratory tests than simply practical trials of Service gear. An invention in its first stage may be quite unsuited for immediate use as it stands and special arrangements are required to see whether it is of any value or not. It becomes part of the work of the lab to develop and modify the invention until it is in the form directly applicable to Service requirements.' Associated with this was the need for 'a small wireless station some 200 to 400 miles from Portsmouth for W/T experiments,' perhaps a ship at Queenstown, or in Scotland; the latter option was eventually adopted.

Shortly before the war the Postmaster General, Herbert Samuel, was writing to the First Lord, Winston Churchill, on the question of how best to organise scientific research

> 'on behalf of the State into the problems of W/T, in order that the Government may in future be as independent as possible of commercial companies in developing 'long range' and also 'ship-and-shore' wireless services. The researches made by the Admiralty must no doubt remain independent on account of their secrecy, but there may be matters in which a new Organisation of State Research might be useful to your department ...'

Churchill noted that a report on this subject was already being prepared within the Admiralty by Rear Admiral Charlton, DCNS, but like so much else, all this was overtaken by events.

By the outbreak of war in 1914 it was clear that the W/T section at *Vernon* needed to be greatly expanded yet again, and many young scientists and engineers were recruited, some commissioned as RNVR officers, both to assist in the development of equipment and to help maintain it. W/T had become an accepted means of communication in the fleet, although regarded more as a supplement to the well tried and tested visual signalling methods than as a primary system. There were still severe limitations in range and reliability, mutual interference was a problem, and the number of sets fitted was no more than a couple of transmitters per ship. Battleships and battlecruisers had a high power set of 14 kw with a range of about 500 miles, and a 1 kw auxiliary set. Cruisers had a 1.5 kw standard ship transmitter, range about 100 miles, and an auxiliary set, while small ships had only a single 1 kw 'destroyer' set with a designated range of 50 miles.

Most submarines had also been fitted with a 1 kw transmitter by the outbreak of war but this only gave them a range of about 30 miles, which of course meant that it was no use from most of their patrol areas. In any case, when submerged, submarines could neither transmit nor receive. If they were deployed for some specific purpose, such as a possible movement by the High Seas Fleet, Commodore Keyes at Harwich sometimes accompanied them in a destroyer and if he received important intelligence and wanted to redispose them, he would steam about with a black ball hoisted which meant 'Surface', and if the submarine saw this and did so, he would then pass the message by V/S. Carrier pigeons were also used from submarines but they were unreliable and the distance from base was often too great.

Royal Marine Signallers

Royal Marines appear to have served as 'Signallers' in ships as early as 1877, when Lance Corporal Turner was in HMS *Goshawk*, and Sergeant Bird in the *Revenge*. This practice continued for many years, as there was a shortage of Naval signalmen at the time. One Admiral however did not approve:

> '*We have tried the Marine as a Signalman, and as might have been expected, he has failed. He probably knows the signals and writes a good hand, but he lacks smartness and nautical intelligence,*'

wrote Vice Admiral Sir Edmund Fremantle in the Navy & Army Illustrated in 1896.

Referring to his own naval signalmen, he added:

> '*I remember a military passenger in the Centurion who was much impressed with these qualifications in our signalmen, and said to me "We have nothing like it in the Army."*'

Fremantle's slur on the Marines was swiftly refuted in their magazine, *The Globe and Laurel*:

> '*In actual signalling duties the Royal Marine is probably the better man as from his long training in morse, in addition to the special naval course all had to go through of two or three months, he can send and read signals, more particularly by night, at rates that are totally unintelligible to the ordinary signalling staff ...*'

In August 1889 prizes for proficiency in naval signalling were instituted, ranging from 10s to 25s, increased two years later to as much as 40s, to attract candidates, but this lasted only until 1895 when it was found possible 'to dispense with the further training of Marines as naval signallers, enough seamen having been trained.' This was somewhat premature, as shortages persisted, and worsened when ships began to be fitted with wireless. In 1908 the Admiralty approved that the complement of flagships should include a Royal Marine Signalling Instructor, while two signallers were to be included in all ships with a Marine detachment.

Marine Signallers had to be trained in V/S and W/T and heliograph for military operations and for duties on board ship, since signallers belonging to detachments embarked in cruisers and above would join up with the ship's communications staffs when on board. Up to 1923, they were trained at the RMLI Signal Schools at

A course of RMA Signallers at Eastney, 1903. The use of morse (by heliograph and wig-wag) and semaphore were widely taught and used, while bicycles were the main means of transport.

Chatham, Plymouth and Forton, and the RMA Signal School at Eastney. After amalgamation of the RMA and RMLI, instruction was centred on Chatham Signal School, which was commanded by the Superintendent of Signalling. There were small signal training cadres at Plymouth and Portsmouth, and military signalling was taught at the army Signal School at Catterick.

Some RMA and RMLI officers were trained in W/T at HMS *Vernon* from the earliest days of wireless; an Order in Council issued in August 1903 authorised the payment of an allowance of 2/6d a day to an officer appointed to *Vernon* 'to instruct officers and men in wireless telegraphy'. In the same year the Admiralty defined the duties of these W/T officers on board ship as: '...to assist in W/T under the torpedo officer and, after instruction, to take charge in ships bearing no torpedo officer ...'

In 1907 further appointments were authorised, and all W/T Instructors became eligible for the allowance, wherever they were serving. This was referred to by the First Lord in a statement on the naval estimates: 'Steps have been taken to provide the more general supervision of wireless telegraphy in sea-going fleets and squadrons by training Marine officers in wireless telegraphy duties.' In 1912 the Admiralty decided that these allowances would have to be increased to 3/6d 'in order to attract suitable candidates.' Marine officers also served in charge of a number of wireless stations (which also qualified them for the 3/6d).

Royal Marine officers acted as W/T instructors at *Vernon*, and subsequently in the Signal School, for many years, while at sea a number of Marines served as Squadron W/T Officers or for instructional duties in the Grand Fleet, both before and throughout World War I.

The Dinner and Smoking Concert

OF THE

Signal and Wireless Staffs

Mediterranean Fleet

HELD AT THE

Royal Clarence Theatre, Malta

FRIDAY JANUARY 5th 1912.

UNDER THE PATRONAGE OF THE

Signal and Wireless Officers, Mediterranean Fleet

COMMITTEE.

PRESIDENT.
Henry H Rowe, Ldg Sig. H M.S Exmouth

TREASURER
Stanley Johnstone, Yeo., H.M.S. Swiftsure.

SECRETARY
Claude A Smith. Ldg. Sig., H.M.S Exmouth.

REPRESENTATIVES.

Bacchante -G Blenkins, L.S.	Hampshire-G. L. Bullimore, H Y
Castille-W. H. Fuller, H Yeo.	Hussar-J. Donovan, Sig.
Cornwallis-T. Glanville, Yeo.	Lancaster-E. J. Hudson, P.O.Tel.
Destroyers-J. Ramsay, L.S.	Orontes-G. Pusey, L.S.
Diana-S. A. Brookes, Yeo.	Russell, T. Atkinson. Sig.
Duncan-J Wailling, L.S.	Suffolk, H. Watts, H Yeo.
Egmont-P. Mc Cole, Sig.	Triumph-W. Crane, L.S.

Chapter Five

World War One

'... received your letter just before we left Wei-hai-wei ...
we had to complete with coal as quickly as possible and
prepare at once for war. We had not the faintest idea who
the war was going to be with ...'

Yeoman Reeves in HMS *Hampshire*
writing to his wife on 2 August 1914

Two important developments occurred early in the war. First, a new sensitive valve amplifier had been associated with the Bellini-Tosi aerial system to give a means of direction finding, and by early 1915 five DF stations had been set up on the east coast to give coverage of the North Sea. This enhanced the intelligence being derived from the interception of German naval wireless traffic, much of which was of course in cypher. DNI, Admiral Oliver, asked the Director of Naval Education, Sir Alfred Ewing, to investigate the possibility of breaking this, and the latter got together a team which included a number of masters from Osborne and Dartmouth, whose cadets had gone off to sea.

Second, their efforts were helped enormously by the capture of two German code books soon after war began. One was from a German merchant ship and was found to be the same as that used by auxiliary vessels and minesweepers, as well as by zeppelins; the other and more important book came from the cruiser *Magdeburg* which had been wrecked in the Baltic in September 1914; this book was eventually passed on by the Russians. It took some weeks to work out the system but before the end of 1914 some of the German naval traffic was being decyphered. This section developed into the renowned Room 40.

Coronel and the Falklands

The first major naval engagements of the war occurred in the South Atlantic, where Britain had a squadron of ageing ships on the North America and West Indies Station, under Rear Admiral Sir Christopher Cradock. The main threat in the area was from two German light cruisers, *Karlsruhe* and *Dresden*, which were preying on shipping in the Atlantic. *Karlsruhe* was eventually destroyed by an internal

J Ruberry,
a Post Office Telegraphist,
became a naval intercept and
DF operator at Hunstanton on
the east coast. He said they
could tell the difference between
submarine and zeppelin
transmissions by their 'note'.
The zeppelins were just audible
when tuning up in their
hangars, so it was often
possible to predict when sorties
were about to take place.

explosion while in the Caribbean in November 1914, but *Dresden* disappeared.

Communications, or the lack of them, together with late or erroneous intelligence, meant that Cradock was left without much support and a vast area of sea to cover. Wireless telegraphy between England and the South Atlantic was difficult, contact being spasmodic and often only possible for a few hours a day. On top of this, the Admiralty was slow to appreciate the intentions of von Spee who had a squadron of modern ships, including the armoured cruisers *Scharnhorst* and *Gneisenau*, on the China station. The Germans set off across the Pacific, coaling at suitable places or from colliers. In mid-September the Admiralty told Cradock that there was a strong possibility of this squadron appearing off South America, and that the old battleship *Canopus* and the new cruiser *Defence* were being sent to reinforce his squadron.

In fact *Defence* never arrived, and *Canopus* was so slow that she was unable to keep up with Cradock's ships and took no part in the forthcoming battle. Von Spee's squadron was then reported steaming North West from Samoa and the threat appeared to have receded. This report was misleading, and Cradock was taken by surprise when the German force was sighted off Coronel on 1st November 1914. The British squadron consisted of the armoured cruisers *Good Hope* (flag) and *Monmouth*, light cruiser *Glasgow*, and armed liner *Otranto*.

Chief Yeoman George Spencer was serving in the *Otranto* and wrote an account of the battle to his wife a few days later:

> *'We had been scouring all through the islands off the coast of Chile trying to get information - dangerous work for this big ship as most of them are badly charted - we were ordered to Puerto Montt, a small German colony, to get news, we could not obtain any but I expect they telegraphed the enemy ... we joined up and signalled results of our searches, at about 2 o'clock the admiral made a signal to say he could hear German wireless very strong and expected that it was ahead ... at 4.30 we observed smoke off our starboard bow and reported it to Glasgow, as we got closer we found that it was two large armoured cruisers and two protected cruisers ... we at once wirelessed Good Hope who had got out of sight and reported them. We were ordered to form in single line ahead in the order Good Hope, Monmouth, Glasgow and Otranto, at that time we were nearest to the enemy having the least speed, but we became the rear ship on forming up.'*

Accounts by Reeves, Ruberry and Spencer are in the Imperial War Museum

Describing the battle, he commented:

'As for Otranto, she seemed to bear a charmed life, a broadside fell just short of us, one broadside and several individual shots fell just astern, my word they did whistle ... at 7.40 a big explosion took place on the Good Hope ... at about 7.50 the Good Hope went and (with) an explosion on the Monmouth at 7.53 the action finished. Glasgow hit three times on water-line and 4 men wounded only, Otranto no casualties and no hits. We then steamed away to the Westward at full speed and the Glasgow to the North West being chased by the enemy ... but at daylight there was no sign of them.'

Otranto went about 200 miles South of Cape Horn and then returned safely to Montevideo. *Glasgow* also escaped.

From: Invincible
To: Inflexible

The utmost harm may be done by indiscreet use of wireless. The key is never to be pressed unless absolutely necessary.
= 180345 Nov 1914

Some thirty British warships, including the battlecruisers *Invincible* and *Inflexible*, were deployed under Vice Admiral Sir Doveton Sturdee to track down the Germans. The communication orders required W/T silence to be maintained, except when essential at night, and then on minimum power. A simple procedure to allow the senior officer to 'change the wavelengths quickly and secretly' was introduced. The morse sign for a particular pendant was to be made ten times and ships were then to shift frequency without answering. Thus Blue Pendant meant 'shift to R tune', Compass pendant 'shift to S tune', and so on.

In the event, von Spee unwisely hung around off Valparaiso for some days and then decided to attack Port Stanley in the Falklands. By this time, not only was the *Canopus* there, but also Sturdee with the two battlecruisers and five cruisers. When the Germans were sighted on 8th December the British ships were still coaling, but they put to sea within a couple of hours, chased and overhauled the Germans.

Captain Malden, Royal Marines, *Invincible's* W/T officer, who had actually served at the W/T station in the Falklands before the war, described the battle in a letter written the next day to his wife:

'We have won a great Victory over the enemy after one of the longest sea-fights ever ... On Monday night I was sent ashore late, and took some dispatches for the Admiralty and the Minister at Rio de Janiero to be telegraphed. I got on board about 12.50 a.m. and went to the wireless office, remaining there till about 3 a.m., as I was suspicious of some signalling, ostensibly from some Argentine stations. At 8 a.m. I noticed that we had ceased coaling, and the Flag Lieutenant came in and said "You are all adrift, a four-funnelled cruiser has been sighted". By 8.45 a.m. more ships had been signalled by the shore look-outs. The Canopus, an old battleship stationed here as a fort, fired four rounds at them, apparently made them think a bit. About one and a half hours later we sailed.

'All the enemy were there, some distance away on the horizon, Scharnhorst, Gneisenau, Leipzig, Nürnberg and Dresden, also two colliers. Can you imagine such a stroke of luck? We had come 8,000 miles to find them, and they had come and found us the moment we arrived. All they expected to find was a few small ships, and they were going to take the Falkland Isles. I am frightfully pleased, as we had been trying to disguise our identity by false wireless signals all the way down, and apparently had been quite successful.'

With their superior speed the British quickly over-hauled the Germans, opening fire on the *Scharnhorst* and *Gneisenau* at 16,000 yards.

'Not long after there was a violent crash just above the W/T office, and we were filled with clouds of black smoke ... our Wireless Office is below armour and is in the after part of the ship. No serious damage was done, though the fumes were beastly. The Wireless worked splendidly, and we were getting signals and making them nearly up to the end ... we had developed a speed of 27 knots, and left the Inflexible. About 4 o'clock the Scharnhorst suddenly stopped, heeled over, capsized and sank. We then tackled the Gneisenau, assisted more or less by the Inflexible. At about 5.45 the Gneisenau followed her consort ... the Wireless worked to the last, when some wire netting fouled the aerial and we had to clear, rather an unpleasant job under weakening fire.'

By the end of the day the *Gneisenau, Nürnberg* and *Leipzig* had also been sunk, as were the two colliers after their crews had been taken off ('A wanton waste of coal', complained Their Lordships!). In Sturdee's report he commended the good work of Captain Malden and added:

'The enemy used W/T until shortly before SMS Scharnhorst was sunk, and endeavoured to jam our signals. Immediately this attempt was made all ships changed Tune by preconcerted signal from 'Q' to 'W', after which the enemy's interference became totally ineffective.' [1]

Malden's letter concluded:

'The Admiral was very complimentary last night about the Wireless, and though I say it myself, I think we did well to keep the enemy in the dark. Many people said that Wireless could not be used in action: that is utterly disproved. Wireless had to take the place of visual signals owing to the smoke. I hope that they will call our battle The Battle of the Falklands, as it is rather a nice name.'

After the battle *Invincible* visited the River Plate and Malden went to the wireless station at Ceritos to send telegrams to the Admiralty. The local operator warned him that the *Seydlitz, Moltke* and *Von der Tann* were in W/T contact with Montevideo, and must therefore be in the Atlantic. A signal to the Admiralty quickly established that these

Inflexible's W/T office, situated in the superstructure 'was so badly damaged by gun blast that the ship was unable to send on power or read long range signals for some days ...' HMS Kent also suffered damage which affected her switchboard and main transmitter; although she could receive, '...it was impossible to communicate with her for 24 hours - thus she was useless for any further cruiser duties and in the meantime her fate caused apprehension ...'

[1] Report on W/T in the battle (ADM137-304)

HMS Vindictive had been sent to Ascension Island in November, after Coronel, to act as a W/T relay. Captain Malden was subsequently sent back to the Falklands to set up a more permanent naval W/T station. His account of the battle was published in 'The Communicator', Vol.22, No.6, 1975.

ships were definitely in the North Sea. One theory was that some of the merchant ships sighted by the British force on the way south had mistaken them for Germans, and these rumours had then been spread by the many wireless stations in South America that were heavily subsidised, or even run by, the Germans, with the aim of frightening off British trade. 'The callsigns of these ships were often made and we picked them up on one or two subsequent occasions, so it turned out we were hunting our own shadows,' commented Lt Cdr Dannreuther, *Invincible's* gunnery officer.

Dresden was later trapped off Chile. 'Our luck turned,' said Vice Admiral Hickling, then a sub-lieutenant in the *Glasgow*. 'We intercepted a signal in Telefunken, the German wireless with a distinctive note ... Earlier we had captured the German merchant vessel code ... the book lay on the Captain's table and every officer spent a few hours a day trying to solve the puzzle. A few days later Charles Stuart, the Signal Officer, bounced up on the bridge: 'I think I've got it, sir - "Am proceeding Juan Fernandez meet me there 9 March very short of coal."' *Glasgow, Kent* and *Orama* caught up with her on 14 March and after a short exchange of fire the *Dresden* blew herself up.

The Grand Fleet

Jellicoe was appointed second-in-command of the Grand Fleet at the end of July 1914, and a few days later, as war appeared to be imminent, was instructed by the First Lord, Churchill, in accordance with a pre-arranged war plan, to take over as C-in-C. 'My staff then comprised ... a Flag Lieutenant, three signal officers, three wireless officers (very soon reduced to two), two signal boatswains ... each signal officer had his own special duty, one being responsible that all signals for tactical movements made visually were also made by 'short distance' wireless telegraphy. One wireless officer worked in the main office and one in the auxiliary office.' [2]

[2] *'The Grand Fleet 1914-1916'* by Admiral Viscount Jellicoe of Scapa

The information on the High Seas Fleet's movements being received from Room 40 emphasised the dangers of unrestricted wireless transmissions, and this was reinforced by several British intelligence successes in the first year of the war. Jellicoe again:

> *'...the extreme importance of reducing signalling by wireless at sea to an absolute minimum, except in the presence of the enemy, all tended to concentrate attention on the efficiency of our signal arrangements. Wireless signalling by ships at sea had to be stopped ... As time went on we felt that the enemy might be able to ascertain the class and in some cases even the name of the ship so signalling. This we deduced from the fact that we ourselves made progress in this direction. The fact of a German fleet being at sea, for instance, could hardly be disguised if much use was made of wireless signals. We naturally concluded that the enemy could similarly locate any of our squadrons.*

'When the Fleet was in cruising order at sea by daylight, arrangements were made to pass signals in and out between the most advanced cruisers and the Fleet Flagship by searchlight, except in the presence of the enemy ... All fleet manœuvring when much to the southward of the latitude of Kinnaird Head was carried out by visual signalling.'

The 24" Signal Projector had been introduced in about 1906, the Aldis lamp made its appearance during the war, and the 10" SP shortly after.

In any case the battle fleet always operated in close formation and visual signalling was the normal method of manœuvring; it had been worked up to a high degree of efficiency and speed, with repeating ships stationed clear of the main formation so that flag signals could be seen easily by all ships, otherwise they could be difficult to read because of funnel smoke, low visibility or distance from the flagship. The rules allowed wireless silence to be relaxed as soon as contact was made with the enemy. But the use of wireless was not neglected.

'So proficient did the ships become under the organisation introduced by the Fleet Wireless Officer, Lieutenant Commander Nicholson, assisted as he was by the very efficient wireless officers and wireless personnel, that (when silence was no longer necessary) I could handle the Battle Fleet by wireless with as much ease and rapidity as by visual signals. At the beginning of the war ten minutes to a quarter of an hour would elapse before I could be sure that all ships had received a manœuvring wireless signal ... In 1916 the time rarely exceeded two or three minutes.'

Nevertheless, W/T was still a relatively new and untried means of communication, and its potential for linking ships out of visual touch, and for signalling at night, was not always fully appreciated, and this led to some unfortunate 'missed opportunities' during the coming struggle.

Signal Intelligence and Actions in the North Sea 1914-15

An early intelligence success occurred in October 1914 when the Germans sent four old destroyers to mine the Northern entrance to the Downs. Wireless intercept and Room 40 detected the movement and a small British force was despatched and sank all four German ships. To cap this, a few months later a fishing boat hauled up a safe which contained another code book from one of these destroyers; this was a diplomatic code, also used by some detached warships.

The Germans' next sortie, to bombard Yarmouth and Gorleston, was not detected by intercept, but on 14 December Room 40 deduced that their battlecruisers would leave the Jade river early next day and return the same evening. In case this was another bombardment Beatty's battlecruisers and the 2nd BS were sailed to try to get between them and their base. The British force was quite well placed, as the Germans did bombard Scarborough and Hartlepool, but bad weather and lack of co-ordination between the searching forces allowed them to escape. The light cruiser *Southampton* (Commodore

In his book 'Germany's High Sea Fleet in the World War', Admiral Scheer comments: 'The English received news of our movements through their directional wireless, which they already had in use but which were only introduced by us at a much later period ... the stretch of the English east coast is very favourable for the erection of these direction stations ... the English had a great advantage as they were able to obtain quite accurate information as to the locality of the enemy as soon as any wireless signals were sent by him. In the case of a large fleet, where separate units are stationed far apart and communication between them is essential, an absolute cessation of wireless intercourse would be fatal to any enterprise.'

Lieutenant Commander
Ralph Seymour

Seymour was the son of Sir Horace
Seymour, Deputy Master and
Controller of the Royal Mint,
and a descendent of the first
Marquess of Hertford, whose
family name was Seymour.
Beatty may have been influenced
by his background, but at all
events they seemed to get on well;
writing in April 1913 Beatty said
he had '... trotted my round little
flag lieutenant for a good long
walk - I like him very much, more
than I did my first one. In fact I
like all my staff. They are all
intelligent and charming ...'

Goodenough) sighted and engaged the van of Hipper's Scouting
Group, but a badly addressed signal from Beatty, intended only for
Nottingham and *Falmouth* - 'Light cruisers resume your position for
look-out. Take station 5 miles ahead (of the battlecruisers)' was
passed on to the 2nd LCS, causing them to break off contact. Beatty
blamed Goodenough, but the use of a wrong callsign and ambiguous
wording of the signal must have been the prime error. But for this,
action would probably have been joined, although as it turned out, the
High Seas Fleet was being sailed to support Hipper, albeit rather
tardily, so Beatty could have faced a much superior force.

Beatty's signal officer and flag lieutenant was Ralph Seymour,
who has come in for much criticism, and has been blamed for many
of the communication 'failures' during these encounters as well as
later at the Battle of Jutland. Seymour however was not a signal
specialist, in the sense that he had not done the long course, although
he had previously been flag lieutenant to Admiral Sir Edmund Roe,
C-in-C Mediterranean, and had then spent some weeks at the Signal
School before joining Beatty. Long signal courses had started about
ten years earlier, a succession of jobs as flag lieutenant having
previously been the normal way of 'qualifying' in signals, and some
officers were still following this path. Seymour however was never
shown in the Navy List as qualified (S).

In January 1915 a signal sent to Admiral Hipper, giving the
operational plan for a reconnaissance of the Dogger Bank area by the
German battlecruisers, was deciphered by Room 40 just in time for
the Admiralty to order Beatty and the Harwich force to an intercepting position. The Grand Fleet was also sailed in support, although too
far away to get there in time. The two battlecruiser forces duly met
early on 23 January and the Battle of Dogger Bank ensued.

In the event, Hipper was behind schedule so that the British
forces did not get between him and his base but met him head on.
Hipper turned for home and it became a stern chase; the British
overhauled the Germans, and both Hipper's flagship, the battlecruiser
Seydlitz, and the armoured cruiser *Blücher* were badly damaged.
However Beatty's flagship, *Lion*, was also hit repeatedly, her dynamos
were put out of action which resulted in a wireless failure, and she
dropped out of the fight. Just after *Lion* was hit, submarines were
reported on the starboard bow and Beatty signalled a 90 degree turn
together to port, but unfortunately without indicating the reason. This
caused considerable confusion: 'For nearly five minutes this signal
remained flying, giving us all plenty of time to comment on it' wrote
Tiger's captain, 'I remember asking my navigating officer if he could
explain the meaning of it, for to my mind it seemed to mean breaking
off the action.'

'Course North East' was hoisted as *Lion* dropped astern, and
Beatty then ordered 'Attack the rear of the enemy'; unfortunately
Lion only had two halyards remaining, and this was hoisted along-
side the course signal, and was interpreted as 'Attack the rear of the

enemy bearing North East'. By ill-luck, this was where the crippled *Blücher* was lying, so off sped the battlecruisers towards *Blücher* while Hipper's force disappeared over the horizon. Beatty then decided to emulate Nelson and signal 'Engage the enemy more closely' only to be told that the group for this was no longer in the Signal Book! 'Keep nearer the enemy' was substituted but it was too late. *Blücher* was sunk, and a victory of sorts had been achieved, while the German C-in-C, von Ingenohl, was relieved of his command as he had exceeded instructions not to risk his ships. At least signal intelligence had done its stuff.

Beatty subsequently revised his Battlecruiser Orders, stressing the need for flexibility, and including 'Signals must be brief'. As Roskill says in his biography [3] of Beatty, he might also have added 'and absolutely clear'. The new instructions also said '...cruisers in sight of the enemy must continue sending off information even though (wireless) interference may prevent them hearing any reply to their signals'.

Writing to his mother [4] after the action, Seymour made only brief mention of signalling problems:

> '... the Lion got some heavy bumps, and then she listed over rather rapidly and we had to stop one of our engines. At the same time, or just before, a submarine was reported on the starboard bow ... it was really most unfortunate, as all our ships turned on the Blücher instead of pursuing the remainder and leaving the Blücher to the Indomitable as was the Admiral's intention. To make matters worse, all the electric supply failed, preventing us from getting a signal by wireless or searchlight, to correct the mistake.'

While this was going on in the North Sea, the Admiralty decided to extend the shore station wireless network. Marconi had developed 30kw spark-gap transmitters with a range of some 1,000 miles and stations were set up in British Guiana, Bathurst, the Cape, Aden, Ceylon, Mauritius, Seychelles, Hong Kong and Singapore. 150kw sets were produced for the Falklands and Ascension, and the world-wide network was more or less completed with stations at St Johns Newfoundland, Bermuda and Jamaica, a high powered 'Imperial' wireless station in Egypt, plus contributions from Australia (at Perth and Sydney) and New Zealand (Bluff Harbour and Awanui).

At home, some sixteen additional stations were established around the coast to cope with the large number of trawlers, drifters, yachts and other small vessels engaged in patrols and minesweeping. More frequencies came into use, mainly higher ones for use by the small ships with low power sets, and lower frequencies for the more powerful shore stations.

In April 1915 the 'Y' service, as the intercept organisation was called, reported that analysis of signal traffic indicated that the High Seas Fleet was about to sail. The report was produced and acted upon so promptly that the Grand Fleet actually put to sea an hour before the

Marder quotes the Scarborough incident as 'the first of four serious errors made by Seymour, the second being at Dogger Bank, the third and fourth at Jutland ... Beatty at the time regarded the first two as accidental and did not hold Seymour to account ... Years afterwards, however, the Admiral told a friend "He (Seymour) lost two battles for me!"'

Nevertheless, in his Despatch after Jutland, Beatty praised him for having 'maintained efficient communications under the most difficult circumstances despite the fact that his signalling appliances were continually shot away ...' Seymour was awarded the DSO and noted for early promotion 'for very valuable services in the action and throughout the war.' He remained with Beatty when the latter became C-in-C, and was promoted Commander in June 1917.

Arthur Marder,
'From Dreadnought to Scapa Flow'

[3] *'Admiral of the Fleet Earl Beatty'*, S W Roskill

[4] Quoted by Lady Seymour in her book *'Commander Ralph Seymour, RN'*

Germans! However the latter were covering a local minelaying operation and were back in harbour a few hours later. After the same sort of thing happened a few days later, the British began to wonder whether the Germans had turned for home because they had intercepted the Grand Fleet's wireless transmissions, even though silence had been kept so far as was possible; in fact the Germans were unaware that the Grand Fleet had sailed on either occasion.

In the middle of May 1915 the new DF network had its first success, obtaining fixes on the German flagship covering a minelaying operation north west of Heligoland, but no action developed.

The Signal Book was amended within a few months of the Dogger Bank to include a group for 'Engage the Enemy more Closely', and also one for 'The Admiral is unable to make signals by W/T.'

Marder quotes Fisher on this incident: 'In war the first principle is to disobey orders. Any fool can obey orders!'

By this time the 'I' (Intercept) method of signalling from shore had been introduced, to avoid the need for ships to break wireless silence to acknowledge receipt of each message. Signals for the C-in-C and ships at sea were transmitted from one high-powered shore station to another, e.g. Scarborough to Rosyth, the latter then repeating the signal back, so that there was a double chance of it being received correctly by the fleet. Signals were normally in cypher, and to disguise the increase in traffic when the fleet was at sea, a constant flow of signals was transmitted, many of them dummy ones. Rosyth's transmitter at that time was of relatively low power and was sometimes difficult to pick up, particularly on the other side of the North Sea, but on the whole, in spite of the fairly primitive sets fitted in ships, and the shortage of telegraphists, wireless signalling in the fleet seems to have been quite efficient.

At the end of May 1915 'Y' indicated another sortie by the High Seas Fleet and the Grand Fleet put to sea. The Germans were sighted by the British submarine *E6* which tried to torpedo the battlecruiser *Moltke* but missed. The *E6* attempted to report this sighting but its low power transmitter was unequal to the task and so the news didn't reach the Admiralty until she returned to harbour. This was another short minelaying sortie so again no contact was made between the fleets. The German minelayer *Meteor* did lay a minefield and returned home safely, but she undertook another sortie later in the year to lay mines off Cromarty, when she also sank an armed boarding steamer. Her signal reporting this was intercepted and DF'd, light cruisers were sailed to intercept her, and she was caught and sunk off the Horns Reef.

By the end of 1915 the High Seas Fleet had made a number of sorties; in almost every case some warning had been given by the 'Y' service. The Grand Fleet had sailed on five of these occasions, and indeed spent a high proportion of its time at sea; as Beatty wrote after one trip: "...frequent sweeps in North Sea vastly taxing ... we have been having a most poisonous time. Blowing very hard ... it was a full gale, we lost a top-gallant mast with the wireless..." [3]

The shortage of telegraphists was proving a considerable problem, with the need to man the many newly commissioned ships joining the fleet, as well as the very large numbers of trawlers and other auxiliary vessels requisitioned, Jellicoe wrote: [5]

'We were forced to discharge many of the best operators and replace them with boys trained in the Wireless School established at Scapa Flow. The FWO carried out invaluable work in organising and starting the school. The training of young ratings in visual duties was also taken in hand vigorously under Commander Woods and the signal officers of the Fleet ... The individual efficiency of ships ... could only be maintained if we could spend sufficient time in harbour, during which regular instruction could be given ... The Grand Fleet became, in effect, a great school for turning out trained personnel for the Navy as a whole, whilst still keeping watch over the High Seas Fleet, and controlling the North Sea and its northern exit ...'

[5] *'The Grand Fleet, 1914-1916'*, by Admiral Viscount Jellicoe of Scapa

Left above: 'The Flag Captain of the *Majestic*, flagship of the Channel Squadron, writing a Message on the Slate which the Signal Midshipman will Communicate to the Fleet', read the caption on this photograph, which appeared in the *Navy and Army Illustrated* on 1 June 1901. He is presumed to be Captain E E Bradford, who joined *Majestic* on 17 April 1901, but this could be his predecessor, Captain G le C Egerton, CB.

Left below: Captain Geoffrey Swallow reading the signals when Captain (D) 4th Destroyer Flotilla, 1948-49. His daughter, Patricia Swallow, was also a Signal Officer, and became Director, WRNS in 1982.

Chapter Six

Jutland

'The requirement of practically 100% efficiency in signalling forms a complete contrast to the 5 or 6% efficiency expected from the gun ...'

Signalling played a critical part in the Battle of Jutland. From the technical point of view, the various systems worked reasonably well, at least within the battlefleet. An enormous number of signals were made and received by ships during the battle - some 880 between 1415 31 May and 0215 1 June for example, well over one a minute, are listed in the official despatches, and the vast majority appear to have been received correctly. However this is only part of the story; the signals that were made were sometimes ambiguous; poor visibility and smoke during the battle, and the enormous number of ships spread over considerable distances, severely hampered flag signalling, while W/T or lamp were not always used to back up flag signals as they should have been; Beatty's flagship, *Lion*, was particularly at fault in this respect.

But, more critically, there was a serious failure in enemy reporting - on many occasions, particularly after dark, enemy ships were sighted, or gunfire seen, but no reports were made. Too often it was assumed that the situation was clear to the C-in-C, or it was left to Senior Officers to report, or it was just not thought of. Admiral Sir Angus Cunninghame Graham, who was a lieutenant in the battleship *Agincourt*, attributes this partly to the lack of involvement of the 'command' in harbour training. 'We had constant enemy reporting exercises but for some reason the captain and senior officers never took part and, looking back, this provides one reason for the complete failure of captains and admirals to keep the C-in-C informed'.

The one exception to this failure was Commodore Goodenough, commanding the 2nd Light Cruiser Squadron in *Southampton*, who remembered the main purpose of these ships and whose reporting of what was going on was, on the whole, both clear and frequent. No doubt Goodenough's signal officer, Arthur Peters, deserves some credit for this; his account of the enemy reporting organisation in *Southampton* is given on page 61.

The Grand Fleet had sailed at dusk on 30 May, again as a result of 'Y' intercepts. However some of the subsequent intelligence reports from the Admiralty were inaccurate or misleading. Crucially, soon after midday on 31 May Jellicoe received a report saying that the High Seas Fleet was still in harbour, although they had in fact been at sea for some hours. Captain Thomas Jackson, Director of Operations, had asked Room 40 where DF had placed the callsign 'DK', used by Admiral Scheer's flagship. The answer was "In the Jade", but because of a lack of close liaison between 'Int' and 'Ops', it was not appreciated by the Operations Division that, in accordance with the German's standard practice, the callsign, and the normal W/T operator, were transferred to a shore station when the flagship sailed in order to conceal its departure for as long as possible. Room 40 was aware of this, but did not know that the Operations Division had misinterpreted the situation and intended signalling to Jellicoe that Scheer was still in harbour.

Jellicoe therefore maintained economical cruising speed, thus delaying the eventual contact with the enemy; this also had the effect of keeping the battlefleet and Beatty's battlecruisers further apart so that their outlying ships were out of visual touch. (As it happens, the Germans were equally ignorant of the situation). A later intelligence report which gave more accurate information on German intentions was disregarded by Jellicoe, partly because he had lost confidence in the Admiralty as a result of the earlier mistake. The Admiralty also assumed that Jellicoe knew much more than he in fact did, and later during the night several important decrypts which clearly indicated that the Germans were heading for the Horns Reef route home were simply not passed on.

The first contact occurred at 1415 when the smoke of a neutral tramp steamer was sighted by scouting forces of both sides who turned to investigate. The light cruiser *Galatea* reported two other ships approaching, followed by an enemy report identifying them as German destroyers, and the first engagement of the battle commenced. Both German and British cruisers moved to support, thus destroying the integrity of their respective scouting lines, and some confusing and incomplete reports were sent.

Beatty ordered the seaplane-carrier *Engadine* to send up a seaplane which took off at 1508 and made naval history by transmitting enemy reports from the air. The pilot, Flight Lieutenant Rutland (later known, of course, as 'Rutland of Jutland') recorded that while

Goodenough later wrote to Jellicoe:

'I trust we gave you the information you wanted ... Every light cruiser must have a signal officer just as much as a spotting officer or torpedo officer who should have no other duties to perform.'

Letter of 5 June 1916, Jellicoe Papers, British Library

North Sea and the battle area

Thinking that the High Seas Fleet was still in harbour, Jellicoe signalled to the battlefleet at 1355 on 31 May enquiring at what rate they could fuel destroyers. '(This) shows that I was expecting to remain at sea awaiting events' he wrote later.

The seaplane-carrier Campania (an ex-Cunard liner) should have been with the fleet but for some unexplained reason failed to receive the sailing signal: 'Campania will follow Blanche and be the last to leave.' She eventually sailed four hours late, by which time Blanche had reported her absence. Calculating that she would never catch up, and as there were reports of submarines in the area and she was unescorted, Jellicoe ordered her back.

[1] The term 'Force' might have been more appropriate, but 'Fleet' was used until Jellicoe became First Sea Lord and Beatty C-in-C Grand Fleet.

[2] Evan-Thomas Papers, British Library, ref 52504-06

his observer (Assistant Paymaster G S Trewin) was making his W/T report the enemy turned 16 points. 'I drew his attention to this and he forthwith transmitted it ... I judged by the course of our battlecruisers that our W/T had got through'. In fact, the reports did not reach Beatty, but he did receive *Galatea's* report. Rutland had actually sighted the German light cruisers, which were being recalled to join Hipper's battlecruisers. The plane was recovered by *Engadine* and minor repairs made but, probably because of the weather conditions and low visibility, no further sortie was ordered. 'We could have been of great use,' Rutland wrote later, 'it was the fault of the Navy that we were not used to better effect.'

The Battlecruiser Fleet [1] included the 'fast battleships' of the 5th Battle Squadron, commanded by Rear Admiral Evan-Thomas in the *Barham*, stationed five miles NNW of *Lion*, and the 2nd BCS three miles ENE. The force was steering North when at about 1430, on the strength of *Galatea's* reports, Beatty ordered his force to alter course to SSE. *Barham* was too far away to read flag signals - it was thought at first that *Lion* might have been signalling a zig-zag turn, due about then - and it was some time before *Lion* repeated the signal by light; the original repeating ship, *Tiger*, had become furthest from the 5th BS while on the Northerly course and thus was poorly placed for this purpose, and she appears to have assumed that *Lion*, the nearest ship to the 5th BS, would automatically have taken on the responsibility.

Although widely dispersed, it seems that the battlecruiser fleet was being manoeuvred as a single unit, or at any rate the movements of the three components were ordered by manoeuvring signal from the flagship, and Evan-Thomas appears to have waited until he was clear what was wanted, despite the fact that it must have been obvious that the battlecruisers, enveloped in smoke, were heading off at high speed in the opposite direction. A simple 'Join me' from Beatty might have been a quicker and more flexible means of getting the 5th BS to move in the right direction.

As it was, the stationing of the 5th BS five miles to the NNW (too far to read flag signals, and away from the expected direction of the enemy), meant that by the time the 5th BS had come round they were some eight or more miles astern, and likely to slip further back due to the greater speed of the battlecruisers.

The 5th BS had only recently been allocated to Beatty and they had not worked together before this sortie. Nor, surprisingly, had they been given copies of the Battlecruiser Fleet Orders (BCFOs). As to why they were stationed five miles NNW, Beatty claimed that it was because Jellicoe had allocated the 5th BS to him on the understanding that they should only be used 'in support', to avoid the risk of them being engaged by a superior force because of their supposedly inferior speed to that of the German battleships.

Admiral Sir Charles Madden, Jellicoe's Chief of Staff at Jutland, saw it differently. In a letter [2] to Evan-Thomas some years later (which he asked him to keep to himself) he referred to the situation after the first sighting of the enemy by *Galatea:*

> *'It might be expected that VA BCF would have stationed 5th BS for action or at least ordered it to close which before 2.45 could have been rapidly effected ... the late arrival of the 5th BS in action is mainly attributed to this departure from Fleet custom ... The C-in-C gave the 5th BS to VA BCF so that the result of meeting (Hipper) could not be in doubt, this needed keeping 5th BS close at hand on account of its slower speed ... if the action had opened with 10 British capital ships to 5 German we might not have lost the Queen Mary and Indefatigable ...'*

Interpreting what actually happened on this occasion, and others, is not easy. There are many discrepancies between signal and navigational records - in *Lion* they sometimes varied by as much as seven minutes - and in practice it is doubtful if the exact time of hoisting - and executing - flag signals would always be logged; also the time taken to code, transmit and decode signals sent by light or W/T, even using the simple groups from the signal book, is not always appreciated. But there is no doubt that on the occasion of the alteration to SSE *Lion* failed to ensure that the signal reached *Barham* quickly, and Evan-Thomas was slow to react.

The two battlecruiser forces, commanded by Beatty and Hipper, met in mid-afternoon. Inevitably the 5th BS were late joining in, only getting within range of the enemy after *Indefatigable* had blown up and *Lion* had been badly damaged, but once engaged their gunnery was effective and relieved the pressure on the battlecruisers. However *Lion's* wireless had been put out of action and Beatty's signals now had to be transmitted by light to the *Princess Royal* for onward transmission by W/T, adding to the problems faced by Ralph Seymour, and further reducing the exchange of information between Beatty and Jellicoe who was still very much in the dark.

By this time Hipper had altered course to the South East in order to lead Beatty on to the German battle fleet coming up fast from the South. *Southampton* first sighted them, signalling at 1638: 'Have sighted enemy battlefleet bearing approx SE course of enemy N'. At about the same time *Lion* sighted smoke to the south east, and then the van of the battle fleet; at 1640 Beatty ordered the battlecruisers to wheel to a northerly course, both to avoid Hipper's trap, and to lead the Germans towards the Grand Fleet. He signalled to the C-in-C: 'Have sighted enemy's battle fleet bearing SE. My position 56 36 N 6 04 E'. This transformed the situation for Jellicoe, who increased speed and wirelessed to the Admiralty 'Fleet action is imminent', while Goodenough in the *Southampton* amplified his earlier report with details of the position, course and composition of the German battlefleet.

The 5th Battle Squadron continued heading SSE towards Beatty, covering the latter's reversal of course with accurate and effective gunfire on the German battlecruisers, but they had neither seen the German battlefleet, nor received *Southampton's* signals, so were

The Grand Fleet Battle Orders included the following:

'Signal Procedure in Action. The Admiral will make manoeuvring and action signals by W/T, as well as by visual ... The 'executive' is to be acted on by whichever method it is received first.'

'To assist in recognition of our flotilla leaders (other than light cruisers) and destroyers in day action, these vessels are to be prepared, at short notice, to whiten one funnel with wash. In addition, all destroyers, when co-operating with the Grand Fleet, are to fly the Black Flag at the main when in action.'

Lieutenant Stephen King-Hall in Southampton recalled that Goodenough ignored Beatty's alteration of course to North. 'We disobeyed the signal, or rather delayed obeying it, for two reasons. Firstly, we wished to get close enough to the High Seas Fleet to examine them and report accurately on their composition and disposition; secondly we had hopes of delivering a torpedo attack on the long crescent-shaped line of heavy ships ... It was a strain steaming at 25 knots straight for this formidable line of battleships, with our friends going fast in the opposite direction ...'

The situation at about 1650 as the
BCF reversed course

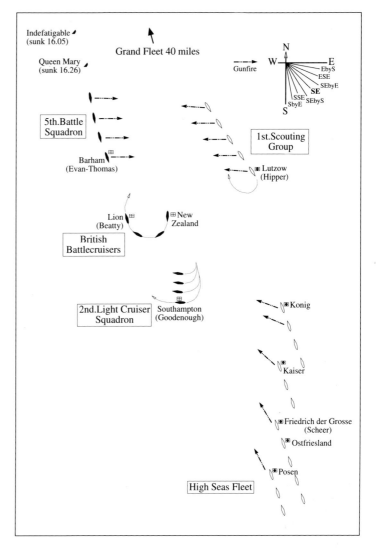

unaware of the situation that was developing. Beatty turned his
battlecruisers 4-points to starboard so that they would pass the 5th BS
on opposite courses, port-to-port, which they did at about 1650 (with
the result that for a period the battlecruisers blanketed the battleships'
fire). At the same time Beatty had hoisted the signal for the 5th BS
to wheel to starboard, although there appears to have been some
delay in executing the signal, perhaps because *Lion* had several other
signals in hand, and the 5th BS ended up further astern than intended,
having been ordered to 'Prolong the line.'

During the run North, which lasted about an hour, the superior
speed of the British ships told and by 1730 they were out of range
ahead of the German battlecruisers, who were unaware that they, in
turn, were being led into a trap.

Meanwhile Jellicoe was advancing in the general direction of the
Germans with his 24 battleships in Organisation No.5 - 'Divisions in

line ahead disposed abeam to starboard'. The aim was for the battlefleet to form a single line ahead of, and roughly at right angles to, the van of the enemy's battlefleet ('crossing the T') so that all ships would have clear arcs of fire; this would also allow the British ships to concentrate their fire on the leading German ships, while most of the latter would have their line of fire masked by their own ships or be out of range.

To achieve this successfully Jellicoe needed to know the direction from which the enemy was going to appear, and when, since the manœuvre to change the formation would take some time to complete. But although over two hours had elapsed since the first battlecruiser engagement, he had received only eight accurate reports (six from the *Southampton*), and a large number of indeterminate ones, punctuated by long periods of silence. Beatty's first report "Enemy battle fleet bearing SE", received in *Iron Duke* via *Benbow*, had become garbled in transmission, and there was a lack of comprehensive follow-up reports; Beatty seems to have made none during the run North.

At 1800 the battleship *Marlborough*, on the starboard wing, reported sighting *Lion* to the SSW. Although the enemy were still out of sight in the mist, this did reveal an eleven mile difference between the plotted and actual position of *Lion* which was much closer than expected and on the starboard bow rather than dead ahead. At 1802 Jellicoe altered the course of the battlefleet to South ('leaders together, rest in succession'), then signalled to *Lion* 'Where is the enemy's battle fleet?' to which Beatty replied 'Enemy battlecruisers bearing SSE'. Jellicoe altered course again at 1806 to SE, at about the time when *Lion* fortunately caught a glimpse of Scheer's van on the horizon and signalled 'Have sighted enemy battle-fleet bearing SSW'. This was received in *Iron Duke* at 1814, and confirmed almost immediately by a report from *Barham*.

The movement and deployment of the Battlefleet from 1800

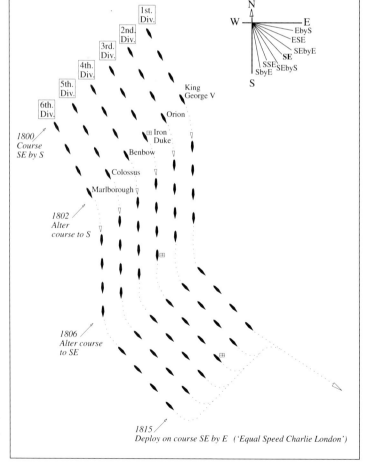

There was no time to lose. Jellicoe wrote later:

'My first impulse was to form on the starboard wing column in order to bring the fleet into action at the earliest possible moment, but it became increasingly apparent, both from the sound of gunfire and reports from Lion and Barham, that the High Seas Fleet was in such close proximity and on such a bearing as to create obvious disadvantages in such a movement.'

Furthermore, to prevent his own 'T' being crossed, the leading ship would then have had to make a large turn to port, the remainder following behind, with the enemy rapidly getting closer and the danger of the manœuvre not being completed in time.

Jellicoe took no more than a minute to make up his mind, and told the Fleet Signal Officer, Commander Alexander 'Sammy' Woods, to hoist 'Equal Speed South East'. As the fleet was actually steering South East, Woods asked if he could make it a point to port, so that it would be clear that the deployment was to be on the port column. Jellicoe agreed, ensuring that there was no doubt by repeating 'Equal Speed South East by East', and at 1815 the signal 'Equal Speed pendant CL', or in signalman's language 'Equal Speed Charlie London', was hoisted and transmitted by wireless and lamp. The actual meaning given in the signal book was 'The column nearest SE by E is to alter course in succession to that point of the compass, the remaining columns altering course leading ships together, the rest in succession so as to form astern of that column, maintaining the speed of the fleet'.

This manœuvre has been the subject of intense analysis over the years and with few exceptions the experts have come to the conclusion that Jellicoe made the right decision. Donald Macintyre, in his book *Jutland*, wrote:

'The deployment of the Grand Fleet, in the nick of time and in spite of sparse and inaccurate intelligence, in a manner most perfect to bring a devastating concentration of fire onto a portion of the enemy fleet was a masterpiece of fleet manœuvre that has rarely been equalled and never excelled.'

Furthermore, although there were failures elsewhere, communications within the battle fleet worked admirably. An American, Commander Holloway Frost, writing in 1936, commented:

'We must heartily commend the visual communication system of the Grand Fleet. We particularly like the laconic wording and the great rapidity with which the despatches were sent from ship to ship. Radio communication was also very rapid and the errors were kept to a very small percentage ... the entire communication system had grown to be very efficient and it is doubtful that it can be equalled even today, despite many technical improvements.'

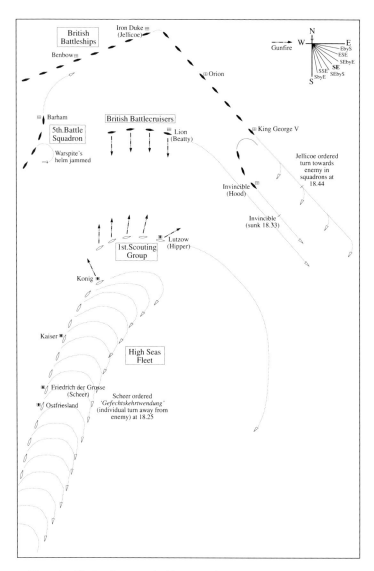

The situation at about 1830 during the deployment

Jellicoe had indeed succeeded in 'crossing the T', and Scheer found himself heading straight at the British battle line which was in an arc some seven miles long ahead of him. Visibility was poor, due both to haze and funnel smoke, and neither Jellicoe nor Scheer could see much of what was going on, their ships firing at whatever targets emerged from time to time out of the mist. Very soon Scheer decided to extricate himself, and ordered his well practised 'battle turn', or *Gefechtskehrtwendung*; this was in effect a turn together of 180 degrees, but conducted in rapid sequence with the rear ship turning first, which allowed it to be performed when in a bent line and was supposed to reduce the risk of collision.

When the Germans disappeared from sight at 1842 Jellicoe and most of his senior officers assumed this was due to the thickening mist. Some ships, such as the light cruisers, saw what was happening but failed to report, and it was some time before Jellicoe altered course, rather cautiously in stages, to follow the enemy; Beatty raced ahead in pursuit but for some reason, never satisfactorily explained, *Lion* wasted time by turning a complete circle, with his battlecruisers following round in succession. Jellicoe was also worried about being led over minefields or submarines, an anxiety reinforced just before 1900 when *Marlborough* was torpedoed.

Yeoman Atrill in the Marlborough noted: 'Signal ratings' war stations were below armour, but there was an arrangement that allowed halyards to reach them via a chute through the mast, so that flag signalling was still possible while we were all under cover.' Although under cover, they weren't actually below armour.

Scheer decided to reverse course again at about this time, ordering another 'battle turn', and *Southampton*, under heavy fire, was again in a position to report this at 1904. Why Scheer turned back towards Jellicoe, thus bringing his battle line back into the devastating fire of the Grand Fleet, is something of a mystery; he probably thought the latter were further to the south and hoped to escape by slipping across their rear. One German account has him explaining: 'I think it will surprise and confound the enemy! They won't know what I am about'. According to his Flag Lieutenant, Weizacker, his real intention was 'to leg it for home!'

Thus battle was joined again, the British being nearly as surprised as the Germans, many turret crews having been allowed to come up for a breather. The German battlecruisers took the brunt of this phase; Hipper's flagship *Lützow* was badly damaged, and her wireless aerials were shot away. Hipper spent some time in the torpedo boat *G39*, searching for an undamaged ship to which to transfer. Having tried the *Seydlitz* and the *Von der Tann*, he eventually made it to the *Moltke*, resuming command of his battered squadron after some two hours.

His battlecruisers had relieved the pressure on Scheer sufficiently for him to execute a third 'battle turn', but the disorganised state of his battle line made this a tricky manœuvre:

> *'For several perilous minutes the ships of the 5th and 6th Divisions and the fleet flagship were proceeding at slow speed very close to one another and almost in line abreast, and it was only the seamanship and splendid tactical training of the admirals and captains that prevented collisions.'* [3]

[3] Official German Record

Worsening visibility and attacks by German destroyers which laid heavy smoke screens, and forced the Grand Fleet to make a turn away, coupled with the lack of reports from the light cruisers, meant that the High Seas Fleet disappeared westward while Jellicoe was once more unsure of the actual situation, and was slow to bring the fleet round to a south-westerly course. He thought, however, that he was well placed between the Germans and their base.

At 1940 Beatty again reported being in sight of the enemy, but his own position was given wrongly and it was 2000 before this was sorted out. Further confusion ensued when Beatty signalled to Jellicoe at 1947: 'Submit van of battleships follow battlecruisers. We can then cut off the whole of the enemy's battle fleet'. This again was not much help to Jellicoe, but Admiral Jerram in the *King George V* was ordered to do what he could with the 1st Battle Squadron which was leading the fleet. By this time *Lion's* position was again uncertain and Jerram headed off on what turned out to be a divergent course. He was brought back into touch when the 4th Light Cruiser Squadron sighted three German battleships in the twilight and attacked them with torpedoes, but Jerram was doubtful about their identification and decided not to open fire. The 2nd Battle Squadron had also seen the Germans, but in the uncertain situation also took no action. Thus Jellicoe was robbed of his last opportunity of bringing about a further encounter before dark.

Beatty was in touch with, and engaging, the enemy intermittently until about 2045. Dusk was falling and Jellicoe had no intention of engaging in a night action so, assuming that the Germans would choose the southern route home via the Dutch coast and the Ems to reduce the risk of running into the Grand Fleet again, he set course so as to be in a position to intercept them at daylight. At 2141 Jellicoe received a signal from Beatty, originated some forty five minutes earlier, reporting the enemy steering WSW, which appeared to confirm Jellicoe's assumption. However since then the Germans had turned back to a southerly course and Scheer had told all ships to make for the Horns Reef. This became known to Room 40 from 'Y' intercepts but, as mentioned earlier, not all of these were passed on, and the Germans' intentions were not appreciated by Jellicoe until it was too late.

At 2100 the two fleets were on slightly converging courses with the leading ships only about five miles apart. Neither C-in-C was aware of this, the Germans gradually dropped back and then moved across astern of the Grand Fleet. There were a number of engagements between various light forces, and from time to time gun flashes lit up the night sky, but again few useful enemy reports were originated. One action was seen by ships of the 5th Battle Squadron; *Malaya* identified the leading enemy ship as apparently *Westfalen* class, but her Captain decided not to open fire since the ship ahead had not done so. (It was indeed the battleship *Westfalen*, leading the High Seas Fleet). *Valiant* was in no doubt that it was an enemy battleship but she did not open fire because the flagship, *Barham*, had not done so. The Admiral did not open fire because he had received no orders and assumed that the *Iron Duke* must have observed the action and had a good reason for not firing! None of these ships made an enemy report.

At 2345 the *Seydlitz* blundered through the British fleet, between the 2nd and 5th battle squadrons. She was sighted by *Agincourt* whose Captain wrote afterwards: 'I did not challenge her so as not to give our Division's position away.' She was also sighted by *Marlborough*, and by *Revenge* whose 6-inch crews were ordered to open fire but they were outside their turrets watching the destroyer actions, and by the time they had closed up *Seydlitz* had disappeared.

Captain D12 in *Faulknor* was engaged in the night actions, including a successful attack by his flotilla with torpedoes which sank the old German battleship *Pommern*. He made three enemy

Opposite: The situation at 2100

Marder commented: 'It was a cardinal rule not to do anything at night that might disclose the position of the battlefleet. The most stringent orders were therefore in force forbidding signalling by light or by W/T. For the same reason it was thought undesirable to show up the battlefleet through gunfire or by challenging an unknown ship. Even when an unsatisfactory reply was made to a challenge, battleships did not open fire.'

Nevertheless, Grand Fleet orders did emphasise 'the utmost importance that reports of sighting the enemy should reach the Admiral without delay ... full use must be made of all the visual and W/T lines of communication which are available.' However the same Memorandum did discourage a too liberal use of W/T ... 'which should be reserved for messages of the first importance ...'

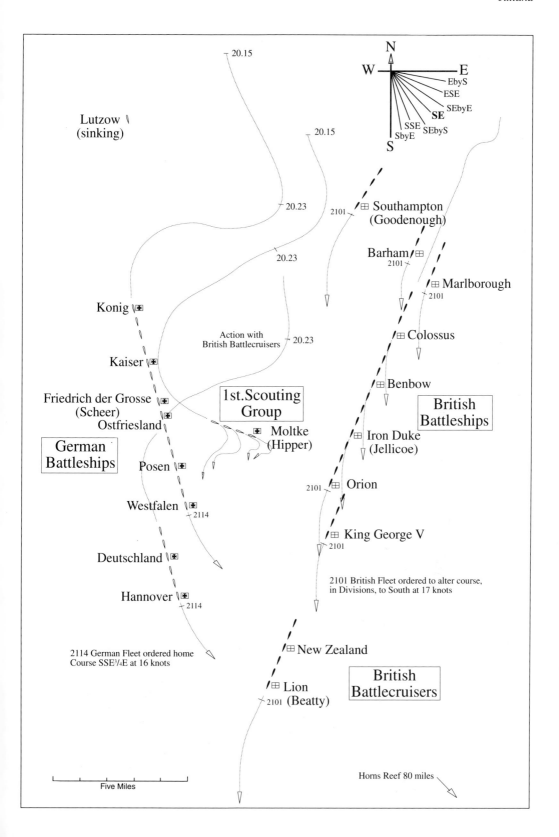

20.15

Lutzow
(sinking)

20.15

20.23

2101 ⊞ Southampton
(Goodenough)

Barham ⊞
2101

20.23

⊞ Marlborough
2101

Konig ⊞

Kaiser ⊞

⊞ Colossus

Action with
British Battlecruisers   20.23

/⊞ Benbow

1st.Scouting Group

British Battleships

Friedrich der Grosse ⊞
(Scheer)
Ostfriesland

⊞ Moltke
(Hipper)

⊞ Iron Duke
(Jellicoe)

German Battleships

Posen ⊞

2101 ⊞ Orion

Westfalen ⊞
2114

⊞ King George V
2101

Deutschland ⊞

2101 British Fleet ordered to alter course,
in Divisions, to South at 17 knots

Hannover ⊞
2114

2114 German Fleet ordered home
Course SSE¾E at 16 knots

⊞ New Zealand

British Battlecruisers

⊞ Lion
2101 (Beatty)

Five Miles

Horns Reef 80 miles

N
W ——— E
EbyS
ESE
SEbyE
SE
SSE SEbyS
SbyE
S

reports, none of which were received by the C-in-C. Referring to the first of these, which reported 'Enemy battleships in sight. My position 10 miles astern of 1st Battle Squadron', Jellicoe commented in his Despatch: 'This signal was unfortunately not received in the battlefleet owing to telefunken interference.' Whether this was due to deliberate jamming or simply problems with the relatively primitive wireless equipment and the general confusion, it is not possible to say, but it was certainly very unfortunate that none of *Faulknor's* reports got through. Despite all the activity and gunfire astern of him during the night, Jellicoe seems to have remained convinced that the German battlefleet was to the west of him and heading for the southern route home.

Recognition at night was certainly a difficult problem. Coloured light recognition signals could be compromised, or misinterpreted; the challenge and reply system was also open to compromise - indeed on several occasions German ships intercepted British recognition signals and used them in reply - one British ship which had lost hers in the battle asked the next in line what the current ones were, and the Germans are reputed to have read the answer! Jellicoe commented: 'The German system of recognition signals is excellent. Ours is practically nil.'

By dawn it was all over. An Admiralty report received at 0329 placed Scheer only one hour's steaming from the safety of the Horns Reef and Jellicoe realised that he no longer had any hope of catching the enemy.

'Ten Commanders' on the staff of the C-in-C, Grand Fleet, July 1916

Standing (L to R):
G Blake (G)
TFR Calvert (1st Lieut)
N O'Neill
WD Phipps (Signals)
RL Nicholson (Fleet Wireless Officer)
CM Forbes (Flag Commander)
Sitting (L to R):
RM Bellairs (War Staff)
Hon MR Best (W/S)
PR Stevens (W/S)
ARW Woods (Fleet Signal Officer)

Although communications were far from perfect, most failures were to do with the content of messages, and the almost complete lack of effective enemy reporting. In his Despatch after the battle Jellicoe wrote:

> *'The signals were worked with smoothness and rapidity by Commander Alexander Woods, assisted by the other signal officers, and all ships responded remarkably well under difficult conditions. My Flag Lieutenant, Lieutenant Commander Herbert Fitzherbert, was also of much service to me throughout the action. The high state of efficiency of the W/T arrangements of the Fleet and the facility with which they were worked before, during and after the action is a great testimony to the indefatigable work carried out by Commander Richard Nicholson. His services have been invaluable throughout the war. A special word of praise is due to the wireless departments in all ships'.*

Enemy Reporting in *Southampton*

The most glaring fault at Jutland was the lack of enemy reporting by ships in touch with the enemy. The only ship with a consistently good record was *Southampton*, and the description [4] by her signal officer, Arthur Peters, of how this was handled, is of interest.

[4] In a note to the Tactical School. Godfrey Papers, Naval Historical Branch

> *'Our bridge coding organisation ... was simplicity itself, consisting merely of myself and a plotting officer (Sub Lt RNR). The commodore and the navigator, myself and the Chief Yeoman were the only people on monkey's island, except I think, one other signalman to watch our own fleet; the plotting officer was in the charthouse just below, and the navigator informed him by voice pipe every time we altered course or speed. The commodore normally confined his instructions to such broad orders as 'Report that enemy', pointing at it; 'Report those cruisers altering course'; 'Tell him some more enemy are coming in sight from the SE'; Report the course of the enemy battlecruisers', etc; the navigator would give me the bearing of the enemy, and either he or the commodore the course; the latter would then concentrate on getting the ship in the best place for keeping the enemy in sight, and I was free from all worries except getting the report through.*
>
> *'I made no plain language version of the reports; I simply jotted down a bearing and a course, went into the charthouse and coded the report direct from the signal books, two copies (actually I think I made three, the third being kept for the record - I still have them!); as I coded I asked the plotting officer for a position ... one copy was then sent by messenger straight to the W/T office; I had inserted all the prefixes etc., with the exception of callsigns, which were put on by the coding officer (doctor or paymaster) who kept watch in the*

W/T office; the message was made at once, the bridge being informed by buzzer when it was through. The message was then passed out of the cabinet to the coding officer, decoded by him, and the plain language version sent up to me on the bridge. This I compared with the original 'shorthand' version. The second copy was used for sending the message by signalling projector.

'The success of the method, such as it was, was mainly due to absolute confidence between the commodore and myself; he relied on me to interpret his wishes in the best and briefest way available in the signal books; this is a very rare trait in admirals! Much time was saved by cutting out (making) an original plain language version, but this is of course risky ... if a mistake in a course or bearing was made no one ever knew whether it was my mistake in coding, or the commodore's or navigator's, but to the commodore that was immaterial, he being a 'big' man! - sufficient that it was 'our' mistake, for which he would take the blame.

'In addition we had done a vast amount of coding exercises in harbour for the past two years, so that both the coding officers and myself were really at home with the books ... and we always concentrated on reporting the enemy being our primary duty, and didn't care much what our squadron (always in open formation) or our fleet were doing.

'With regard to remarks on the lack of success of others, few people other than the three light cruiser squadrons had really made a thorough study of reporting the enemy; many admirals and captains still thought they only had to say something, and that exact sentence would be magically wafted without delay to the addressee!'

The Tactical School commented that in the Grand Fleet, the C-in-C himself conducted coding exercises which were designed to train officers in making enemy reports. It also pointed to the need for each ship to have an officer who had done a short course in signals and who would be free from other duties 'to attend to signals from the moment the enemy are sighted and (who) would be responsible that information is correctly framed and passed. The senior signal rating is fully occupied with the work on the bridge and cannot be expected to censor signals or their destination.'

Some other Comments on the Battle

Angus Cunninghame Graham: [5]

> '5 *'Random Naval Recollections'*, published in 1979

'The requirement of practically 100% efficiency in signalling forms a complete contrast to the 5 or 6% efficiency expected from the gun. The gun's five or six hits however produce so spectacular a result that the other ninety four rounds are allowed to fall forgotten and unregretted into the sea. Of the limitations, the chief of these was the shortage of trained

signalmen and telegraphists, brought about by the wartime expansion of the Navy, and the rapid development of wireless telegraphy. The strength of the signal personnel in the Grand Fleet was therefore inadequate, and the responsibility for reading important signals often fell upon boys still in their 'teens. The chance of renewing battle on the morning of 1st June was thrown away, not by ships losing touch with the enemy during the night, but by their failure to report. The chief cause of this failure is the want of an officer in each ship to take over this duty. Costly cruisers are built, one of their chief functions is to be the 'eyes of the fleet' and yet it is left to their captains and navigators to share between them the duty of telling the Admiral what they see.'

Subsequently, KR & AI included a requirement for every ship to have an officer told off to take charge of signals. A further step was taken in 1927 by giving Sub-Lieutenants a fortnight's signal course.

*　　　*　　　*　　　*　　　*

David Joel was Flag Lieutenant to Admiral Gaunt in the battleship *Colossus*, with Mr W R Paris as his Signal Boatswain. Joel wrote:

'I shall never forget the gallant destroyer Acasta heavily hit and hove to in the swell and wash of the great battle line not a cable away flying Flag 6 meaning 'I am sinking'. Her crew were fallen in and cheering each ship as we raced by. We had a few hits and some of our 4-inch anti-torpedo ammunition blew up unpleasantly close to the conning tower. About this point I desired to make use of my gas mask which was in a heavy wooden box, but my Admiral, of small stature, was standing on the box in order to see out of the slit in the conning tower. I remember admiring a fine Leading Signalman (Chandler) who was out in the open repeating all signals down the line by searchlight; except for those on the bridge, I suppose no one else was so exposed. In the middle of all this my Admiral told me to make a signal to our sub-division 'Remember Belgium, and the Glorious First of June'. Our communications were over-loaded, and feeling that no one liked Belgium, nor would the first of June mean much to many people, I remonstrated, but the Admiral over-ruled me, as Admirals do.'

*　　　*　　　*　　　*　　　*

Evan-Thomas did not speak out until 1923 when he heard that the draft Admiralty Narrative implied that he was to blame for delays both at the turn to SSE and again later back to the North; not only did he dispute this interpretation but he was upset that he had not been asked for his comments on the draft. After an exchange of correspondence [6] with the staff involved, he eventually sought a

[6] Evan-Thomas Papers, BL 52504-06

meeting with the First Lord, but he had hardly entered the room when they were interrupted by Beatty (First Sea Lord) and 'I was more or less thrown out.' He presumed that Beatty did not want him putting his side of the story.

In his correspondence about the narrative, referring to the turn to the SSE, Evan-Thomas said:

> '...delay was caused by the idea that as no signal was made to turn, the Vice Admiral wished 5th BS further to Northward to prevent enemy escaping in that direction - that was the idea at the moment in my head ... (due to intense smoke) it was impossible to see what Lion was doing until most of the Squadron had turned ... as Lion had been signalling to Barham with a searchlight previously to this turn, and had made all alterations of course by that method, there was no reason why a signal should not have been made for the Barham to turn with Lion by searchlight, or if not by wireless, had he wished her to do so ...'

Vice Admiral Sir Geoffrey Barnard, who was Evan-Thomas' nephew and godson, wrote in 1962 that:

> 'He told me that he thought Beatty's staff signal arrangements were "... lamentable. They didn't even bother to read the Grand Fleet signalling instructions ... they hoisted wrong signals and forgot to haul them down ..." My uncle also referred to Beatty's "non-existent enemy-reporting arrangements."'

On the turn to the North, Barnard says:

> 'It was quite clear to me that Beatty's staff hoisted the wrong signal and then forgot to haul it down ... the signal to the 5th BS to turn to starboard 16 points was the wrong way ... if Beatty wanted them in close support behind him he would have made the turn to port and executed it long before the flagships were abreast. My uncle says the Turn signal was still close up when he passed abeam of Lion on opposite courses at combined speeds of more than 50 knots.'

In 1927, as a result of an article by Winston Churchill, which Evan-Thomas (and others) thought was full of inaccuracies and again criticised the 5th BS, he wrote a long and somewhat intemperate letter to *The Times*. But by this time he had suffered a stroke, and his memory of the events eleven years earlier differed from those of many others. He died the following year at the age of 66.

*   *   *   *   *

In correspondence [7] with Cunninghame Graham, Admiral Sir Douglas Nicholson commented on the fact that the 5th BS had been ordered to alter course in succession to the North at about 1650, thus coming under concentrated fire at the turning point:

[7] Cunninghame Graham Papers, Churchill College, Cambridge

'Had the squadron turned together this could not have occurred and moreover appreciable time and distance would have been saved. Turning together however was at the time so out of fashion as to be almost forgotten and its use discouraged.'

This is something of an exaggeration; turns together were used, e.g. for avoiding a torpedo threat, and indeed in many of the manœuvres which had been introduced into the signal books. Commenting on the German 'battle turn', Nicholson himself wrote:

'Masterly it may be, but new it is not ... its great value at sea was brought most clearly to light in the 1870s by Admiral Sir Geoffrey Phipps Hornby, who may justly be said to have laid the foundations of all subsequent systems of handling ships in company under steam. To his devising also we owe the science and present systems of 'Forming and Disposing' and 'Equal Speed' signals and manœuvres, the latter being entirely constructed on the turn together principle.'

[8] *'Admiral of the Fleet Earl Beatty'*

Roskill [8] quotes Beatty writing to Jellicoe saying he was in favour of using 'Blue' turns but only by a squadron, not when all squadrons were together, 'which as you say, would not be desirable. But with 4 or 5 ships we have found it works very well.' But Vice Admiral Carrington, who had been navigator of *King George V*, says that both Jellicoe and his Master of the Fleet were opposed to the use of the turn together because of the risk of collision, and it was never used in Grand Fleet exercises and manœuvres.

Nicholson also remarked on another problem:

'From long experience as a Flag Lieutenant in the Fleet from 1891 to 1897, and in this century as a battleship Captain and junior Flag officer, nothing is harder or demands more unceasing attention than accurate station keeping when in long single lines ... to have to do these things just before, or in action, when the Captain should be free to attend to the fighting of his ship, is an uneasy business.'

*   *   *   *   *

[9] In his book *'Conflict of Style'*, a study of command and leadership styles in the Royal Navy, with particular relevance to the Battlecruiser Fleet and Jutland

Quite apart from the accuracy with which the times of hoisting and executing flag signals (two very different things), might have been logged, Dr Andrew Gordon has pointed out [9] a number of anomalies in the records which do nothing to help historians deduce the facts. Two examples:

a. The following sequence of signals for the 5th BS is listed in the Admiralty's Official Despatches:
1. *2.17   Turn in succession to N by E;*
2. *2.32   Turn together N by W;*
3. *2.40   Turn in succession to SSE.*

This sequence of signals is most unlikely to be correct; the ships are in line ahead after No.1 and on a line of bearing after No.2, from which a turn in succession is not possible.

b. Another sequence, addressed to the 5th BS:
1. *4.30   Turn together 4 points to port.*
2. *4.31   Negative Turn together 4 points to port.*

4.30 is shown as the time of despatch (ie, execution) of No.1, and it cannot possibly have been aborted by No.2. It could only be cancelled, before execution, by hoisting the 'Negative' on a separate halyard, and hauling them both down together.

No doubt these entries are incomplete or inaccurate, but they do illustrate the difficulties in interpreting the records.

Equal Speed Charlie London

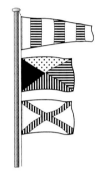

The Deployment signal at Jutland was adopted as the unofficial badge of the Signal School after the battle. As the School was housed in the Barracks, it formed part of HMS *Victory* and thus had no separate official badge of its own. It was displayed in the School, and was used as a blazer badge.

When the Signal School moved to Leydene in 1941 it became an independent command as HMS *Mercury* and thus acquired an official ship's badge. However the Deployment signal is still displayed, and it is flown at the Signal School on special occasions.

Chapter Seven

The Signal Division and the
Development of Wireless

'Codes of Signals have been used for centuries...
they are conveyed by flags, semaphores, balls, guns,
lights, rockets, bells, horns, whistles, etc. and a half
century since were carried on with incredible ability.'

Before the war there had been no Department at the
Admiralty with responsibility for all aspects of Signalling.
The Superintendent of Signal Schools was in effect the
Admiralty's adviser on visual signalling matters, and carried out
trials and experiments as necessary on new equipment. Under the
Director of Naval Operations there was one W/T officer on the staff
of the Assistant Director, Torpedoes (AD Torp). *Vernon's* W/T
Department virtually controlled the policy and design of wireless
equipment and wrote the necessary instructions.

As has been seen, individual signal books were written at the
Signal School, usually by an officer appointed for the task. By 1911
a complete revision was considered necessary, and a Signal Books
Revision Committee, later called the Signal Committee, was formed,
initially under Captain Richard Peirse, followed by Captain Sydney
Fremantle, and accommodated at RN Barracks, Portsmouth. As
Fremantle commented in his memoirs: [1]

'The increasing speed of ships and the improved reliability
and more general use of wireless telegraphy had necessi-
tated constant modifications in existing books, which were
encumbered with many slips embodying such changes ... the
effect of which was a liability to cause dangerous misunder-
standings, especially of manœuvring signals.'

Most of the books had been completed by May 1914, and some issued
for trial in the Fleet. On the whole they were well received, but they
had not been issued to foreign stations before war broke out, thus:

'... it was considered that the partial introduction ... would
be likely to cause much confusion. So the time and trouble
which my very able and experienced committee had devoted
to their task was very largely wasted.'

[1] *'My Naval Career, 1880-1928',*
Admiral Sir Sydney Fremantle

After a discussion with Prince Louis of Battenberg, First Sea Lord, at which Fremantle had pointed out the defects in the Admiralty organisation, he put up a detailed scheme for the formation of a Communications Department. This was overtaken by the outbreak of war, but the nucleus of the Signal Committee was kept in being, moved to London and formed the Signal Section of the Operations Division, under the Naval Assistant to the First Sea Lord. Fremantle again:

> *'The Signal Division (sic) was duly formed and, accommo-dated at a requisitioned office in Victoria Street, we started business with a small staff consisting of two experienced Commanders for the visual signalling and the W/T work respectively, a paymaster Lieutenant Commander for codes and cyphers, and two elderly Civil Service clerks. We very soon found that there was more work than could be done with so small a staff. The preparation of French, and later Italian, Allied Fleet Signal Books, necessarily under careful pre-cautions to preserve secrecy, I undertook myself ... but the principal business was in connection with codes and cyphers.*
>
> *'Pre-war it would take up to two years to produce a new cypher, but with the addition to our staff of a large number of women, we soon reduced this time to a month, and by the end of the war I believe the Division had a personnel of 300 and were able to prepare a new cypher book in a week.'*

The possible loss of secret books was a worry - the practice was for signal books, when not in use, to be kept in a wooden box with a lead bottom, to be thrown overboard if the ship was in danger of being captured. When a box from a ship that had run aground was found floating with the books intact, it was decided to fit each signal book with a slab of lead in its cover.

The Signal School played a large part in producing codes and cyphers, but had no access to the War Room, and thus to the movements of ships and squadrons, nor to the Intelligence Department, which seriously affected the quality of the codes and cyphers being produced, and complicated the distribution arrangements.

The W/T organisation was also soon found to be inadequate, mainly due to the lack of co-operation between the technical, and the operational and intelligence departments. Thus in 1917 a considerable re-organisation took place - first, on 20 June 1917 *Vernon's* Wireless Section moved *en bloc* to become the Experimental Department of the Signal School, the title of the Wireless Commander being changed to Experimental Commander. Then a couple of months later, the material side of V/S and W/T was transferred to the Director of Torpedoes and Mining (DTM), which now came under the Controller (3rd Sea Lord); Commanders Salmond and Candy became responsible 'for all matters connected with the design and development of W/T, Sonic Telegraphy (S/T) and Electric Signalling material, keeping in close touch with the Signal Division.'

Bertram Ramsay joined the Signal Section in February 1915. 'Ramsay had one of those comparatively rare brains, capable of grasping and retaining an extraordinary knowledge and appreciation of detail without ever losing sight of the overall picture.'

'Full Cycle', by W S Chalmers

On 18th August 1917 the Signal Section became a separate Directorate under DCNS, supervised initially by the Naval Assistant to the First Sea Lord, until on 8th October Commander R L Nicholson was appointed, as an acting Captain, to be the first Director. At the same time, the Signal School was given access to Operational and Intelligence information.

The Signal Division was defined as being responsible in the Office Memorandum of 18th August as being responsible for all Naval, Mercantile, Allied, and Military W/T, S/T and Visual Signalling (including the allocation of pendant numbers), Recognition Signals, Signal Books, Codes and Cyphers, and 'dealing with all messages (whether W/T, S/T, Visual, landline or cable).' The Division was not responsible for personnel or material but was to act in an advisory capacity, being consulted as necessary.

This led to some conflict of interest between DTM and DSD, so in April 1918 a further Office Memorandum laid down that DSD was to advise on all questions involving V/S, W/T and S/T policy, while DTM was to be responsible for all matters connected with the design and development of W/T, S/T and Electric Signalling material. This OM also laid down the duties of the Superintendent of Signal Schools - advice to DSD and DTM on visual, W/T and S/T matters; planning of W/T and S/T installations including design specifications, inspection and fitting; experimental work; and the instruction, training and examination of Signal and Telegraphist personnel.

The Signal Division provided a Duty Signal Officer for DCNS, so that one was always available to advise the operations staff in the same manner as a signal officer afloat. This much improved the general conduct of Admiralty communications and of the W/T organisation. However there was still a problem; as DSD commented: 'The organisation whereby War Registry [2] is utterly divorced from Signal Division and manned by persons with no knowledge of the dangers of transmitting badly drafted messages and of misusing codes, (has) undoubtedly led to the enemy gaining a great deal more information than he should.' But co-operation with War Registry gradually improved, and although it remained quite separate, DSD became in effect responsible for all matters of communication policy and practice.

Lack of adequate co-operation with the Army resulted in interference between Army and Navy communications, so in June 1917 a Joint Naval and Military W/T Committee was set up. This grew into the W/T Board, which was joined by the Air Force and the GPO.

A further reorganisation occurred in early 1920 when Office Memorandum of 1st April announced the transfer of the Signal Division from DCNS to the Controller:

'*As from 6th April 1920 the duties at present performed by DOCD, DTM, and the Superintendent of Signal Schools in connexion with the provision, organisation and maintenance of, and training of personnel in, W/T, R/T, S/T and V/S will*

[2] War Registry, civilian manned, was in effect the Admiralty's Main Signal Office, responsible for routeing and distributing messages.

be combined and dealt with by a single Department under the Controller with the title of Signal Department. The Head of the Department will be known as the Director of Naval Signals, and will be on a footing similar to DNO and DTM. The Communications Division of the Naval Staff has ceased to exist as such.

'The post of Superintendent of Signal Schools will be abolished, but the Officer in Command of the Signal School will act in an advisory capacity to the DNS ...

'The word communication as applied to Signals, W/T and other forms of telegraphy is no longer to be used and it is to be replaced by the word signal.'

The Signal Department remained under the Controller until World War II, although DSD had a responsibility to VCNS for operational matters. This somewhat unconventional arrangement was formalised in 1941, with DSD being responsible to the Controller for material matters, dealt with by DDSD(M), and to VCNS for operational matters, handled by three other deputies, for V/S and W/T, RDF, and 'Y'. In November 1943 these functions were separated - the Signal Department became a Division of the Naval Staff, while a new Radio Equipment Department was formed '...responsible to the Controller for all matters connected with Research, Design, Trials, Development and Production of all equipment making use of electro-magnetic waves (except airborne and ammunition).' This of course included supervision of the Admiralty Signal Establishment.

*   *   *   *   *

There was a great upsurge in the use of wireless after the first war. The early arc and spark transmitters were gradually replaced by the first valve sets, again working in the range 100-300 kHz. The big ship sets were Types 35 and 36, while destroyers had Type 37, the latter having a working range of about 500 miles, although they could often be heard at 1,000 miles or more. Another set, the Type 34, was introduced for exchanging gunnery spotting information. There was also a low powered transmitter known as the Type 43, which used a pair of NT1 valves - the first transmitter valves introduced into naval service. This was housed in the auxiliary office and used for harbour wave, having a range of about ten miles, though much greater ranges were achieved around dawn in the summer months.

John Meadows[3] wrote:

'The wireless office was situated on the lowest deck of the ship, accessed by climbing down a vertical ladder, the watertight door at the top of the shaft normally being clipped shut. Not an action station for anyone who suffered from claustrophobia!'

'In the later 1920s a new breed of transmitter began to come into use, the Type 48 as the main set in big ships, and

In Minutes on Admiralty files of the time the Director was variously referred to as DSD, DNS or DOCD; DSD, signifying either Division or Department, seems to have been the generally accepted title.

Commander John Meadows joined the Signal Branch as a young telegraphist in 1928, and had a job for his first few months as a 'sweeper' in the Experimental Department, then housed in wooden huts on the edge of the parade ground at Portsmouth Barracks. This experience seems to have led him to become a radio enthusiast who not only understood how radio worked, but later became adept at putting it over as an Instructor at the Signal School for many years.

[3] Letter to the author

the Type 49 for destroyers. These were more complex and more powerful but still operated in the LF and MF bands.

'The first thermionic valve receiver, known as the model C, which replaced the crystal set, had a number of separate coils and condensers which could be adjusted to receive a given frequency. Each unit was screwed into a silent cabinet lined with copper sheeting, the various items being connected together with number 10 gauge copper wire which was fashioned to connect either horizontally or vertically, never at any other angle. These wires were invariably polished with brasso, as were the contacts on the inductance boxes and their moving arms. This made the items on the bulkhead gleam purposefully, thus inviting communication with the outside world, but bits of dried brasso between contacts did nothing to improve the efficiency of the rig!'

Buzzer lines were fitted to connect the various wireless offices and remote positions, and sometimes also the communication department messes. This facilitated the general administration of the communication department, and also allowed signal officers, who had to learn morse at 22 words per minute on the long course, their only chance

A Battleship's huge roof aerials

to practise it! 'It was a brave chap who responded to the callsign 'SO', although there were some, like Dickie Mountbatten and Christopher Bonham-Carter, who could handle it well', said Meadows.

Chief Tel Bill Hoskins, who joined the Navy in 1917, remembers his first ship, the *Triad*, proceeding to the Dardanelles just after the war. There was still a danger from mines, and mine warning signals were broadcast every hour from Malta:

> *'Radio receivers had not progressed beyond the crystal stage and although the combination of carborundum, steel, telerium and bornite proved fairly efficient, the operator had to keep on his toes.'*

Hoskins was drafted to the *Caesar* where the equipment was:

> *'just a spark transmitter and crystal receiver, but the aston-ishing thing was the amount of work carried out with other ships and even direct to Malta ... success was due to aerials made up of six foot cane spreaders holding six legs of 19 SWG phosphor bronze wire between very high masts ... after dark one saw the firework display caused by the corona discharge across the insulators from the aerials to the wooden mast, which indicated a lot of wasted power!'*

When in *Centurion* in the Mediterranean, Hoskins recollects keeping in touch with *Renown*, with the Prince of Wales embarked, as she sailed for India:

> *'We were still working with* Renown *when she had reached the Persian Gulf, a distance of some 1,700 miles. I spent many hours on watch with my mouth open as we found that hearing was improved by holding one's breath, though not for too long!'*

Chief Tel Austin was a young Ordinary Telegraphist in *Royal Sovereign* in 1922:

> *'The ship was fitted with a Type 2 spark transmitter and what was then a modern Type 34 valve transmitter in the main W/T office; the second office, situated just aft of the Boys' messdeck and a deck below, was equipped with a Type 1 spark and a Type 16 arc transmitter.*
>
> *'Neither the Warrant Tel nor the Chief Tel were entirely au fait with the modern transmitters. The second W/T office was a very confined space, the transmitters being in the usual 'cage', the door to which was fitted so that, when opened, power to the transmitters was cut off, although the cage door contacts remained alive. To enter the narrow door one had to squeeze past a protruding shelf just above the deck which held the transformer supplying the sets.*
>
> *'One day when I was at my cleaning station in the 2nd W/T, the valve transmitter ceased to work. The Chief was sent for; as he squeezed through the cage door his shins collided*

'Before money is spent on wireless stations, it is essential to ascertain precisely what advantages would be secured in return. What were the probabilities that they would be 'jammed' in time of war; that they would be put out of gear by evilly disposed persons?'

R F Wilkins,
Committee of Imperial Defence,
29 June 1914

with the transformer shelf, and to prevent himself falling he grabbed the frame of the cage door right on top of the safety contacts. He duly received a very nasty shock. Being somewhat inexperienced and naive, I made the mistake of laughing out loud ... I myself then suffered considerable discomfort from the Chief ... but I did learn not to laugh at other people's misfortunes, particularly if they happened to be one's senior!'

Accidents in the 'cage' of the old transmitters were not uncommon. In the early thirties, the Chief Tel of the Penelope was careful to move the actuating arm of a magnetic switch to bring on the power supplies with a 12-inch ruler, but he had failed to notice that it had a thin metallic strip let in to one edge. The 10,000 volts which routed itself to earth through the ruler and the Chief Tel did him a good deal of damage.

Soon after the war, planning had begun for a world-wide system of shore W/T stations. These were originally intended to have low frequency transmitters, but at about this time it was realised that high frequency transmissions could be reflected from the ionosphere and thus travel long distances. HF had other advantages - less powerful transmitters and smaller aerials could be used, which saved money, and many more channels were available in the HF band than in the LF. Thus an 'Empire' chain of HF stations was gradually established including Ottawa, Esquimault, and Halifax in Canada, Bermuda, Aden, Bombay, Ceylon, Singapore, Hong Kong, Durban, the Falklands, Belconnen (Australia) and Wairouru (New Zealand).

Semaphore and Morse ('Wig-Wag') exercises, and Marching Manœuvres at the Barracks, Portsmouth, in the 1930s

It should be mentioned at this point that the 'Government Code and Cypher School' had been opened on 1st November 1919, at Watergate House, Adelphi (Marconi's old headquarters, as it happened). Supervised by DNI, its first Director was Commander Alastair Denniston, RNVR, a German speaking master from Osborne naval college, who had been brought into NID to work on German naval cyphers. The GC & CS took over responsibility for compiling and printing all Government Codes and Cyphers, including reviewing the security of those in use, and giving advice to all concerned.

In 1922 responsibility for GC & CS was transferred from the Admiralty to the Foreign Office, and the organisation moved to Queen's Gate, but the naval intercept and DF stations remained under the Admiralty. Denniston was Director until 1944, when he was succeeded by another naval officer, Sir Edward Travis. A signal officer, Sir Clive ('Joe') Loehnis, who joined in 1935, was Director from 1960 to 1964, though by then it had become known as the Government Communications Headquarters (GCHQ).

Mountbatten - the Signal Officer

Lord Louis, as he was known in the Navy, had a considerable impact on the world of signals between the wars. Apart from his forceful personality, he became a knowledgeable and enthusiastic specialist in wireless, and could handle a key or tune a transmitter as well as most telegraphists.

He joined the Signal School for the Long Course in 1924, but had shown an interest in signals many years before. 'I remember having miniature semaphore and morse flags made for me by the Signalmen of my father's flagship, HMS *Drake*, in 1905, (and) I learnt to use both quite well.'

In 1920 he had been Flag Lieutenant to Rear Admiral Sir Lionel Halsey in the *Renown* for the Prince of Wales' Empire tour.

> 'The Admiral was well versed in the old Fleet Signal Book which had recently been replaced by the Fleet Code. He used to say to me: "Flags, hoist MY to the escort". I had to look up MY in the old book and find it meant 'Proceed in execution of previous orders'. I then had to look that up in the new book and give the order to hoist KF. This taught me that Flag Officers should not try and tell the Flag Lieutenant how to make the actual signal.' [4]

Mountbatten went straight from the Long Course to Greenwich to do the Higher Wireless Course (known as the 'Dagger' course because of the symbol that then appeared against one's name in the Navy List), his results being good enough to qualify him to be an Associate of the Institute of Electrical Engineers. After a short spell as Flag Lieutenant to the Admiral Commanding Reserves, in 1927 he became Assistant Fleet Wireless Officer, Mediterranean Fleet. Here he made his mark with a series of two hour lectures to junior officers; these were

Loehnis did the long course in 1928. 'We used the Barracks' parade ground for marching manœuvres, there were two masts for flag-hoisting, and we did semaphore and flashing exercises, the latter from a masthead light which we read from the wardroom. Peter Reid was our star turn.'

[4] 'An Old Communicator's Reminiscences'
The Communicator, Vol.22 No.4, 1975

HMS *Drake* at Halifax, Nova Scotia, 21 October 1905

Drake was flagship of Rear Admiral Prince Louis of Battenberg. Writing to General Griffiths, who had been Captain of Marines on board at the time, Lord Mountbatten said: 'I well remember my father telling me how he had the necessary signal flags made on board in order to be able to hoist Nelson's original signal.' In fact, the numeral flags flying are from the 1799 Signal Book, whereas those actually used at Trafalgar were from the revised version introduced in January 1804 as a result of the compromise of the 1799 book. In 1885 someone in the Admiralty, who was unaware of the change in 1804, no doubt because he referred to an unamended copy of the signal book, pronounced the flags used on Trafalgar Day to be wrong, and they were changed back to those of the 1799 book. This was finally put right in 1908 after the new Admiralty Librarian, W G Perrin, investigated the matter.

The apparent admiral's flag at the main represents the Telegraph flag which indicated that the message had been coded up using Popham's Vocabulary Code.

subsequently published and distributed to every ship. In 1929 he returned to the Signal School, the intention being that as a 'Dagger' he should join the Experimental Department as an application officer, but he thought this might mark him out as too much of a technical specialist and he was able to arrange a mutually agreeable swap with Geoffrey Burghard to head the W/T instructional staff as 'W One' instead.

There is no doubt that he was an excellent instructor ('Full of ideas, most of which are excellent ...' noted the Captain), and Peter Dawnay remembers his lectures being both lucid and amusing. He thought that the existing documentation was inadequate and one of his contributions to the Branch was to reform the system of reference books. His main effort was directed towards producing a new *Handbook of Wireless Telegraphy*, known as BR222, which was the 'Bible' for telegraphists and, regularly updated, remained so for many years. 'I spent my spare time writing a book called Notes on W/T sets ... an enormous loose leaf volume with circuit diagrams and photographs of every W/T set...' he noted. He claimed to oversee the production of every drawing and photograph, in conjunction with his assistant, Chief Telegraphist Horace Brooks (who was to remain with him for many years, and no doubt did much of the donkey work). He set up the Drawing Office to produce the definitive version of the diagrams, and also wall charts - in colour, for the first time.

Lord Louis is probably best remembered by the telegraphists who served in the Mediterranean Fleet in 1931 and 1932 when he was the Fleet Wireless Officer. Flag signalling had reached a peak of efficiency in the first decades of the twentieth century, but in the W/T department both morale and operating standards left a good deal to be desired. Although wireless was by then well established, the telegraphist, hidden away in the W/T office down below, was not as close to the 'command' as the signalman; his responsibilities were just as great and mistakes could have serious consequences, thus it was all too easy to end up with the brickbats while the bouquets were apt to be somewhat sparse. Mountbatten recognised that the telegraphists were short of 'esteem' and that it was necessary to give them a sense of 'belonging', but that this also required senior officers to be educated into the potential of wireless and the importance of the telegraphist.

On the practical side, he introduced a procedure whereby any signalling error had to be reported immediately it was detected. This led to the (erroneous) belief that he had a receiver which he regularly manned at his house at Pieta in Malta. It was of course largely the vigilance of his own staff at the communications centre at Castille that kept him in the picture, but this potentially invidious procedure worked because it was approached in the right frame of mind, not least because he took a lot of trouble to get to know a good deal about every ship's W/T department. He set up a system of personal documentation which stood him in good stead then, as well as in later years, and was the basis for his renowned 'personal touch'.

Chief Tel Bill Hoskins recalls the communication exercises at Malta: 'Questions on any subject were hoisted at the signal station and answered by both wireless and flag signals - all on a competitive basis - for everyone to see who was first and last, and there was often a request for an operator's log for scrutiny. These exercises ... were instrumental in producing some of the finest wireless operators in the world. Mountbatten was the most efficient man at any job I have ever met - he *was* the wireless department of the Navy.'

During his final week as FWO, Lord Louis laid on a Wireless Signalling Demonstration at the Castille. Quick-shift scenery was put up, hiding a large switchboard enabling the receivers at Castille to be connected to loudspeakers on appropriate waves. Ships, aircraft and a submarine took part, as did the Admiralty, and the audience were invited to originate messages which were then heard being transmitted and the replies received. The demonstration covered peace time communications, wireless discipline and the detection of offenders by the note of his transmitter, and the restrictions of a war situation. The finale showed the Remote Control Office of the Fleet Flagship as the first enemy reports began coming in.

Mountbatten certainly had a good technical understanding and considered himself something of an expert. He met Marconi aboard the latter's yacht Electra in 1926 and was shown round the experimental transmitting room. 'The questions I asked soon floored him as his knowledge was still fairly primitive. He therefore sent for his senior scientist to answer my questions.'

Letter to P L Green,
21 February 1979
Broadlands Archives

Lord Louis conducting the Wireless Signalling demonstration at the Castille

The Remote Control Office is on the left, and the Bridge of HMS *Keith* on the right. The circuits are labelled, left to right: Med. HF wave (Day), Admiral's wave, Aux wave, Reconnaissance wave, and Destroyer wave. The High Speed Transmitter is in front of Lord Louis, with the PO of the Watch at the back, and the High Speed Receiver at the extreme right. The board at the back lists the ships and authorities on each wave. The coding Office is below the right hand board.

On completion of the last of the three 'shows', Lord Louis went to the Receiving Room to thank all concerned.

> *'To my horror I heard the 'laughing sign' (— —·· — —)*
> *being transmitted on Auxiliary wave. I caught one of my*
> *favourite operators red-handed on the key. Then I did a*
> *terrible thing; I said "You've made a fool of all we've been*
> *working for. You asked if I could send you home six months*
> *early; I had agreed. That is cancelled. You will join the sloop*
> *leaving tomorrow for six months in the Red Sea. It is*
> *summer, and the Fleet will soon know who had the last*
> *laugh". He took it like a man. This splendid chap was the*
> *first who wrote to volunteer for the Kelly in 1939. He*
> *certainly had the last word.'*

Peter Dawnay, then flag lieutenant in the 1st Cruiser Squadron wrote:

> *'He inspired terrific enthusiasm and loyalty from his team*
> *of telegraphists ... there is not the slightest doubt that he*
> *brought the Fleet up to the peak of wireless efficiency and*
> *good discipline, which was very strict.'*

Royer Dick, the Fleet Signal Officer, considered Lord Louis 'the outstanding Signal Officer of his generation.' A slightly different view was expressed by Admiral Jerram:

> '*As FWO Mountbatten was a bit too ready to sweep with
> a new broom. He was forever re-writing the Mediterra-
> nean Fleet Wireless Orders and became the bogey of the
> printing staff!*'

No doubt any other FWO would have taken much the same action,
but certainly Lord Louis was much respected by the communicators
of the fleet at this time, and indeed by all those who served on his
staff.

The Larken Committee

In July 1932 Lord Louis had returned home to give evidence to the
Larken Committee, which was enquiring into the conditions of
service, pay and functions of the Signal and Telegraphist branches.
The main problem arose from anomalies in the pay structure, which
meant that some senior communication ratings were paid less than
their seamen counterparts. In addition the promotion ladders were
stagnant, while it was felt that as communication ratings tended to be
the pick of the new entries they would have advanced much more
quickly in other branches. This resulted in good men leaving the
Service because they had not reached Petty Officer rate before
completing their first twelve year engagement. Furthermore, in
comparison with other branches, their hours were longer, they were
hard pressed during fleet exercises, they still had to keep watches
when in port and, when ships were detached from the fleet, the
telegraphists still had to work as hard as ever. On top of all this they
had much more responsibility than the seamen.

The Committee pondered the old chestnut of whether the Signal
and Telegraphist branches should be amalgamated or indeed
completely separated; it was decided they should 'be kept together.'[5]
It did recommend that their rates of pay should be identical, and other
anomalies were ironed out. The problems of watchkeeping, responsibilities, stretch, entry qualifications and other matters which the
Committee also considered were very little different from those
which have continued to be familiar to the Branch ever since.
Interestingly, of the 57 witnesses called by the Committee, no less
than 20 were ratings.

[5] Board Minute, 13 July 1933

Chapter Eight

The Experimental Department

*'There was never any shortage of ideas - more were
generated than could ever be worked on'*

By 1918 the Experimental Department had settled down within
the Signal School, and a new Experimental Commander was
soon to be appointed. This was James Somerville, a (T) and
W/T specialist, who was particularly interested in radio and all its
ramifications. At the begining of the war he had been the W/T officer
on the staff of BS1 in the *Marlborough*, then Fleet W/T Officer to
Vice Admiral de Robeck who was in command of the Dardanelles
operations, where he won the DSO. He remained with de Robeck
when the latter returned to command the 2nd Battle Squadron in the
Grand Fleet. Thus he came to his new job with a wealth of valuable
sea experience.

Somerville was renowned for his witty, sometimes rather rude,
signals. 'His signal repartee was a constant joy' says Rear Admiral
Roy Foster-Brown, his flag lieutenant when Somerville became
RA(D) Med in 1936:

> *'He retained a schoolboyish approach to things all his life ...
> but his jests were not always appreciated - the flag lieutenant
> to a cruiser squadron admiral begged me to stop Somerville
> sending such signals. But when the flagship switched on a
> brilliantly illuminated name plaque 'SOUTHAMPTON', off
> went the following: 'As a shareholder in the Southern Railway
> Company I must protest at what can only be called pilfering
> of one of the platform signs ...' There was no response to this.'*

Admiral of the Fleet
Sir James Somerville

Somerville had under him in the Experimental Department some 35
civilian technical staff under the Chief Technical Advisor, H A
Madge, about 60 draftsmen and clerks, as well as four naval officers.
The latter became known as Application Officers, their job being to
interpret the Naval Staff Requirements to the scientists, to monitor
the progress of new projects, and to keep the Naval Staff informed of

scientific developments. In practice this meant being closely associated with each project to ensure that developments kept in step with operational requirements and didn't stray into interesting but less relevant directions, while at the same time representing the views of the scientists to the Naval Staff, especially where the stated requirement was clearly unreasonable or unattainable, or might profitably be revised to achieve a more realistic result.

The Application Officer did not need to be a technical expert though a degree of competence and plenty of common sense was advisable; more important was his ability to get on well with the civilian staff and to gain their confidence. He also had to retain the confidence of the Naval Staff who understandably wanted new projects turned into production equipment as fast as possible and fretted at any delays, while the scientists usually had a better idea just around the corner - 'jam tomorrow, but never jam today'. The Application Officer therefore found himself very much 'the jam in the sandwich'.

The Application Officer arrangement has continued in the Navy to this day. Dr David Kiely, in his book 'Naval Electronic Warfare', comments:

'Naval Application Officers maintain a close dialogue with equipment designers from the earliest stages of a project, and they ensure that the special features required for naval use at sea are known to the civilian designers. (They) behave as 'Expert Users', not as engineering designers, and the unique contribution they make is most valuable.'

The future organisation and staffing of the Experimental Department was considered by a committee which reported in 1919 and recommended a substantial increase in both naval and civilian staff. This was not received very favourably by the Treasury because of 'the War Cabinet decision that a war of large dimensions within the next ten years is not to be regarded as a possible contingency, and the reductions being made in the Navy ...'. However Their Lordships argued that it would be 'a tremendous mistake to acquiesce in reducing on the same scale the personnel concerned with thinking, designing, research and experiment, otherwise at the end of ten years we shall have not merely a small fleet, but a small fleet ten years out of date in all its equipment and organisation.' [1]

The Treasury insisted that the Signal School was not a Research Institution, its function being to work out the practical application to Naval needs of wireless developments, but after discussion and much argument about the pay of the civilian staff, agreement was reached in 1920 on a new complement which still allowed a substantial increase. ('It would anyway have been impossible to fill all the posts originally proposed', commented DSD, Captain J K im Thurn!).

Amongst those scientists who joined the Experimental Department of the Signal School during the war or soon afterwards were George Shearing as head of the scientific staff in 1919;

In his book 'Fighting Admiral' Donald Macintyre quotes an early example of Somerville's wit. As Executive Officer of HMS Ajax, in the Black Sea, he had been presented with a Russian bear, which he named Trotsky. From time to time Trotsky would amble down the gangway and swim over to another ship where his arrival on deck caused a certain amount of dismay. On one occasion the Commander of the flagship thought he had scored when he signalled:

'Your bear has just visited us and says he came to find a clean spot on which to sit down.'

Somerville trumped this by replying: 'Our bear has returned and reports his search was unsuccessful!'

[1] Board Minute of 6 October 1919 (PRO ref. ADM116-1845)

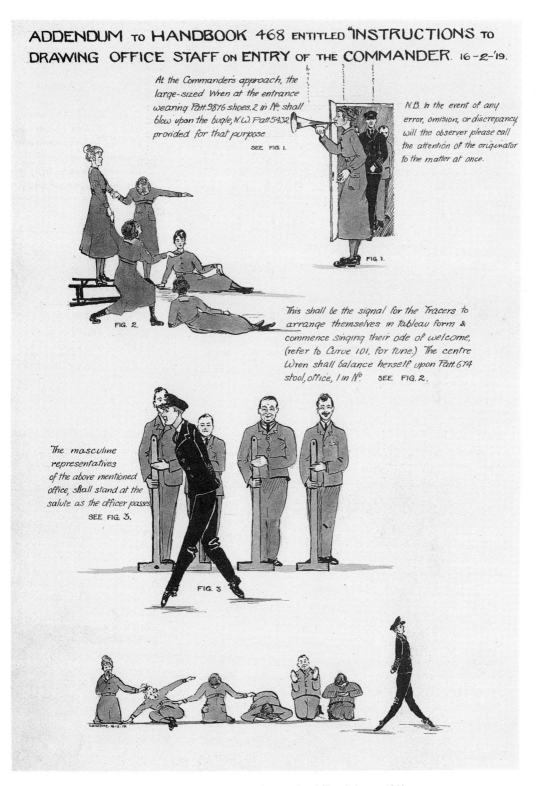

The Experimental Commander, James Somerville, inspects the Drawing Office, February 1919

The W/T Department on board HMS *Warrior (Vernon III)*, 1916

Front, sitting on deck (L to R): H Morris-Airey, BS Gossling, TF Wall, HB Howell GL Glen-Bott, GD Dewar, Sinclair
Seated (L to R): Capt Miles RM, Prof CL Fortescue, Lt Cdr Loveband, Cdr Prendergast, Cdr JK im Thurn, Cdr Kennedy-Purvis, Henry Madge, Cdr Pitcairn, 2 u/k.

Morris-Airey relieved Madge as Chief Technical Adviser in 1919. A number of the scientists were commissioned in the RNVR at that time.

(Sir) Frederick Brundrett, who later became 'The Secretary' (head of the civilian staff), a particularly influential figure who was later Chief of the Royal Naval Scientific Service; Cecil Evershed, who relieved Brundrett as Secretary; and Cecil Horton.

The integration of the scientists within the Signal School was a unique arrangement which had great beneficial results. Professor John Coales, FRS, joined the Signal School on Trafalgar Day, 1929:

> *'Those naval officers I dealt with, who had been to some extent hand-picked by DCNS, were certainly the most intelligent group of men I have ever had to work with. Civilians were treated in every way as equals of the naval officers and were looked on as 'Scientific Gentlemen'; we were made members of the Officers' mess ... naval and civilian staff treated each other with respect, and close friendships developed.*
>
> *'The civilians were often at sea, sometimes for prolonged periods, thus seeing the conditions for themselves, and this frequently inspired new developments. But no one had a monopoly of ideas - they could come from the*

Madge resigned at the end of September 1919 to become a Missionary, and was succeeded as Chief Technical Adviser by Harold Morris-Airey. Brundrett, who had been his mathematical assistant, recalls:

> *'Madge used to resign about once every month. He was an able theoretician and was often seen lying on his stomach on the carpet dictating abstruse papers to the typist.'*

Quoted by O.L. Ratsey in *'As We Were'*, the history of ASWE 1896-1946

The Royal Naval Scientific Service was only formally established in 1945, although the idea had been conceived in 1938. Sir Charles Wright, who was the Navy's Director of Scientific Research, became its first head, and the complement after the war was about 1,100 Scientific and Experimental Officers. The RNSS as such ceased to exist in 1970, as a result of the Ministry of Defence reorganisation.

application officers, the instructional staff, the scientists, the Admiralty or from sea. There was never any shortage of ideas - more were generated than could ever be worked on.'

The cruiser *Antrim* was used for Signal School propagation trials between the UK and Freetown, Sierra Leone, in 1922. Transmitting aerials tried included two 12 inch diameter 'sausages' with 20 wires, 209 feet long for the outward trip, and four of 32 wires homeward. The receiving aerial was a single 'sausage' 440 feet long. Transmissions by *Antrim* and Horsea Island were on wavelengths between 1,100 and 4,800 metres.

The section which was principally involved in developing short wave direction finding, known as X4, was run by Cecil Horton for some sixteen years; he was joined in 1923 by Cecil Crampton and in 1930 by John Coales, amongst many others. As well as the development of HF DF, the work included research into radio propagation; at one stage Robert Watson-Watt, then head of the Radio Division of the National Physical Laboratory, accompanied Horton on a prolonged cruise in HMS *Yarmouth* to investigate the nature of atmospherics and carry out short wave propagation trials. The close association between the Signal School and NPL continued in the 1930s when the possibility of radio echo detection began to be considered and led to the eventual development of RDF, later known as Radar.

Hugh Malleson was the Application Officer for DF in 1930.

'The MF DF in big ships was clumsy and inefficient, consisting of a Bellini-Tosi arrangement of long wires between the funnels. Calibration meant anchoring in a special position in Stokes Bay while the biggest dockyard tug towed the ship round in circles, and bearings were taken of a shore transmitter. A time consuming procedure, which had to be repeated for three or more frequencies.'

Having left the Navy, Malleson was recalled in 1938 to join Crampton and the DF section again.

'By this time a small frame aerial had been designed, and calibration involving a vessel fitted with a suitable transmitter to circle the ship had become standard practice.'

Roy Foster-Brown remembers Crampton saying later on that the HF DF project was in trouble and might even have to be abandoned, because for various reasons, such as the low height of ship's masts, they were having great trouble in achieving a worthwhile bearing capability - 'We can't do any better than plus or minus 25 degrees'. 'But that's marvellous - just what we want' was Foster-Brown's reply; a rough bearing of that sort was a great improvement on nothing at all! This was a good example of the vital importance of the scientists and naval staff working closely together. As it eventually turned out, it was regularly possible to obtain bearings to within a few degrees.

By about 1930 Horton concluded that the best HF DF development would be to use a rotating frame coil, and the cruiser *Achilles* was designed with a single tube foremast to take this at the masthead. Later a fixed system to cover MF as well as HF was produced, given sea trials in *Concord*, and fitted in the new Town class cruisers, starting with *Newcastle* in 1936.

Evershed's team, X5, started work on radio remote control in 1919 and the first system was fitted in the battleship *Agamemnon*, which was used as the target ship for full calibre shoots. An improved system was fitted in *Centurion*, which took over from *Agamemnon*, and was used as a target ship for many years, mainly in the Mediterranean. The skeleton crew which took her to sea transferred to her control ship, the *Truant*, and later *Shikari*, and *Centurion* was then manœuvred by remote control. This work led on to the use of radio controlled motor torpedo boats and eventually to the 'Queen Bee' radio controlled target aircraft developed by the Royal Aircraft Establishment and used extensively for AA target practice.

David Joel was in command of *Truant* in 1923 when she was both the Signal School trials ship and control ship for *Agamemnon*.

Centurion and *Shikari*

> '*It was quite uncanny for all one had to do on my bridge was to dial an ordinary telephone, for example 90, and she would turn to, and accurately steer 090°. It was the same to adjust her speed, and even to discharge a smoke screen, but one disadvantage was that we could never quite stop, and never start, her reciprocating engines. I had to go alongside her often in fairly rough weather in mid-channel with her steaming at 6 or 7 knots, and take off her skeleton crew. This was a tricky job! Sometimes my charge would not be the old 'Aggie' but a CMB, the predecessor of the MTB. These were very fast ... Truant had the reputation of being the fastest destroyer afloat, perhaps 36 or 37 knots, but even so I had to zig-zag the CMB in order to keep her within range.*'

Lieutenant Commander the Hon. Henry Cecil, who also had the honorary rank of Squadron Leader, with his team in front of a 'Queen Bee' radio controlled aircraft, about 1935

By the early 1920s, as well as X4 (DF) and X5 (Remote Control), other sections included X1 to develop Receiving systems, X2 for Transmitters, X3 Valves, X6 Underwater Signalling, and X7 Visual Signalling and Infra-red. The Application Officers attached to the sections were designated A1, A2 etc., later changed to C1, C2, to distinguish them from those of other specialisations who arrived when the Department became involved in, for example, gunnery radar. Apart from the transfer of the Underwater work (X6) to HMS *Osprey* in 1927, the organisation remained largely unaltered for some fifteen years, until a major reorganisation took place in 1937.

The Development of Naval Radar

In 1928 Leonard Alder, a brilliant radio engineer on the Signal School staff, proposed a scheme for the detection and location of objects by radio; in accordance with the normal procedure, he and CSS, Captain Salmond, took out a provisional patent (No.6433/28 dated 1 March), which read, in part:

> *'This invention relates to methods and means for the employment of the reflection, scattering or re-radiation of wireless waves by objects as a means of detecting the presence of such objects and of determining the positions, directions or distances of such objects.'*

This clearly described what later came to be known as RDF, and then Radar, quite precisely. In the Admiralty, DSD and the Director of Scientific Research (DSR) apparently failed to appreciate the potential of this idea, nor to consult the appropriate scientists. 'A distressing lapse for which we were responsible in DSR's department ... It taught us a lesson, but too late,' wrote Sir Charles Wright after the war.

[2] *Journal of the RNSS,* 1947

Cecil Horton commented: [2]

> *'(The patent) gives convincingly and lucidly the fundamental principles on which the various types of radar have been developed. Nevertheless nothing was done about that patent and it lapsed; it fell on very infertile soil ... the user had had no previous experience of radar on which to base his sense of value.'*

Interestingly, Watson-Watt, in his book *Three Steps to Victory*, quotes Marconi, speaking in New York in 1922, as saying:

> *'In some of my tests I have noticed the effects of reflection and deflection of these (short) waves by metallic objects miles away. It seems (that) a ship could radiate or project a divergent beam of these rays in any direction which, if coming across a metallic object, such as another ship, would be reflected back ... and immediately reveal the presence and bearing of the other ship in fog or thick weather ...'*

The Army Signals Experimental Establishment at Woolwich also came up with a proposal in 1931 for a pulsed system for detecting

The S/T (Underwater Signalling) team at the Signal School in 1921. Leonard Alder (left) whose 1928 patent for 'radar' was not taken up by the Admiralty; E A Logan; 'Jock' Anderson, who became Chief Scientist of the Admiralty Signal and Radar Establishment 1951-61, and W F Rawlinson, team leader.

ships, in this case for coastal defence. This too got no further as there was no stated War Office requirement.

In 1934 the lack of any effective means of air defence began to cause concern - exercises in the summer of that year seemed to indicate that 'the bomber will always get through' - and this led to the setting up of a Committee to consider whether recent advances in scientific and technical knowledge could help. The Chairman was Henry Tizard and members included Professor Blackett, a physicist who had served in the Royal Navy, Charles Wright, DSR, and A B Wood from the Admiralty Research Laboratory (ARL). At their first meeting in January 1935 a memorandum by Watson-Watt suggested that radio detection of aircraft might be possible. This was quickly followed in February by the report of an experiment in which an aircraft, flying in the beam of the BBC's short wave station at Daventry, had produced a detectable echo in a receiver when it was eight miles away.

Watson-Watt and a small team moved to Orfordness where radio location trials could be carried out in secrecy, under the guise of ionospheric research. A sub-committee of the Committee for Imperial Defence was set up to oversee the work (known as the Swinton Committee after its Chairman, the Air Minister); this was often attended by Churchill who had been instrumental in getting it going, and the Navy's interests were represented by the Controller. In May 1935 they resolved to give every encouragement to the Orfordness trials 'in conjunction with those (trials) required by the Navy', and they gave the scientists something to aim at - a range of detection of 50 miles within 5 years.

'The Controller has decided that the Signal School should start work as soon as possible on the Naval application of the detection and location of aircraft by wireless methods, work on the production of the transmitting apparatus being begun at once.'

DSD letter to CSS,
13 August 1935
ADM 220/70

Meanwhile Shearing, Chief Scientist at the Signal School, who had become involved with the Tizard Committee, said that he thought the most promising line to follow would be 'that in which the aeroplane is used to reflect energy from some source', citing Post Office experience of signals being interfered with when aircraft were in the vicinity. He added that the Signal School was working on the use of ultra short waves for communications purposes, ie about 50cm, using small valves which had been produced in America, but that a magnetron valve capable of working down to about 36cm had been developed.

The Navy had a requirement for small and robust transmitting valves, with envelopes made of silica instead of glass, but because there was little demand for these outside the Navy, the Signal School was forced to undertake both research and their manufacture. This was of importance to the Orfordness team who urgently needed valves of this sort, and DSD, Captain G W Hallifax, was asked to arrange for the co-operation of the Signal School. In his letter to CSS, Captain J W S Dorling, DSD said 'this work appears highly promising and of the greatest importance not only to the Air Force but also to the Navy (where) it may have applications other than for the detection of aircraft'. He said that the Signal School should ask for additional staff if needed.

Dorling agreed that 'every effort should be made to explore the naval possibilities' but asked initially for only one extra Scientific Officer and one Assistant. R A Yeo, who had been working on short wave communications in X2, was seconded temporarily to Orfordness, and the Navy was finally in the RDF business.

After Yeo's return in October, preliminary requirements for naval RDF were formulated - 60 miles warning of approach of aircraft, 10 miles for ships, with precise location at 10 miles and 5 miles respectively. More Scientific staff were asked for, and space was acquired at Eastney Fort East for a hut and two masts to carry aerials, with a clear view over the sea (but the senior Royal Marine Officer, whose view was spoiled, was not pleased!). From this site the Nab Tower provided a useful reference as a standard target.

The Valve Section, X3, were already supplying the RAF with silica envelope valves, and the Navy retained responsibility for valve development for many years, the CVD [3] organisation being set up in 1938 to provide overall co-ordination.

By October 1936 at the Signal School there were still only four scientists and one assistant working on RDF, which had no special priority but was classified Most Secret, so that very few members of the staff knew what was going on.

Meanwhile Watson-Watt and the Air Ministry were pressing for all experimental work on radio location to be concentrated at Bawdsey, near Orfordness. The Signal School resisted this strongly, on the basis that conditions in ships, where problems such as mutual interference with other radio equipment, the effects of gunfire and so

[3] Communications Valve Development, no doubt part of the ploy to keep the RDF work secret.

on, could only be dealt with effectively by their own Experimental Department; furthermore the Navy needed to work on shorter wavelengths, of which it already had some experience, in order to keep the size of aerials small enough for ships. Also, DSD pointed out, the Navy was interested in the detection and location of surface craft as well as aircraft, and ship targets would be essential for experiments and trials, which favoured Portsmouth.

At their meeting in December 1936 the Swinton Committee agreed, resolving that whereas Bawdsey must be the headquarters for research on location of aircraft, '... the Admiralty might prefer RDF location at sea to be investigated at the Signal School at Portsmouth'. [4]

[4] ADR Minute of 9 December 1936 Swinton Committee Papers CAB 16/132

A sea trial of the Navy's first experimental RDF set, known as Type 79X, took place in December 1936 in the Signal School's trials ship, the old coal-burning minesweeper *Saltburn*. Fixed transmitting and receiving dipoles were suspended 50 feet apart on a cable slung between her masts. An aircraft made runs in and out from the ship, contact being held out to 18 miles and regained at 15 miles, although there could be no indication of bearing.

The *Saltburn* was shared with the Navigation School so RDF trials had to be fitted in to their requirements, which sometimes caused unfortunate delays. Trials of experimental rotating aerials fitted on the top of her masts suffered from a lack of time for testing and tuning because she was already committed to a Navigation School cruise, and results were very disappointing, aircraft and the Eddystone lighthouse only being detected at about 7 miles.

Progress was slow, the potential of this new invention not being fully appreciated, but things began to improve in 1937 when a number of important changes took place at the Signal School. Commander the Hon. Henry Cecil joined as the first Application Officer specifically for RDF; he was a gifted member of a distinguished family and made significant contributions to this work over the next four years. Within a month a succinct situation report drafted by Shearing, Horton and Cecil pointed out that the field for experiment and development was so large and indefinite, and the staff available so limited, that it was essential to lay down priorities; it proposed that the less sensitive high frequency work should be put out to commercial firms, and that the detection of aircraft should be given a higher priority than that of surface ships.

In August Dorling was succeeded as CSS by A J L Murray, and in November Basil Willett relieved Bill Wyllie as Experimental Commander. Murray took up the question of priorities, including the problems with *Saltburn*. A full review of the situation was undertaken at a meeting in the Signal School in September, and this resulted in action by the Admiralty to provide more resources, including the promise of a cruiser to replace the *Saltburn* which was too small, while the Signal School undertook to redeploy staff to provide more effort for this work.

Captain the Hon. John Bruce

One of the Application Officers involved with the early development of RDF was John Bruce, son of Lord Elgin. A fellow midshipman before the first war, 'Sandy' Saunders remembers him as 'a smallish, unassuming man, with a great sense of humour. On one occasion when their ship was in Rosyth, John landed to visit his home, Broome Hall. On sighting a party of people being mustered at the main door by a guide for a tour of the Hall, he hung back. Some masterly woman, seeing his hesitation, insisted on his joining the party. He was too shy to explain who he was, so he was solemnly shepherded round his own home until they came across his father, who exclaimed: "Hallo, John! What on earth are you doing?"'

[5] Speech at a Naval Radar Trust dinner, 1990

A new R Division was established, headed by Horton, who led the RDF team more or less continuously from 1937 until 1944. In a tribute [5] to Horton, Basil Lythall, another distinguished RNSS scientist, quoted him as saying:

> *'This establishment failed to see the significance of radar, and as late as 1937 it was a matter of great difficulty to get workshop and drawing office effort put on to it. The reason was always the same - other and more obvious demands took priority.*
>
> *'Virtually every British seagoing radar that saw service in World War Two first came into being under his leadership ... it was owing to his drive and insistence that the Navy entered the war with some ships actually fitted with radar and many more on order. In retrospect, his contribution to wartime radar must be reckoned as the pinnacle in his long record of distinguished achievement.'*

Things now began to move faster. A A Symonds led the Section working on metric RDF at Eastney, John Coales took on all work on wavelengths less than a metre, whether for RDF, communications or D/F, and A W Ross headed a research team on propagation and aerials at a field station at Nutbourne.

The main work was on Type 79 for aircraft detection and location, but with a wavelength of 7.5 metres instead of 4 metres on which the earlier work had been based. This was because suitable electronic equipment for 7.5 metres was more readily available, having been developed for, amongst other things, the new BBC television service. The fact that larger aerials were needed had to be accepted. Work was also concentrated on developing 50cm equipment, more appropriate for surface detection and gunnery control.

Trials of the laboratory model Type 79X, were promising enough for the Signal School to start manufacturing two 'Chinese copies', designated 79Y, and these were the first to be fitted in ships, .*Sheffield* and *Rodney,* in the autumn of 1938, only six months or so after the decision was made to produce them. At the same time work started on 79Z, incorporating experience to date, for sea trials in the *Curlew* [6], and as the basis for manufacturing drawings to be made for subsequent production by industry. No further modifications or 'improvements' were then allowed, and this procedure ensured that urgently needed new equipment was got to sea in substantial numbers in the shortest possible time.

[6] For a time Curlew was allocated the flagship's buoy at Scapa, since this was connected to the shore telephone system, in order to improve the AA defence. She became very popular both with the fleet and east coast convoys as word got around that she could predict when to expect an air attack!

By September 1939 some forty sets had been ordered. *Valiant, Suffolk* and three AA cruisers had been fitted by the end of the year, and many more were to follow in 1940. With the addition in 1940 of a ranging panel to give accurate ranges out to 28,000 yards the set was re-designated Type 279. Work on surface detection and gunnery sets also gathered pace.

Meanwhile Somerville, now Vice Admiral Sir James Somerville, who had been invalided a few months earlier, was called back to the

Admiralty within a day of war being declared as 'Director of Miscellaneous Weapons and Devices' (sometimes known as the 'Department of Whizzams and Dodgers'). Amongst other tasks he chaired the Inter-Service Committee for Radio Interception. But his particular brief was to coordinate and speed up the development and production of RDF.

Things had come full circle - Somerville, who had become the Experimental Commander of the Signal School in 1917, now set about the rapid expansion of the arrangements needed to produce and fit the many types of radar urgently required by the fleet. The groundwork having been laid so capably by Horton and his team, with much credit on the uniformed side due to Willett, Cecil and Bruce, the work at last got the priority it deserved, just in time to have a major impact on the course of the war at sea.

Stephen Roskill, responsible for anti-aircraft weapon developments in 1940, sat on one of Admiral Somerville's committees. After one meeting, he recalled:

'I button-holed Mr Horton and said something like: "The future of RDF obviously lies in its possible use as a rangefinder, and that being so it is essential that the antennae should be fitted on gun directors, as is done with optical rangefinders, and not on top of ships' masts. Can that be done?" Horton replied: "If it could be done, would there be a firm Staff Requirement?" I replied with an

Controller's Minute of 28 July 1939, and Admiralty letter of 10 August 1939

Sub Lieutenant Monty Davenport, RNVR, was called up on 3 September and found himself in the Signal Division to deal with the security of fleet communications. He soon encountered Somerville who asked him to find the Controller's phone number; he had no idea what he was talking about! 'Typical damn useless RNVR', said Somerville. 'Do you know what I do?'

'No', admitted Davenport. 'Well, damned if I do either!' was the reply.

[7] Letter to *The Daily Telegraph*, 25 April 1961

emphatic affirmative and Horton asked me to come to the Signal School to discuss the possibility.

'There were five of us at the meeting - Captain Basil Willett, Horton and Coales of the school's scientific staff, Cdr Lawson of the Naval Ordnance Dept., and myself; and we drew up the requirements for the new radar set in outline.

'Then we had to persuade the Ordnance and Naval Construction departments of the need to fit them ... at the highest priority. I remember very well how a senior officer from the MOD, when told that the KGV class battleships would require 14 radar sets, exploded with "Roskill, you're mad!" I think on completion they actually had 21 sets.

'The first of the 50 cm sets were hand-made under the supervision of the Signal School. Later, at Admiral Somerville's very correct insistence, the tactical set (mainly for anti-submarine use) was given equal priority with the gunnery sets; and from those small beginnings developed the great family of short-wave naval radars made possible by the development of the cavity magnetron.

'Surely this was as good an example of co-operation between Servicemen and Scientists in the naval field as that achieved between Tizard and the RAF in the field of fighter defence. I write this letter [7] because I do not believe the staff of the Signal School have ever been given the credit for their great share in what was one of the most important developments of the whole war.'

'Special Transmitter Made by HM Signal School'

In his book, *Fraser of North Cape*, Richard Humble explains that the above title refers to an Admiralty docket (SD 2247/40) which was kept by Admiral Fraser, then Controller, as a souvenir, and thus is not to be found in the public archives. It records the contribution made by the Signal School to the 'Battle of the Beams' - the successful attempt to deflect the signals guiding German bombers to their targets. Earlier, the RAF had been helpful to the Navy in making available aircraft radar equipment for fitting in escorts (ASV) during the difficult days of the Battle of the Atlantic. The docket reads, in part:

'It was recently discovered that the Germans were making use of W/T beams to guide their bombers on to their targets. The Air Ministry made an urgent unoffical request to the Signal Department for any transmitter which could be used to jam the German W/T beams. The frequency involved was very high and the only transmitter which could be made available was one in HM Signal School, and this required considerable modification.

'The Experimental Department of the Signal School worked on the set night and day for several days, built two

special silica transmitting valves, installed it in a lorry and turned it over to the Air Ministry.

> *'Information has now been received that this set has proved very efficient on trial, and is likely to be of considerable value in the effort to reduce night bombing.*

> *'It is submitted that a signal of commendation may be made to the Signal School.'*

Admiral Fraser marked the docket:

> *'Approved. After action this paper is to be forwarded to Lord Beaverbrook by hand to show that we are not always thieves.'*

Beaverbrook [8] returned it having added:

> *'None the less you are thieves & it is my conviction that you would steal the Crown Jewels if it would help the Navy.'*

Beaverbrook kept the joke going, and later when Fraser congratulated him on becoming Minister of Supply, Beaverbrook replied:

> *'Come and see me any time ... I am always glad to see an Admiral. And as for thieves, I am Ali Baba.'*

'The man who achieved so much for us (in getting RDF to sea), Basil Willett, deserves recognition... Although no one thought big enough in those days, he thought bigger than most. Seldom has the Navy owed so much to one man and the team he leads, such as Horton, Landale, JD Rawlinson, Coales and Crampton ...'

Captain Cunninghame Graham, in a letter dated 22 March 1943. Churchill College, Cambridge, ANCG II 3/4

[8] Lord Beaverbrook was Minister for Aircraft Production from November 1940 and Minister of Supply from June 1941

Chapter Nine

Preparing for War

*'Traditionally, naval communications consisted of V/S
and W/T - what happened on shore was the business of
the Post Office, or the Army, or somebody...'*

U ntil the late 1930s, very little thought or effort had been devoted to planning for the additional Line Telecommunications (L/T) that would be needed ashore in time of war. The only major facilities which were in place were the lines that allowed remote keying of transmitters, and the inter-connection of the world-wide network of transmitting and receiving stations.

Before the war the Signal Department had four sections - Personnel and V/S, Wireless Organisation, W/T Material, and 'Y'. In 1937 Commander Jack Bowen joined to set up a new section responsible for 'line' communications; this section was also given the task of looking after RDF which had just undergone sea trials of the first set, Type 79X. At that time RDF was not recognised as the war winning device it turned out to be, and DSD (Philip Glover, one-time naval tennis champion) was, understandably, more concerned with the problems of getting modern radio equipments into the fleet in large numbers. It wasn't until the outbreak of war, helped by Somerville's arrival on the scene, that RDF got a section of its own.

Until shortly before the war it was the practice to put a break sign between each group in a code or cypher message. Noticing that this was not being done one day at the Castille in Malta, the Duty Signal Officer asked the fixed service operator why he wasn't following the correct procedure. 'There just isn't time when there's a lot of traffic' was the reply, which led in due course to the abolition of that particular, unnecessary, practice.

Mobilisation for the Munich crisis provided a valuable dress rehearsal for war, though on a very small scale, as the manning levels were somewhat skeletal. The L/T operators were either RNVR communicators or civilian women loaned by the GPO, and the Admiralty teleprinter room was simply part of a blocked off corridor. But the strain on the Admiralty's communications during the crisis did give some sort of guide as to what would be needed in wartime, and resulted in a good deal of preliminary work being done. For example, although subsequently found to be too small, a start was made in providing space in the basement for a receiving room, and for coding and cyphering.

At least the need for something to be done about L/T had been recognised. As Bowen wrote:

'Looking back on the gigantic war effort, it is staggering to remember how puny our scale of preparation was as late as 1939. The Treasury still exercised a stranglehold in every direction ... extra money for Defence was doled out as though we were a set of cat burglars asking for a clothing allowance! For example, I was visited by a gravely concerned Treasury gentleman because I had proposed to spend a yearly rental of £18 in order to ensure that the Emergency Fleet Base at Loch Ewe would be promptly connected on the outbreak of war!

'The biggest problem was to make authorities 'L/T minded', and that went for most Signal Officers too! Traditionally, naval communications consisted of V/S and W/T - what happened on shore was regarded as being the business of the Post Office or the Army or 'somebody' - at any rate not the Navy.'

The idea that Naval establishments would need their own system of telephones, and particularly teleprinters, was not easily sold to the powers that be; to most naval officers and Admiralty civilians at that time 'telegraphy' meant handing in a telegraph form at the Post Office. Only about six weeks before the war, a furious Director of the Operations Division wanted to know why a signal telling a ship to sail the next day from a Home Port had been sent by post. Investigation showed that this was the normal practice for all Secret messages not bearing an indication of priority!

Scotland quickly assumed much greater importance than hitherto, with the Clyde and other ports becoming convoy assembly areas, new training establishments being sited in 'safer' territory, and considerable activity in the field of combined operations. Early in 1941, the Admiralty took over the newly built Cambuslang Switching Centre in Glasgow, for both telephone and teleprinter working, staffing the establishment entirely with WRNS.

Flag Officer Greenock and his staff were established in a pleasant house, named Bagatelle, on a hill overlooking the Clyde. It also contained the communication centre, with a large team of over-worked Wrens in the gloomy cellars and basement, and an RNVR Signal Officer, Philip Whipp, later relieved by Eric Lowe, doing the best he could with the very restricted facilities.

By this time David Joel had been appointed Signal Officer, Greenock, but in effect he became responsible for the West Coast of Scotland, with the job of setting up communication facilities to match the increased responsibilities. His first move was to visit the Telephone Manager, Scotland West, whom he found a bit unco-operative at first, perhaps understandably, as the next door Flag Officer in Glasgow only had a staff in single figures and one line to Cambuslang!

Even in wartime difficulties arose in getting things done, and subterfuge was sometimes the only answer. As Bowen recorded: 'We didn't always reveal what we were up to. On one occasion there was an urgent request for a cable to be laid from Aden to the head of the Gulf. As no new cable was available, we simply picked up a modern and expensive Italian one recently laid across the South Atlantic, and re-laid it where we wanted it!'

Joel had resigned some time before the war to become a very successful furniture designer, and had been recalled in 1939. Eric Lowe remembers him with a mixture of affection and at times exasperation.

'There could not have been a better person to get the West of Scotland landline network set up in quick time. 'Solly' Joel was a brilliant showman, and a born fixer, at times totally ruthless, but irresistibly charming.'

David Joel with Rear Admiral
Cedric Holland, DSD 1942-43

*'I talked Battle of the Atlantic, Combined Ops,
ships being sunk, and so on, and he quickly
realised what it was all about, and put the
whole of his large department at the service of
the Navy. Before long a network of private
lines had been established all over the west
coast, roughly doubling the size of the original
peacetime system.'*

Joel decided that a specially designed communications
centre was needed, and also that the ideal site was on
one of the features of Bagatelle, the sunken rose garden.

*'Naturally the opposition was tremendous, but
the Director of Operations at the Admiralty,
Ralph Edwards, also a signal officer, was on
my side and with some judicious signals from
him I got my way, together with the necessary
priority for the building.'*

The communications centre was duly built, and was
manned almost entirely by Wrens, some 40 in each watch.

*'Whipp's assistant was a splendid acting Signal Boatswain,
Paul Wightman, an RFR Chief Yeoman, and owner of a pub
in Cardiff. He found being back in the Navy a comparative
rest, but he controlled 'Signal City' with a firm but fatherly
hand. Included on the staff was a team of Wren motor-cycle
despatch riders - an essential part of the communications
organisation. We also used them as outriders for visiting VIPs.'*

However Lowe recalls that diversion of the Wrens to be VIP
outriders was a constant thorn in the flesh of the Duty Signal Officer!
In any case the Wrens found the heavy Army machines difficult to
handle on icy roads and they were eventually equipped with small cars.

*Waymouth visited his opposite
number in the US Navy at
Argentia (travelling by flying
boat from Poole) to exchange
views. He thought their
communication arrangements
were likely to prove to be quite
inadequate, and when he
showed them the plans for Derby
House he was immediately
asked to fly to Washington to
brief their Director of Signals,
Admiral Redmond.*

*As a result, it seems the USN
recast their ideas, and this visit
helped to encourage the close
co-operation which was to
prove so vital in fighting the
Battle of the Atlantic.*

Much the same sort of activity was going on in the Western
Approaches command, situated initially at Plymouth, with the
headquarters in one of the old Napoleonic forts. Commander Ridley
Waymouth, and his assistant signal officer Fred Stannard, had to plan
for the move of the rapidly expanding command to Liverpool. Derby
House was selected, despite the disadvantage of being in the city, a
likely target for bombers, partly because the GPO trunk line arrangements
would give two alternate main routes out, whereas a site outside the
city, with only one cable route, would leave them more vulnerable.
To cater for complete landline disruption, a VHF link was set up to
control the local W/T station at Preston. In the event, after Liverpool
suffered some severe bombing raids, a stand-by headquarters was
also set up in Knowsley House, some miles outside Liverpool, the
home of Lord and Lady Derby, which was conveniently close to a
main cable route.

The Western Approaches communications staff eventually
totalled over 500, mainly WRNS, and the facilities allowed them to

control any of the main wireless stations in the UK, as necessary, with direct circuits also to the US and Canada.

The Branch Expands

The wartime expansion of L/T facilities was of course a joint effort with the Post Office which actually provided the lines, the expertise and much of the technical equipment. The manning requirements were a different matter; Whitehall W/T was manned in peacetime by members of the Shore Wireless Service - a fine body of ex-RN Telegraphists, whose only fault was that they could be a bit conservative - their reaction to the introduction of 'high speed' working tended to be 'I can make it faster by hand!'

Once war broke out their numbers had to be increased, and the first additions were signal ratings from London Division RNVR and some RNV(W)R training centres, followed as in 1938 by the loan of GPO operators who had some experience of using morse over landlines. In the end the problem was largely solved by the decision which had been taken in July 1938 to re-form the WRNS. At this time the total requirement for all branches of the WRNS was estimated to be about 1,500, and organised training was only introduced as late as April 1939. They were expected to be employed in the UK only, and initially were recruited on an 'immobile' basis, though it was soon realised that some would be needed on 'mobile' terms, primarily in order to balance the demands of the various ports and headquarters.

By 1939 a high standard of both visual and W/T communications had been established in the fleet, and there was a spirit of keenness and efficiency in the Branch, and a determination to 'get signals through'. This was of great importance in maintaining effective communications in the face of the wartime expansion, as regular officers and ratings were spread more and more thinly and with increasing responsibilities.

The first to be called up were reservists and pensioners, the younger ones being given refresher courses and sent to sea, while the older ones were generally more suitable for instructional and administrative work. These were followed by Hostilities Only (HO) ratings, but the plans for training on the scale necessary were quite inadequate and various civilian wireless colleges had to be brought in to help. The Telegraphist branch, some 4,000 strong in 1939, had increased to about 20,000 by 1945, plus 6,000 Coders, and 800 WRNS. A similar expansion of the Signal branch took place, with WRNS V/S, SDO, Coder and telephone switchboard categories being introduced. Some of the shore V/S stations were eventually manned entirely by WRNS.

Many new training establishments sprang up, such as HMS *Royal Arthur* at Skegness, *Scotia* (Ayr), *Valkyrie II* (Isle of Man), and *Wildfire* (Sheerness), all of which trained HO ratings, and *Cabbala* (Warrington) for WRNS W/T. HMS *Condor* (Arbroath) became the

Admiral Sir Percy Noble, C-in-C Western Approaches February 1941-November 1942, outside the Comcentre at Greenock, with Rear Admiral Hill. Noble qualified in Signals in 1908.

'He made several major contributions to victory in the Atlantic ... the victories he won were painstaking, almost wholly without glamour and often not visible as victories at the time,' commented Dr Martin Stephens in his book 'The Fighting Admirals'.

'My success in getting Wrens to the Signal School paid handsomely as we found that we could teach those who became telegraphists to read morse at 25 words a minute in two-thirds the time it took to train men.'

CSS, Captain Cunninghame Graham

Naval Air Signal School, and HMS *Dundonald* (Troon) the Combined Operations Signal School.

The Long Signal Course for officers was halved in length from 12 to 6 months by eliminating ceremonial and much of the theory and technical training, and concentrating on practical and organisational aspects. A separate specialisation of Air Signal Officer was introduced for Fleet Air Arm Observers, trained at the Naval Air Signal School; a new branch of Telegraphist Air Gunners was also introduced for the 'back-seat' of the Fleet Air Arm aircraft of the day, who were also trained at Arbroath. (After the war the Air Signal Officers were 'converted' to (C) specialists, and TAGs gradually faded out as VHF Voice equipment replaced W/T, while any guns fitted were fixed and were fired by the pilot).

In 1940 it was decided to introduce specialist signal courses for RNVR officers, concentrating on shore communication aspects. After a four month course these officers qualified as (Se), and soon proved their worth. A few who had previous sea experience later returned to join the RN Long (S) course.

New Entries at flag signalling instruction in the old training ship *Implacable* (ex-French Trafalgar veteran *Dugay-Trouin*), moored in Portsmouth harbour, with Yeoman George Harrison and a 'Tufnell Box' (which contained miniature masts and flags)

In 1941 Commands were asked if they would accept WRNS officers as signal specialists. Most replied that they would, if they were additional to complement, but C-in-C Western Approaches said they could replace some of his naval officers. Thus in 1942 WRNS joined the RNVR (Se) course at Leydene. Four of the first course relieved RN signal officers at Liverpool, and a few months later C-in-C WA reported that the experiment had been successful:

'They are capable of carrying out many of the naval signal officer's duties although they are handicapped by lack of sea experience.' [1]

[1] BR1076 - History of the WRNS, 1939-1945

(It might be pertinent to ask how many RNVR officers had much sea experience!). By the end of the war over 60 WRNS Signal Officers were serving in shore commands at home and abroad.

The wartime requirement for WRNS Cypher Officers had been realised as early as 1938, and by September 1939 138 had been enrolled and trained, their numbers rising to 350 within a year. The nucleus of a WRNS Coder branch had also been formed before the war, and this too rapidly expanded.

The Civilian Shore Wireless Service was reorganised in 1938, to provide a 'Naval Service of Civilian W/T Operators', [2] to be employed on 'Y' duties at shore intercept and DF stations at home and abroad. The initial complement was for something over 150 operators, many of them experienced ex-RN telegraphists and, as expected, the continuity of service which the employment of civilians allowed gradually resulted in much increased effectiveness. The organisation was augmented in the war by the introduction of the Telegraphist (SO) (for 'Special Operator'), trained in 'Y' duties only.

[2] ADM1-10004. The Admiralty Civilian Shore Wireless Service (ACSWS) as it became, remained as a large and very profesional organisation after the war. In 1964 the ACSWS (together with the Army and RAF equivalents) was absorbed into the Government Communications Headquarters (GCHQ)

Afloat, the limited requirement, principally manning HF DF sets, was met initially by Telegraphists who had been given special training and were borne additional to complement, but in 1943 as the Battle of the Atlantic developed, and with the growing importance of HF DF in the submarine war, it was decided to use Tels (SO) afloat, and they became the nucleus of a new Telegraphist (S) branch. As the use of Radio Warfare techniques and 'Y' intercept afloat developed, the duties and flexibility of this branch expanded and some were trained in special techniques, such as Japanese morse.

As early as January 1940 some of the first Wrens W/T were also trained as Special Operators, the six months course taking place at Soberton Towers (a few miles from Leydene House, which later became the home of the Signal School). On successful completion of training they were rated Chief Wren W/T (SO) and were employed on 'Y' intercept work at Scarborough and other stations on the east coast. Later, a normal branch structure was introduced, and some served afloat as 'Headache' operators in ships escorting east coast convoys, intercepting transmissions from German E-Boats.

The first WRNS to serve overseas consisted of twenty Chief Wrens W/T (SO) who sailed for Singapore in January 1941. A further ten, plus twelve WRNS cypher officers, who were in the first draft for Gibraltar, were lost when the merchant ship *Aguila* was torpedoed. Subsequently WRNS were transported in warships whenever possible.

Manning the 'Monsters'

The 'Monsters' were troopships, such as the *Queen Mary* and *Queen Elizabeth*, which usually sailed independently, relying on speed rather than convoy for their safety. They were treated as naval vessels for communication purposes, and thus carried naval codes and cyphers. Joel recalls that on the first occasion when one of these ships was due to sail from the Clyde, he was asked at very short notice to provide a naval 'crypto' team. As he had no male staff available, he decided that the only answer was to send Wrens:

> *'I knew that if the matter went through normal official channels there would be delays, so I got my Signal friends at the Admiralty to confirm urgently by signal the tentative arrangements I had made, and off they went.'*

Formal approval was duly given for WRNS Cypher Officers and Coders to be employed in the Monsters, usually in small teams of perhaps two or three officers and half a dozen Coders; on special occasions, eg when carrying the Prime Minister, WRNS Signal Officers and a large number of WRNS Cypher Officers were included in the party - as many as thirty for the Quebec conference in August 1943. V/S Wrens were embarked when in harbour but not at sea.

Jean Davies, who was on the first (Se) course in 1942, had the distinction of being the first WRNS Signal Officer to serve afloat, in one of the 'Monsters'. She was also on the staff which accompanied Churchill to the Quebec conference in 1943, and later became the first signal officer to be Director, WRNS.

Seven or eight ships were treated as Monsters, with a round trip to the US of about 14 days, and there could be two or three turn-arounds each week at Greenock, with an incoming ship having up to 10,000 passengers to disembark. When the *Empress of Scotland*, the Canadian Pacific flagship from the Vancouver-Tokyo run, which had no experience of the North Atlantic or sailing unescorted, joined the group, she had to be kitted out at very short notice, so Lowe decided to embark and complete briefing during the trip.

> *'Absorbing all the implications in half a day was too much to expect ... for example, being expected on return to enter harbour at speed without a pilot! And getting used to receiving operational information from women was in those days something of a culture shock too.*
>
> *'All operational signals for the Monsters were classified Hush Most Secret which created a level of top security traffic well above the norm at Greenock. The biggest risk lay in other local traffic going outside the command and containing some linkage to the high level traffic; the Chief Yeomen of the Watch were the only people who saw every one of the thousands of signals classified confidential and below, and they became adept at spotting trouble, while the Duty Signal Officers had absolute authority to block, amend or paraphrase as appropriate.'*

Communications at Sea

By 1939 the Fleet communications organisation was generally sound, though oriented towards fleet actions rather than convoy operations, and based on LF and MF for tactical wireless circuits. VHF was still in the experimental stage, and R/T (later known as 'Voice') hardly used except with aircraft. The requirements for communications with small units in distant waters, and particularly for convoy escorts, and for that matter merchant ships, had largely been ignored.

Voice circuits were not favoured - they were more difficult to control, and there was no written record of what had passed, which was quite alien to naval tradition. In any case, shipborne radio equipment had not been designed for voice operation and circuits generally suffered from poor quality and interference. Nevertheless, the level of aircraft operations, and the introduction of new sensors such as radar and HF DF, meant that more and more circuits were needed for the control and exchange of information. There was a need therefore for direct and rapid communication between those actually plotting and interpreting the information, or directing aircraft. This could only be achieved by the use of Voice; in any case there were no telegraphists to spare for manning any additional circuits.

Morse was retained for normal fleet communications, and of course between ship and shore where strict control of traffic levels and precedences was essential, most messages had to be encrypted, and a permanent record was required. The Fleet was also manœuvred by W/T when V/S was not practicable; this was on LF or MF frequencies which propagate over the horizon, often for several hundred miles, particularly at night, and were thus vulnerable to interception.

"What do you mean, how long is it since I read a biffer?"

('Biffer' is a signalman's slang for a morse flashing exercise.)

One method of reducing the risk was to use low power, with the transmitter slightly off-tune. Results could be erratic, and if a ship de-tuned too much then communication was lost. But the propagation of wireless waves was a subject that was not fully understood then and transmissions were inevitably detected at much greater ranges than expected. Charles Daniel, a senior signal officer then in command of *Renown*, appreciated the dangers and was concerned. 'You stand a good chance of losing a battleship if you go on like that' he commented to the FWA, John Henley. For lack of an alternative, they did go on for the time being, and perhaps were lucky not to lose a battleship!

Manœuvring by W/T was very different from using flags; with

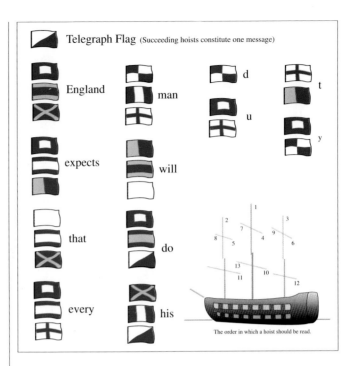

Telegraph Flag (Succeeding hoists constitute one message)

England

man

d

u

t

y

expects

will

that

do

every

his

The order in which a hoist should be read.

Victory's Distinguishing Signal. Her number in the Navy List at the time was 703, the numeral flags in this case being taken from the Signal Book for Ships of War, 1799. When Marryat introduced his 'Code for the use of the Merchant Service' in 1817, ships' names were included, Victory's number in this Code being 937. Again warships were indicated by the Union flag, merchant ships by a 'distinguishing pendant'.

Nelson's signal at Trafalgar - 'England Expects that Every Man will do his Duty'. The groups were taken from the 1803 edition of Popham's Vocabulary Code. The occasion is described in a letter by John Pasco, Nelson's Signal Lieutenant, reproduced in Chapter 1. As is well known, the word 'expects' was used instead of 'confides' because the latter was not in the Code, and for the same reason the word 'duty' had to be spelt out. The exact wording of the signal is often mis-quoted, and indeed the inscription on Nelson's column in Trafalgar Square omits the word 'that'. The correct wording can be verified from the logs of the ships reading the signal, which was of course sent as a series of separate hoists.

The order in which flag hoists are read when more than one is hoisted at the same time is shown in the diagram. The principle is: main, fore, mizzen; starboard before port; upper yards before lower. In practice it would be unusual for more than two or three to be hoisted at the same time, and Nelson's signal would have been transmitted by a quick succession of hoists. According to the logs of ships reading it, the whole signal took no more than about four minutes to transmit.

*'I wish Nelson would make no more Signals,
we all understand what we have to do.'*

Collingwood, 21 October 1805

Plate I

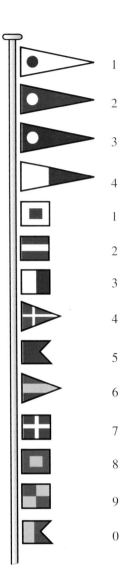

1
2
3
4
1
2
3
4
5
6
7
8
9
0

Opposite Top: King George VI outside the front door of Leydene House, 30 October 1942.

L to R: Cdr Charles St Quintin (Training Cdr), Cdr Colin Buist (Equerry, then serving in the Signal Division), Captain Gerald Warner (CSS), Lt Cdr John Longden (W1), HM The King, Lt Cdr Christian Eliot (V1), Rear Admiral Cedric Holland (DSD), Instructor Cdr Bennett, Captain Hon. John Bruce (Head of Radar Dept.), Cdr C Willoughby (Executive Officer).

Opposite Centre: Queen Elizabeth II outside the front door of Leydene House, 7 June 1991.

L to R: Cdr Christopher McClement (Executive Officer), Lt Cdr Andrew Potter (Supply Officer), Rear Admiral David Bawtree (Flag Officer, Portsmouth), Cdr Martin Knapp (OIC Special Communications Unit), HRH The Duke of Edinburgh, Cdr John Talbot (Cdr Communications and Navigation), HM The Queen, Cdr Charles Roe (OIC User Requirements and Trials Section), Admiral Sir Jeremy Black (CINCNAVHOME), Rev. Harvey Griffiths, Captain Paul Sutermeister (CSS).

Below Top: The Flag of the Lord High Admiral. This version was used as the Admiralty Flag from the 17th Century until 1964 when the Board of Admiralty ceased to exist. The Queen then formally assumed the office of Lord High Admiral and thus now flies this flag in her own right, although it had previously been customary for the Sovereign to fly the Admiralty Flag when embarked.

Below Bottom: This left the Admiralty Board, as it became known, without a flag for some years. In 1977 the three anchor version, used for a period in the 18th Century by the old Navy Office, was authorised for use by the Board.

The shapes of these flags are 1:2 and 2:3 respectively.

Above, The pendants and numeral flags from Marryat's 'Code of Signals for the Merchant Service', 1817. This was similar to Popham's Vocabulary Code, but with more appropriate words and phrases, and many geographical names. The pendants were also used as substitutes, and to indicate groups allocated to the names of individual ships. Other flags were added later, all carefully designed to be different to the naval ones.

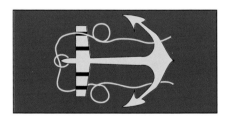

Plate II

The Leydene Staircase.

The self-suporting figure-of-eight staircase, an outstanding feature of the main hall at Leydene House. For many years only senior officers were allowed to use it, partly for fear that it might be damaged by too many people rushing up and down. At one stage a supporting pillar was inserted, but this proved unwise as the stairs needed a certain amount of 'spring'.

Plate III

*Right: 'Equal Speed Charlie London',
the Deployment signal hoisted in
Iron Duke at 1815 on 31 May 1916.*

*The signal aspects of the battle
are described in Chapter Six.*

*A gold, diamond and enamel
nautical brooch, made in
Cowes about 1900, and given
by King Edward VII to Mrs
George Keppel. When this
came up for sale in Geneva in
1989, Sotheby's asked the
Signal School for the meaning.
As the sale catalogue states,
this was provided by Warrant
Officer Tony Murphy, then head
of the 'Tactical' section. At the
time (about 1900) the flags were
Z, pennant 9, red burgee and
W, and the meaning of the hoist
was: 'Position quarterly and
open. I am about to fire a
Whitehead torpedo ahead.'*

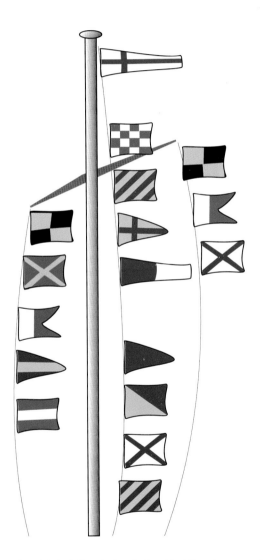

*Above: When Admiral Cunningham's flagship, Warspite, entered Alexandria
harbour after the Battle of Matapan, she flew the signal shown.*

*Pendant 3 superior addressed the signal to 'General Afloat'; the meaning of
the group FUL was 'sunk', so the signal read: 'Zara Pola Fiume sunk.'*

Plate IV

the latter the transmission, receipt and execution of a signal was instantly obvious to the Admiral or Captain, and there was no ambiguity, whereas with W/T there was a degree of uncertainty, and the 'command' could not see what was happening. Raymond Dreyer, FWA Home Fleet in 1943, remembers:

'The most fascinating experience was manœuvring the Fleet by morse on the 210 kHz low power Fleet Wave. A signal would be broadcast and selected ships requested to answer. The FWO, FWA, Staff PO Tel and Staff Leading Tel all listened for these answers. If three of us heard an answer, it was accepted; if less than three, the ship concerned was called again. When the selected ships had all answered the FWO reported to the C-in-C "Ready to Execute, Sir". There were no collisions or near collisions - though on occasion the signal officer of another group of ships, perhaps several hundred miles away at the time, would report on return to harbour that he had heard our 'low power' LF transmissions!'

The desirability of shifting 'tactical' circuits to VHF became evident, not only to reduce the risk of intercept and DF, but also to provide better quality voice circuits, and more channels, but with no suitable equipment available, the use of LF and MF had to continue for some time. When the American TBS became available under the lend-lease programme later in the war, this was fitted as the standard VHF inter-ship tactical or manœuvring net in destroyers and above (but usually only one set per ship), and this had the advantage of providing a common system for use when in company with the US Navy. At the same time, HF became more important, both for long distance communications and to provide additional frequencies for tactical purposes; it was also thought, correctly at that time, that HF was less easy to DF than LF or MF.

When RAF fighters shifted to VHF early in the war a number of east coast escorts were fitted with RAF sets to allow them to communicate with their fighter escorts, and in 1942 fitting was extended to some ships in the Mediterranean. These early VHF sets were crystal controlled, giving better frequency stability and ease of operation; they were known as Type 86 (low power, and generally fitted in small ships) and Type 87 (higher power, and larger ships). Initially these sets covered the band 100-124 MHz, but in later versions this was extended up to 156 MHz to cope with the large number of additional circuits needed. For the first years of the war Fleet Air Arm aircraft were fitted with sets operating between about 4.3 and 6.8 MHz, and it wasn't until 1943 that 4-channel crystal controlled VHF sets covering the band 100-156 MHz became available. As with the ship VHF sets, this produced a large number of possible channels, frequency stability and improved speech quality, but it also meant a major crystal production and distribution problem.

The Broadcast and Ship-Shore Organisation

In 1939 both broadcast and 'I' method were in use for shore-to-ship communications, primarily for general messages; otherwise direct communications on LF or MF had to be established with the local area radio stations for both shore-ship and ship-shore purposes. Traffic capacity was low, and these arrangements soon proved incapable of handling the heavy load of operational and administrative messages. The broadcast gradually became the primary method of passing all traffic from shore to ship, being transmitted on several frequencies simultaneously to give the necessary geographical coverage. The transmitters were keyed from the Admiralty or the area headquarters and, when the flagship was in harbour at Scapa, also by C-in-C Home Fleet for high precedence traffic. Thus the 'Command' could exercise very close control over the traffic being passed, and supervising this was one of the prime functions of the signal staffs.

Fixed Services, 1939

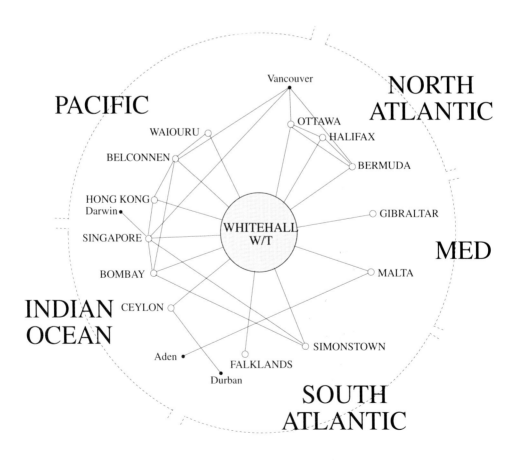

Every effort was made to avoid ships having to transmit; broadcast messages were serially numbered so that ships would know if any had been missed, and could find out from ships in company if they had been read and were relevant, and if so have them passed by V/S. If traffic levels on the broadcast allowed, messages were repeated later. When ships were due to cross boundaries, messages had to be dual-routed on both of the appropriate broadcasts for a period, to allow for uncertainty over the ship's exact movements. In the busiest areas, or for specific operations, more than one broadcast might be needed; the extra ones usually carried particular types of traffic, eg for Flag Officers.

In 1941 trials of a new system to improve ship-to-shore communications in the North Atlantic were carried out, with several shore stations keeping watch on a number of common frequencies. Any station hearing a ship call was to accept the message and pass it on via the fixed service network. This was a great success, and the

Fixed Services, 1945

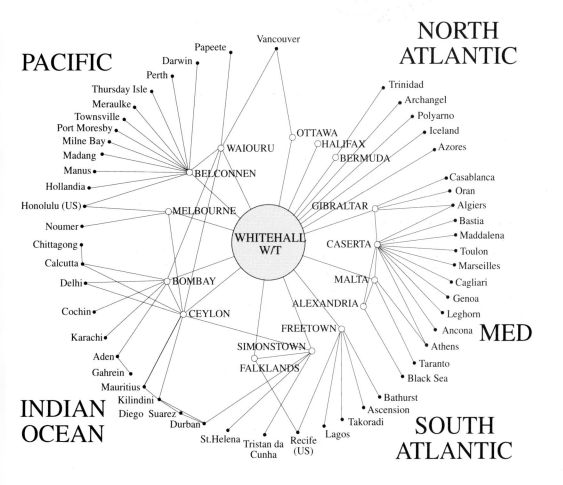

system was introduced in the Atlantic area in 1942, gradually being extended throughout the world. Five common frequency bands were adopted, on 4, 6, 8, 12 and 16 MHz, the Admiralty and Post Office facilities were pooled, and the system was then used by both warships and merchant ships. Frequency prediction charts were produced and issued to ships to help them choose the most suitable frequency for the area and the time of day or night.

A classic example of making the best use of the ship-shore, broadcast and fixed service organisation occurred during Operation PEDESTAL, the Mediterranean convoy operation which fought the tanker *Ohio* and four other ships through to Malta in August 1942. John Buckeridge was then Flotilla Signal Officer in *Ashanti*:

> '*Direct communication with Malta was proving difficult at one stage because of the 'skip' effect, and we found it much easier to raise Whitehall W/T. The latter was highly efficient and all lines were cleared for us. Whitehall re-routed signals direct to Malta, and they were then broadcast using Malta's high power transmitters. Depending on the length of a signal, we could often hear it start to come out on the Malta broadcast before we had finished transmitting it to Whitehall; by this means all our instructions were quickly passed both to our own forces at sea, and to other authorities concerned.*'

When calling on ship-shore, ships identified themselves with a random two letter callsign in order to conceal their identity - the latter would be included in the encrypted text, only delivery groups and passing instructions being 'in clear'. The vagaries of HF transmissions meant that the shore station best placed to hear the ship might not be the nearest; it frequently happened that one in another area or halfway round the world would accept the message; this did not matter as the shore stations were all connected to the world-wide network of fixed services, and the message would immediately be passed on to its destination. Ships ended their transmission by indicating the broadcast which they were reading; the shore station would then send the receipt for the message via the appropriate fixed services for transmission on that broadcast. This procedure also clarified routeing instructions for messages to that ship when there was any doubt about her position, thus reducing the occasions on which she would need to break wireless silence.

The new ship-shore system soon became well established and it was unusual for ships not to be answered by one of the shore stations around the world quite quickly. The US Navy was suitably impressed and eventually adopted a similar system. The heaviest traffic levels were in the area around the British Isles, so in the UK two different shore stations kept watch on each of the five bands with the operators in direct touch by telephone; between them, in difficult radio conditions, it was often

Another example of the ship-shore system in action occurred when the Japanese cruiser Haguro was sunk in the Malacca Strait in May 1945. She had sailed from Singapore to try to evacuate the Andaman Islands, and was sighted by a submarine, while the Eastern Fleet was poised to intercept her. Eric Lowe, signal officer in Royalist which was acting as W/T guard, recalls that the ship intercepted a crucial enemy report from the submarine, which was apparently not picked up ashore, as it did not immediately reappear on the broadcast. After a few minutes, Royalist decided to break W/T silence and re-transmitted it on ship-shore. The message was accepted by Falklands W/T, re-routed on the fixed services to Whitehall and then to Bombay, from where it was immediately re-transmitted on the area broadcast. Within five minutes of Royalist's transmission, it was being read by all ships in the area. The Haguro was subsequently attacked by the 26th Destroyer Flotilla, led by Saumarez, and hit by several torpedoes, in what turned out to be the last RN surface action of the war.

possible to reconstruct the complete message without having to ask the ship for a repetition.

The broadcast and ship-shore systems were closely linked; in particular procedures were developed which ensured that high precedence messages received on ship-shore, such as enemy reports, would automatically and rapidly be re-broadcast so that every ship in the area would know what was going on. This also helped to reduce the amount of signalling within forces at sea.

After the fall of France, a number of units from Allied navies joined the Fleet. These all operated using British signal books and procedures, initially with small liaison teams, but before long, and in some cases without translating the books, they managed on their own and integrated completely into the RN organisation.

Submarines used the same ship-shore system when it was essential to transmit, though this meant putting an aerial above the surface. Messages to submarines were normally sent at routine times by the Rugby VLF broadcast, which could be read by submerged submarines over most of the Home and Mediterranean stations. Later, in the Pacific, submarines read the USN VLF broadcast from Honolulu. Otherwise the ordinary ship broadcasts had to be used, with the disadvantage that they could only be read with an aerial above the surface. [3]

[3] Submarine communications are described in more detail in Chapter 15

Convoy Communications

Convoy escort communications proved a problem, with the rapid expansion of small escorts, shortage of telegraphists, and the lack of suitable equipment in many of the smaller escorts. Most ships had an MF capability, and 2,410 kHz became the universal convoy R/T frequency, though alternatives were available and were sometimes used, for example when U-Boats were suspected of transmitting deceptive messages on the standard frequency. Watch was usually kept on loudspeaker, and a system of guardships on the broadcast could relieve the pressure on communication staffs. However with increasing traffic levels and the difficulty of relaying messages to the other escorts, it was often necessary for them all to read the broadcast. Wireless silence was kept when possible, manœuvring of a convoy being conducted by flags during the day, and inter-ship signalling by lamp, but with large convoys, and at times of submarine attack, the use of radio was essential, outweighing the risk of interception and DF.

The Admiralty had no control in peacetime over equipment fitted in merchant ships, nor over their W/T organisation, which was run by the GPO, with their transmitting station at Portishead and receivers at Burnham, in Somerset. Some traffic, such as radio telegrams, was transmitted on the Rugby VLF transmitter (which belonged to the Post Office) at routine times, different of course to the submarine routines. Most merchant ships carried one radio operator, only larger ships being required to carry two or three, both equipment and operators usually being hired from one of the marine radio companies.

On the outbreak of war the Admiralty took over control from the GPO, and the embryo merchant ship broadcast system - 'GBMS' - came into force. Ships listened at routine times to Rugby and to area stations, otherwise keeping watch on the international distress and emergency frequency, 500 kHz ('Five Ton'). After the fall of France, the Admiralty assumed control of all Allied merchant shipping which then complied with British procedures. When the Americans entered the war the world was divided into two strategic zones, the Admiralty being responsible for merchant shipping in one, and the US Navy Department for the other.

The GBMS organisation proved to be inadequate for the efficient clearance of traffic for a number of reasons - poor coverage by W/T stations, obsolescent equipment, and many ships only able to listen at single or two operator periods. The situation gradually improved as more and better naval W/T stations became available (these often operated both naval and GBMS broadcasts), and more modern equipment was fitted in ships. As additional radio operators became available they were allocated to the bigger merchant ships so that they, at least, could keep constant watch, and from 1942 all Allied merchant ships had to have at least two operators.

In 1942 the GBMS system was superseded by a combined Anglo-American system of 'Broadcasts to Allied Merchant Ships' (BAMS), and the addition of some US Navy W/T stations much improved the coverage. For ship-shore purposes, ships in convoy passed any essential messages through their escort, for transmission when W/T silence restrictions allowed. For inter-communication between the convoy and its escorts, Commodore's and Vice-Commodore's ships, rescue, MAC [4] and HF DF ships were fitted when possible with low power sets for use on 2,410 kHz for intercommunication with the escort. The US used VHF for convoy wave, so stocks of American portable TBY sets were maintained at convoy assembly ports for fitting in important ships sailing in American convoys or with American escorts.

A special signal book, 'Mersigs', was produced for ships in convoy, based on the same principles as the naval signal books, but combining the convoy manoeuvring instructions, and the signals to order them, in one volume. In 1944 this was replaced by an improved version, 'Wartime Instructions for Merchant Ships' (WIMS).

[4] MAC ships carried Hurricane fighters, which could be catapulted off to deal with enemy shadowers, the plane eventually ditching near an escort in the hope that the pilot could be recovered. These ships needed to be able to communicate with the escort, as did others, such as rescue ships which were also fitted with HF DF when equipment was available.

Chapter Ten

World War Two

HMS Falmouth, the C-in-C's Yacht on the China Station, was berthing at Saigon. 'The procedure' wrote John Buckeridge, 'was to berth with one's bows downstream, and this entailed going up river, turning the ship by putting her bows into a paddy field, working the engines to take her stern round, and then going down river to berth. I remember standing on the foc'sle looking into the paddy when a signalman brought me a signal from the Admiralty. It read: "Total Germany." Almost at once another signal arrived: "Winston is back." So I went to war.'

As in 1914, one of the early naval engagements of the second world war took place in the South Atlantic, and communications to and from the area were not much improved. Falkland Islands W/T had only one antiquated Marconi MF transmitter with an output of about 3kw, to which an HF attachment had been added. This could do no more than maintain a shore-ship broadcast on 8,555 kHz, interrupted at intervals for commercial traffic to the nearest cable link at Cerrito, near Montevideo (to avoid breaching Uruguay's neutrality naval traffic had to be disguised as from the Governor of the Falklands), while at night it also had to exchange commercial traffic with the GPO station at Dorchester, as well as naval traffic with Whitehall.

This imposed serious delays on signals from the Admiralty, and also from C-in-C South Atlantic at Freetown, whose traffic was routed via Whitehall. To help overcome these difficulties, in addition to the Falklands broadcast, ships listened every four hours to Rugby VLF.

The River Plate

The pocket battleship *Graf Spee* had left Germany before war broke out, and had been commerce raiding very successfully in the Atlantic and Indian Oceans since late September 1939, refuelling periodically from her supply ship *Altmark*, to which she transferred captured merchant crews. She was being hunted by a large number of ships in eight groups.

Force G, under Commodore Harwood, consisting of the *Ajax* (flag), *Achilles* and *Exeter*, sighted her early on 13 December. *Graf Spee* had expected to meet searching cruisers singly, and was somewhat unnerved to come across three. Harwood had earlier signalled his plans: 'My policy with three cruisers versus one pocket battleship. Attack at once. By day act as two units. First Division

(*Ajax* and *Achilles*) and *Exeter* diverge to permit flank marking. First Division will concentrate gunfire.' Thus the ships knew what to do without further orders.

Although *Exeter* and *Ajax* both suffered considerable damage (and lost their wireless aerials, which disrupted inter-ship communications) *Graf Spee* failed to make the most of her gunnery advantage, and eventually escaped into Montevideo. Harwood had tried to order the *Cumberland* to join him from the Falklands, by transmitting on the Falklands broadcast frequency, allowed in emergency for direct communication between ships; but it was difficult to get through and the first *Cumberland* knew of what was going on was when she intercepted a signal from *Exeter* saying 'All my turrets are out of action...'[1] Other groups, mostly off the coast of Africa, were re-routed urgently.

Graf Spee had used much of her ammunition and assumed that a strong British force would have gathered off the Plate, a notion that British intelligence encouraged. The British Naval Attache at Buenos Aires had rigged up W/T reception facilities at the Embassy in order to monitor the Falklands broadcast and the ship-shore frequency to Simonstown and Freetown, and this helped to guide the diplomatic activity which ensued, aimed at keeping *Graf Spee* in harbour for as long as possible. International law allowed merchant ships a 24 hour start from a neutral port before an enemy warship might sail, and British ships were therefore sailed from the Plate at intervals to delay *Graf Spee*.

In fact reinforcements were still hundreds of miles away, but after consulting Berlin, Captain Langsdorff took his ship down river on 17 December and then scuttled her. He committed suicide three days later.

A British scientist, Bainbridge-Bell, was flown out and, posing as a scrap metal dealer, was able to board the wreck and examine her Seetakt radar, used for rangefinding, which had a 'mattress' aerial attached to the gunnery director, just above the optical rangefinder. This was the first concrete evidence of Germany's progress in the development of naval radar, of which we previously had little knowledge. Bainbridge-Bell collected some 'scrap' samples, which included bits of the aerial, and these were analysed by the Signal School. It was assessed as a 60cm set with a maximum range of about eight miles. (None of the British ships involved had radar).

This was not quite the end of the story, for the *Altmark*, which lay low in the Atlantic for some weeks, eventually headed home through the Denmark Strait, being reported off the Norwegian

The River Plate action

[1] Report on W/T aspects of the battle ADM1-10727

Ajax launched her Seafox aircraft to spot fall of shot. Unfortunately its radio was tuned to the reconnaissance and not the spotting frequency, and it was some minutes before it was retuned. In the meantime, Achilles had been hit and having lost contact on the gunnery concentration net had reverted to individual control, but the Seafox was not aware of this, reporting Achilles salvos to Ajax; the latter corrected for Achilles fall of shot and not her own and thus for a time she consistently fired over.

coast on 15 February 1940. The Home Fleet was deployed to try and intercept her.

Lieutenant Commander Frank Jupp was then a Signalman in the destroyer *Cossack*, with D4, Captain Philip Vian:

> '*D4 was organising a search with the cruiser Arethusa and four destroyers. Arethusa first sighted the Altmark on 16th February, and the nearest destroyer was ordered to intercept her, but the Altmark slipped into Jossing Fjord.*
>
> '*Entering the fjord Cossack was met by Norwegian patrol boats, which told her that she was contravening the neutrality act and requested her to leave. Captain Vian pointed out that British prisoners were on board the Altmark but was met by a categorical denial by the Norwegians, who said she had already been searched with negative results, and suggestions for a joint Norwegian/British search were not accepted. Proceeding outside territorial waters, Cossack informed the Admiralty of the situation; confident of their information, the Admiralty authorised Cossack to re-enter the fjord to rescue the prisoners.*
>
> '*Altmark turned a searchlight on Cossack's bridge to blind her, and went full astern to try to ram her, but herself ran aground. Cossack then nudged her bows alongside Altmark. Communications with both the Norwegians and the Altmark were, literally, by shouting or by arm and fist waving - very effective!*'

Altmark's track and Jossing Fjord where she was eventually intercepted

The boarding party was led by the First Lieutenant, Lieutenant Commander Bradwell Turner. Vian recorded the incident in his book *Action This Day*:

> '*Turner anticipated Cossack's arrival alongside Altmark with a leap which became famous. P O Atkins, who followed him, fell short and hung on by his hands until Turner heaved him on deck... When Turner arrived on Altmark's bridge, he found the engine telegraphs set to full speed in an endeavour to force Cossack ashore. On Turner's appearance the Captain and others surrendered, except the Third Officer who interfered with the telegraphs. Turner forebore to shoot him ... The prisoners were under locked hatches in the holds; when*

these had been broken open Turner hailed the men below with the words "Any British down there?" He was greeted with a tremendous yell of "Yes! We're all British". "Come on up then" said Turner, "The Navy's here!"'

A total of 299 prisoners arrived on deck and were transferred to *Cossack*. There were some casualties, all German, and *Cossack's* steering gear suffered slight damage.

Vian records that a letter of congratulations from the First Sea Lord had complained that he and the First Lord:

'... had spent a sleepless night because, whilst Altmark was crying blue murder to the world on commercial wave, Cossack had made no signals informing Admiralty and the C-in-C of the situation.

'This was all too true. I believe our guardship on commercial wave had not liked to break W/T silence to tell us of Altmark's signals, and we had failed to dismantle her radio set, being quite unaware that she was using it. Sir Charles Forbes (C-in-C) on the other hand, defended our silence. He had, he said, relied on us, and never slept better!'

The Norwegian Campaign - Spring 1940

The Norwegian campaign was the first large-scale operation in which all three arms of the Service - navy, army and air force - were engaged. There was no unified command set-up, and an unusual feature was that the naval commander in the operational area, Admiral of the Fleet the Earl of Cork & Orrery, was senior to the C-in-C Home Fleet.

The campaign took place in an area where W/T communications are notoriously difficult. There were other hazards too - patrolling in the Denmark Strait, *Devonshire* had encountered a severe blizzard which caused her aerials to ice up until they reached a diameter of four inches which then brought the whole lot down. At the same time an ionospheric black-out started which was so severe that the whole HF spectrum went completely dead, though LF transmissions were subsequently found to be better than usual. This left the ship with a problem, recalled Reggie Paul, CS1's signal officer:

'If we sighted a German battleship, how could we report it? At first it was absolutely impossible to get aloft to rig a roof aerial and HF jury aerials could achieve nothing. Eventually, after 36 hours and with a great deal of risk, we managed to get a roof rigged from the after funnel to the mainmast and just managed to raise Scapa on 107 kHz. The HF blackout went on for four days.'

When ships were in some of the Norwegian fjords, they found it difficult to communicate with the outside world at all. Paul again:

'It was nearly impossible to raise Whitehall on HF during the day on any frequency covered by the ship's fairly elderly

David Bromley-Martin, Squadron Wireless Assistant to BC1 in Renown, also had problems. They fell in with the Scharnhorst and Gneisenau which were retiring after covering the German landings at Narvik. *'As the battle ensigns were being hoisted, an 11" shell cut the halyards, passed through the centre strut of the tripod mast and exploded a hundred feet or so further on, showering the flagdeck with splinters. The flag deck crew were luckily undamaged but somewhat astonished.'* In a brief encounter Renown scored three hits on Gneisenau, but the Germans escaped into the Arctic gloom. Ten German destroyers as well as transports were in Narvik, and the 2nd DF under Captain Warburton-Lee in Hardy were sent in to carry out a surprise attack. They sank or damaged three destroyers and several other ships but Hardy and Hunter were lost; Warburton-Lee was awarded the VC.

BC1's flag was shifted to Warspite for the second Battle of Narvik a few days later - a battlecruiser being less suitable for manœuvring in the narrow waters - in which the remaining German ships were sunk. *'Once in the fjord all external communication was cut off by the high surrounding mountains ... it was a little eerie for a battleship and a large force of destroyers to be in action with absolutely no contact with the outside world.'*

transmitters, which had a 'ceiling' of about 15 MHz. The BBC however came in nicely on 20 or 23 MHz.

'Outside the fjords things were better, though still difficult. No propagation data was available then, and a good deal of guesswork had to take place. In the open sea it was usually possible to raise the UK on lower frequencies, reflected from the lower E-layer, but this meant relatively low angle radiation, and as soon as the ship entered a fjord this was cut off by the mountains. East of North Cape the mountains to the South were less lofty and signalling via Malta was often the best answer.

'Communication between ships in different fjords was also a problem, but 3,700 kHz generally did the trick, probably via the ionosphere. However the Norwegians had a useful chain of coastal aeronautical stations each of which could communicate with its neighbours. We co-opted these, and roughed out a combined procedure for relaying RN messages, and passing them to ships. It didn't work well, but it was a lot better than nothing.

'An interesting moment was when Devonshire received two messages almost simultaneously by this system - one from an ex-German prize reporting a U-Boat, and the other from a British submarine reporting a German merchant ship. Fortunately the submarine's torpedoes missed!'

The force sent to evacuate Namsos consisted of *Devonshire* (CS1) and a mixed bag including French cruisers and auxiliary transports. Apart from a rapid conference before leaving Scapa they had not met before.

'Off Namsos we suddenly ran into thick fog and only just had time to form single line ahead. The fog persisted and it became necessary to turn 180 degrees by W/T, Anglo-French code being the only available medium. The message took half an hour to clear and the timing of the executive signal was an uncomfortable decision, precipitated by the proximity of the rocks. Everyone turned after a fashion except the French flagship Montcalm, who missed Devonshire's stern by inches. She had received the signal all right, but unfortunately it had not been reported to the bridge!'

The force eventually crept in to Namsos by sending the *Kelly* ahead to feel her way in using asdic, and transmitting W/T signals on which *Devonshire* was able to home by DF (this is reminiscent of a very similar incident some twenty five years before, mentioned in Chapter 19, when eight battleships ran into fog off Norway, and Angus Cunninghame Graham had to manoeuvre them by siren).

The Loss of the *Glorious*

Communication problems played a part in the loss of HMS *Glorious* and her escorting destroyers *Acasta* and *Ardent* on 8 June 1940. With

Ark Royal (Vice Admiral Aircraft Carriers) they had been part of the escort of a convoy evacuating troops from Norway, but had been given permission to proceed ahead independently.

Ships had been directed to shift from Narvik area frequencies to Home Station frequencies on crossing latitude 65N, which in the case of *Glorious* would have been on the morning of 9 June, but it seems that she actually changed over at 1300 on 8th when some 300 miles north of this latitude; the reason for this is not known.

She was intercepted by the German battlecruisers *Gneisenau* and *Scharnhorst* in the Norwegian Sea in position 69N 4E just after 1600 on 8th, and all three ships were sunk by gunfire within two hours. The only report received by the British was at 1720 when *Devonshire*, some seventy miles away, picked up part of a weak signal on 3.7 MHz (a Narvik area frequency) addressed to VA Aircraft Carriers from *Glorious*, which she read as: 'My 1615 2 PB 1640 ...' That was the only signal received by any British ship or W/T station, and its significance was not appreciated by *Devonshire*; it was assumed to be corrupt and anyway not addressed to her. Furthermore, with the King of Norway and most of the Norwegian cabinet on board, she would have been loth to break wireless silence herself.

Route of *Glorious* and convoys

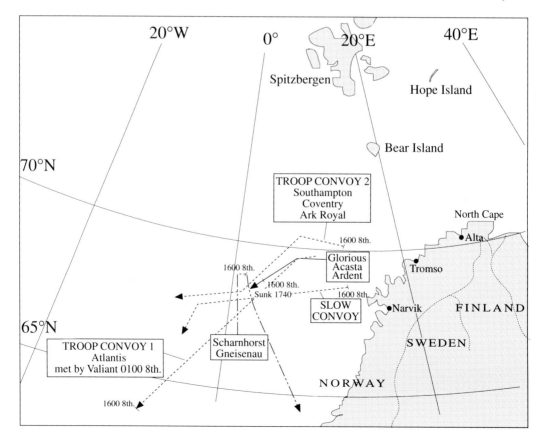

Half an hour earlier, at 1652, the B-Dienst (intelligence) group on board *Gneisenau* had intercepted the original report (that timed 1615) on 8.29 MHz (a Home Fleet frequency). This was recorded as:

'MTA v OW2 O-U 2BC 308 15 030 154 GQOX 11 = 1615'

(To Scapa W/T from *Glorious*: Most Immediate. 2 battle-cruisers bearing 308 15 miles course 030 my position 154 69N 04E 11 miles = 1615.)

The group's log also records that no British station was heard to answer or relay this signal. At 1719 the *Gneisenau* intercepted the beginning of a further transmission from *Glorious* on 3.7 MHz which they immediately tried to jam by transmitting bogus signals on the same frequency using British callsigns and procedures; this must have been the signal picked up by *Devonshire*, and which appeared to refer to two pocket battleships. [2]

[2] The author is indebted to Captain Vernon Howland, RCN, for providing him with details of his research into the radio aspects of this action

Ships in the Narvik area were keeping watch on 3.7 Mhz on 8 June, but Fleet Air Arm wave had been shifted from the normal 253 kHz to 230 kHz because of 'intolerable interference'; possibly *Glorious* did not know of this change, as there is evidence that she tried 253 kHz, as well as 8.29 MHz, before transmitting on 3.7 MHz. The ship's main aerials were damaged during the action, and the transmission on 3.7 MHz may have been made on an aircraft set, which was fitted in the Remote Control Office (RCO).

It is not known if the destroyers attempted to send enemy reports; they should have done so, but the possibility that they left it to *Glorious* cannot be discounted.

Glorious had no aircraft ranged ready to take off, and no air patrol, nor were any of the three ships fitted with radar, so they were surprised by the appearance of the Germans. In a gallant action, the destroyers laid smoke screens and attacked with torpedoes; *Acasta* scored one hit on *Scharnhorst*, causing considerable damage and some casualties.

A Telegraphist Air Gunner, Bob McBride, had manned his Swordfish which was 'piped away' at about 1605, after having visited the RCO and been given 253 kHz as his operating frequency. He had just tuned his set, probably about 1630, when he heard the ship transmit an enemy report: 'I was wearing headphones - the noise nearly blew my head off!' The flight deck was wrecked shortly after, and no aircraft took off.

The fact that the German warships were in the area was not known to the C-in-C or the Admiralty until the morning after the action, when the hospital ship *Atlantis* met HMS *Valiant* and reported having seen the German ships the previous day when they attacked a troop transport, the *Orama* (which was empty except for some German prisoners). The scale of the disaster only became apparent later on 9 June when the German radio reported that *Glorious* had been sunk.

Curiously, the Germans were not entirely satisfied with the action

- on return to Trondheim Admiral Marschall was accused of disobeying orders (to attack shipping at Harstad), endangering his ships, and expending too much ammunition. In mid-June he was relieved by Vice Admiral Lutjens. A few days later the *Gneisenau* was torpedoed by the submarine *Clyde*, and both battlecruisers were in dockyard hands for several months.

The damage to the German ships did prevent them taking any further action against the British convoys, and none of the troops being evacuated from Norway were lost.

*   *   *   *   *

One of the few survivors was the Warrant Telegraphist in *Glorious*, Mr E E Blackwell, who became a prisoner of war. He had in fact been relieved by Warrant Tel Clark, but was still on board. The following extracts are from Blackwell's report [3], written after he had been released in 1945.

Blackwell remembers leaving the DF office, at the after end of the flag deck, on his way to tea:

> *'Passing the chart house, at about 1615, the Captain stopped me and asked: "On which wave do we make an enemy report?" I replied: "253 kHz, but knowing the area, would suggest HF as well." As I finished speaking, action stations sounded, and the Captain thrust a message into my hands, saying: "Then make this, quickly, both waves."*
>
> *'Entering the RCO I called to the two operators to switch on main and second office W/T sets. Handed the original signal to the 253 kHz operator for transmission and told the HF operator to carry on calling, whilst I made a copy of the signal for him. The message was self-evident, reporting two Deutschland class battleships.'*

It will be noted that Blackwell must have confused the two reports, hardly surprising after a lapse of five years. He goes on:

> *'An order to switch on the beacon came from the plot. Mr Clark having arrived in the RCO now took over, and I left to attend to the beacon ... returned to RCO to hear that main W/T aerial had been carried away. Left for Main office - casualties on deck outside. Gunfire from enemy constant ... made my way to flight deck to estimate extent of damage to aerial - the after W/T mast on starboard side had been shot away. Huge hole in flight deck, with two or three Swordfish blazing at the edge. Abandon ship piped. Went to plot - heard Captain say "Give her all you've got, Chief." He then called: "Cancel abandon ship."*
>
> *'Could see Ardent and Acasta through the smoke screen and they appeared to be going in to the attack. Splashes all around them.*
>
> *'In plot Signal Officer told me there had been no answer*

[3] Report dated 16 July 1945 (ADM1-19406). The communication difficulties during the campaign were investigated by DSD (ADM199-478). No evidence was found of any W/T or 'Y' station picking up a report from *Glorious* or the destroyers.

to our enemy reports. I suggested we tried to get through on Narvik waves, either by shifting frequencies on the main set, or by utilising aircraft GP sets, one of which was fitted in the RCO and one in the main office. He favoured the latter and ordered RCO to get on Narvik reconnaissance, while I went to main office to put the set there on Narvik HF. Heavy crash, apparently near main office - valve in main transmitter broken - still trying to get through on GP set.

'Abandon ship piped again ... list to starboard increasing. All confidential books collected, placed in steel chest and transported by main office personnel to port side - awkward journey, owing to the now big list ... steel chest thrown overboard. I went over the side and stood on rubbing strake - pushed along by men edging aft, until I reached a break and fell into the water.'

Blackwell and three ratings were eventually picked up by a Norwegian trawler, which was making for the Faroes but was sighted by a German aircraft and forced to return to Norway, where the four of them became prisoners of war. Thirty five other survivors (only one each from *Ardent* and *Acasta*) reached the Faroes in the Norwegian motor vessel *Borgund* and were returned to the UK.

Admiral Sir Bertram Ramsay and Dunkirk

Bertram Ramsay asked to specialise in Signals and did the long course in 1908/9. He is said to have chosen signals because he liked to dress immaculately and was not inclined to get involved with 'nuts and bolts'; furthermore 'Flag Lieutenants don't coal ship!' [4]

His first signal job was as flag lieutenant to Rear Admiral Sir Colin Keppel in the *Albemarle* in the Atlantic Fleet, with Ernle Chatfield as Flag Captain. Chatfield wrote:

'He was a bright young Lieutenant of great ability and keenness, but lacking in tact. The difficulty was, he tried to run me through the Admiral; such as coming on the bridge when we were about to unmoor at Oslo. We were the only ship present, and without consulting me he hoisted a signal for Albemarle to unmoor and weigh southern anchor first. Which, of course, I ignored, as it was the wrong anchor! Then he ran against David Beatty, Captain of the Queen. In a squadron signal exercise off Dover, Ramsay made a signal: 'The Queen's signalmen are a disgrace to the Fleet.' David Beatty came aboard the Albemarle at 9 o'clock the next morning in frock coat and sword, and made a furious complaint to poor Colin who, like me, knew nothing about it.'

Dover was to figure again, rather more prominently, later in Ramsay's career.

He was critical of some of the old fashioned ideas and thought a more scientific approach to the study of war was needed. In 1912, when

[4] *'Full Cycle'*, by Rear Admiral W S Chalmers

the Naval War Staff Course was introduced, Ramsay applied and joined the second course in 1913. Then to *Dreadnought* as Signal Officer, Flag Lieutenant and War Staff Officer to Rear Admiral Gamble, BS4.

Shortly after the outbreak of war the Fleet had one of its first submarine alarms.

> *'The Fleet Flagship hoisted the signal: "Submarine in sight" and dashed off to starboard followed by us, going full speed. After steaming away for about twenty minutes we altered back to our original course and secured the guns. I had been down below about 30 seconds when again six blasts on the siren were heard. I dashed on the bridge to see the Iron Duke altering course to starboard with the signal for altering to port flying. Nothing came of this attack.*
>
> *'Considering we were at imminent danger of being torpedoed there was marvellously little excitement on board. People will not realise the danger, and everyone wants to leave his post and have a 'look see'. Another amusing thing happened - the officer in charge of 'Y' turret, which has a Maxim gun mounted on it, thought the bugle he heard was 'repel aircraft', so he rushed to his station and seeing an object in the sky immediately aimed at it and fired. On looking again, however, he saw it was a kite being flown from the Iron Duke for trial.'*

Ramsay was Executive Officer of the battleship *Benbow* with James Somerville as his captain, commanded two cruisers, then became an instructor at the Imperial Defence College. He commanded the *Royal Sovereign* before being promoted Rear Admiral in 1935.

A spell as Chief of Staff to Admiral Sir Roger Backhouse, C-in-C Home Fleet, came to an abrupt end after disagreement over the staff organisation - Backhouse was bad at delegating and liked to deal with all problems, however small and however overloaded he became, leaving the Chief of Staff to be a sort of senior consultant, when required. Ramsay, with his War Staff experience, couldn't stand this and eventually asked to be relieved, went on half pay, and in 1938 was retired.

However he was nominated as Flag Officer Dover in the event of war, and during the Munich crisis began setting up the headquarters. There were no communication facilities but his newly appointed flag lieutenant, James Stopford, had taken the precaution of bringing with him from the Signal School a portable W/T set which he could just fit in his car. He found that the old Port War Signal Station had been converted into a public lavatory but, undaunted, he set up his equipment and, much to his surprise, it worked.

By September 1939 Ramsay, now Vice Admiral on the retired list, was back in Dover. 'My flag is flying today for the first time over the signal station at Dover Castle, so I am once again an authority' he wrote to his wife. Initially under the C-in-C Nore, he soon became an independent command as Vice Admiral Dover,

Admiral Sir Bertram Ramsay

Early in 1915 Ramsay was appointed to the newly formed Signal Section of the War Staff, where his recent experience in the Grand Fleet was of great value in preparing the new signal books. After commanding a small ship on the Dover Patrol, and then the destroyer Broke, he went as Jellicoe's Flag Commander and War Staff Officer for the latter's post-war cruise in the battleship New Zealand to the Dominions and India, to advise on their naval needs in relation to the defence of the Empire. Included were recommendations, largely adopted, on such matters as training and the signal communications organisation.

Admiral of the Fleet Sir Roger Keyes wrote to Ramsay: 'The wheel of fortune turned well for you and I am so glad - your courage in declining to remain in a false position with Backhouse gave you an opportunity which might not have come your way in the normal course ...'

with Captain L V Morgan, another signal officer, as his Chief-of-Staff. Offices had been provided in the old tunnels under the cliffs, but the staff was totally inadequate, and the enormous amount of coding and cyphering had to be done at first by the Secretary, Flag Lieutenant and Chief Yeoman at a small table using any scraps of paper to hand. Soon, of course, the staff was augmented, mainly with Wrens, most of whom had not yet received their uniforms.

James Stopford used to play golf with Ramsay when time allowed. 'The Admiral was a good golfer ... mine was very different, but it was quite clear that if I did not give him a game, a new Flag Lieutenant would be found, and by the time of the invasion of the Low Countries I was down to scratch!' When Stopford was re-organising the communications systems, Ramsay asked for direct telephone lines between Dover and Boulogne and Dunkirk. This was not supported by the Admiralty who preferred wireless and considered the rental cost of £500 a year unwarranted. But in the end the telephones were provided, and when French resistance collapsed and the British Army had lost most of its equipment, they became invaluable. Stopford's last conversation on the phone to Boulogne was with a German, and of course the line to Dunkirk in particular proved vital during the evacuation and was kept going to the very last.

```
ROUTE X 55 MILES
ROUTE Y 87 MILES
ROUTE Z 39 MILES
```

The Dunkirk evacuation area

Vice Admiral Somerville, visiting Dover, realised the strain Ramsay was under and volunteered to stay on, taking over at night to allow Ramsay to get some sleep. Communications were difficult, not only to Dunkirk but along the beaches. A naval W/T set was established at the shore end of the mole at Dunkirk, but this broke down owing to sand in the generator. Generally messages had to be passed by some convenient ship's radio. The telephone at La Panne, one of the evacuation beaches, was in constant use by Army staff officers who, hoping to achieve a measure of security, used Indian dialects! Captain Howson, a signal officer who had been sent over with the beach parties, found that the only way to communicate with the Army was to take his messages by bicycle to La Panne.

The King visited Dover several times, once in a fierce blizzard. Ramsay wrote:

'It was strange to hear him say that it was lucky he had put on his second-best cap and his old trousers. Somehow one does not expect kings to have old pairs of uniform trousers or old caps.'

One of those at the sharp end of the evacuation was Signalman Les Mallows, RNVR, who was in his first ship, the paddle steamer *Princess Elizabeth,*

'... now one of His Majesty's minesweepers, which would move according to my reading of the signals addressed to her. The thought struck me that I had better get them right!'

117

After four trips, during which they survived unscathed, they arrived back at Dover to be told the operation was complete.

> *'However there was not much rest - next morning Flag E was hoisted at the Castle Signal Station, meaning a General semaphore message was to follow. Two signalmen stood at right angles to each other and began transmitting:*
>
> *'"From V A Dover. I had hoped and believed that last night would see us through but the French who were covering the retirement of the British rearguard had to repel a strong German attack and so were unable to send their troops to the pier in time to be embarked. We cannot leave our Allies in the lurch and I must call on all officers and ratings detailed for further evacuation tonight to let the world see that we never let down an ally."*
>
> *'This was probably the first time any of us had realised that the French were holding off the Germans while the British were taken off.'*

'I know of no other sailor whom I would sooner have seen responsible for extricating the B.E.F.'

Lord Alanbrooke

The ship set off once more to Dunkirk, where they found a berth alongside the high jetty.

> *'With the tide low, heaving lines were thrown up to cries of "Attrapez cette ligne", and "Tirez, Tirez" as the lines came down again, but eventually a gangway was rigged and the first French soldiers crept gingerly down, throwing their rifles into the water as they came. This seemed rather a waste and instructions changed to "Apportez les fusils et donnez-les-moi!"'*
>
> *'All went well and the ship arrived back at Dover next morning, queuing to find a berth alongside. Dog tired, the sailors propped themselves at the guardrails watching the mass disembarkation. At that moment we had the quiet satisfaction of seeing our Allies forming orderly ranks on the quayside, with the white cliffs of England as a backdrop.'*

Commander J P Gibbs to Ramsay: 'I was delighted to see about your KCB for, if ever a man deserved it, you do ... War is hell when you and I can't go to the Derby ...'

By the end of Operation DYNAMO over 338,000 British and Allied troops had been evacuated.

Matapan

With the entry of the Italians into the war in 1940, the focus of attention turned for a time to the Mediterranean, where a major pre-occupation was fighting convoys through to the besieged island of Malta.

With Andrew Cunningham C-in-C Med based in Alexandria, and Vice Admiral Somerville commanding Force 'H' at Gibraltar, there were some lively activities - an Italian attempt to intercept an east-bound convoy in November 1940 was beaten off by Somerville at the Battle of Cape Spartivento, Genoa and Tripoli (Libya) were bombarded, and the Italian battle fleet in Taranto harbour was decimated by carrier-borne aircraft.

Complete wireless silence was in force during the withdrawal after the attack on the Italian fleet in Taranto. Vice Admiral Sir Stephen Berthon remembers that Illustrious therefore had to transmit the result of the attack by V/S: 'She chose to do this by flags, presumably so that the whole fleet could read it. Hoist after hoist spelt out the great news that two battleships had been disabled, three cruisers sunk, and so on - the longest flag signal I have ever seen. One could sense the cheering in each ship as the Yeoman reported the meaning of each hoist.'

In May 1941 came the evacuation of Greece and Crete, with heavy casualties, followed later in the year by the sinking of the *Barham*, and then in December damage to *Queen Elizabeth* and *Valiant* as a result of attacks by human torpedoes in Alexandria. But the gloom in 1941 had been relieved by an outstanding success earlier in the year.

Although Italian naval cyphers had been broken before the war, and this continued until June 1940 when the Italians joined in, they introduced new cypher systems for both surface and submarine fleets in July, and the flow of Sigint from these sources largely dried up. However some military and naval traffic was decrypted from time to time, and in March 1941 intercepts indicated that a naval operation was due to take place, probably in the Aegean area, with a D-Day of 28 March.

Admiral Cunningham decided that an immediate reaction by the Mediterranean Fleet would probably lead to the operation being postponed, so while British convoys were re-routed away from the area, the battlefleet (*Warspite, Barham Valiant*) and *Formidable* stayed in harbour until after dark on 27th. That afternoon Cunningham went off to play golf, confident that this would be noticed and reported back to the Italians by the Japanese consul, another keen golfer.

The Eastern Mediterranean showing the battle area

Italian air reconnaissance reported the fleet in Alexandria on the 27th, and although Admiral Iachino in the battleship *Vittorio Veneto* was surprised next morning when he encountered British cruisers south of Crete, he still believed that there was no threat from the battlefleet. By this time however the latter were only some 70 miles away, and in their second attack in mid-afternoon *Formidable's* Albacores scored a torpedo hit on *Vittorio Veneto*.

Iachino turned for home, his flagship still being able to steam at about 19 knots, and the British battleships, with a maximum speed of 24 knots, were going to have a hard job to catch up with him. There had been conflicting reports from aircraft on the positions, composition and movements of the Italian forces, so *Warspite's* Swordfish was catapulted just before 1800 to try and clear up the situation. The observer, Lieutenant Commander Bolt, sighted the *Vittorio Veneto* half an hour later, and shortly began initiating a series of valuable reports.

'We passed our reports by W/T direct to Alexandria W/T station at a distance of some 400 miles. We had carried out a great deal of practice with this station during dawn anti-submarine patrols from Alexandria and it was very satisfying that P O Pace,

HMS *Valiant* in 1941

Her Type 279 radar played a vital part in the Battle of Matapan.

my telegraphist-air gunner, was able to clear some dozen Operational Immediate messages in a matter of minutes. These signals, repeated by Alexandria W/T to Malta and Gibraltar, were received immediately in Whitehall W/T and the Admiralty had them nearly as soon as the C-in-C in Warspite.'

It then became clear that the Italians had concentrated and were some 45 miles ahead steaming at about 15 knots. At 1940 a dusk attack by *Formidable's* aircraft scored a torpedo hit on the cruiser *Pola*, though this was not known at the time.

Three ships, *Valiant*, *Formidable* and *Ajax*, were fitted with Type 279 radar, and *Orion* had an early type of fixed aerial ASV, 286M. The cruisers were some way ahead of the battlefleet when at 2040 *Orion* detected a stopped ship; this was assumed to be the *Vittorio Veneto*. Then *Ajax* picked up the same target, and Cunningham altered course towards these detections, some twenty miles ahead. Less than an hour later, *Valiant's* radar also detected what she reported as a large ship, at a range of nine miles on the port bow.

It was assumed that destroyers would be in company with the *Vittorio Veneto*, and a prudent manoeuvre would be for the battlefleet to turn away to avoid a possible torpedo attack. Tom Brownrigg, the Master of the Fleet (Staff Navigator), described the scene:

'The C-in-C was recommended to turn away - Blue Four. But he said: "If that's the enemy we will turn towards and find out what sort they are and how soon we sink them: Four Blue!" It thus occurred that for the first time in a night action a battlefleet turned towards an unknown force of enemy ships.'

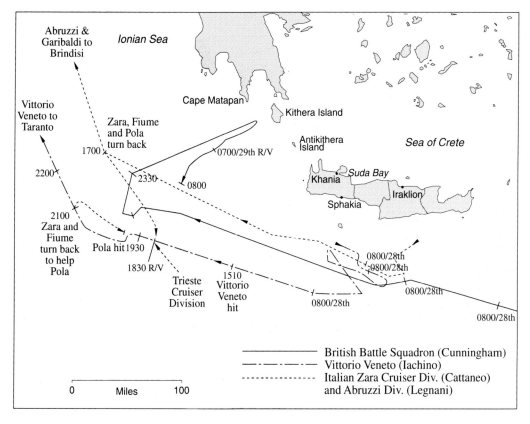

The Battleship action at Matapan

⁴ ADM 220-26

Geoffrey Barnard, the Fleet Gunnery Officer, recalled:

> '*ABC turned the battlefleet together to investigate, handling the fleet from this moment until midnight in the same way that he would have handled a division of destroyers.*'

As they were led in by reports from *Valiant's* radar, several more darkened ships were seen fine on the starboard bow, crossing ahead of the fleet. These were the *Zara*, *Fiume* and four destroyers. The battlefleet was turned together to starboard into line ahead to open their 'A arcs', the destroyer *Greyhound* switched on her searchlight which lit up one of the cruisers, and the three battleships opened fire.

In *Valiant*, the fire control table had been set to radar range as soon as *Zara* and *Fiume* had been sighted, and her first broadside was seen to hit *Fiume*, the right hand target; fire was then shifted to *Zara*, and the five broadsides fired at her were also seen to hit. ⁴

Thus Sigint had provided the opportunity, the radar assisted approach positioned the British battlefleet perfectly for the brief night action that followed, and radar ranges helped to achieve hits from the first broadside. The three Italian cruisers and two destroyers were sunk. Casualties on the British side were the loss of three aircrew from *Formidable*.

This was a far cry from the first world war when the aim was to avoid a night action between capital ships at all costs!

The Signal School Moves to Leydene

Back at home, things were hotting up. The German bombing which intensified in the autumn of 1940 brought the war to the dockyard and to the doors of the Signal School. The Commander, Laurie Durlacher, later wrote:

> *'During the blitz we were fairly badly damaged, and after each raid in which we suffered I had to plan how to reorganise instruction for the next day ... it was tough having to train intensively by day and with few undisturbed nights. We suggested that we should move before being bombed out of doing our job. The official reply was that it was not Their Lordship's policy to earmark alternative accommodation but this would be found when absolutely necessary - ie when existing premises were completely destroyed!'*

In May 1941 Admiralty House and the Tactical School, which was used as the local headquarters, were badly damaged and the C-in-C and his staff moved out to the stand-by HQ at Fort Wallington. In 'The Portsmouth Letters' Admiral Sir William James wrote:

> *'As we are on reclaimed ground we cannot dig deep shelters and (during air raids) all my operational people, including Wren coders, signalmen and telegraphists are bunched up in the basement of the Tactical School and one bomb could have killed the lot. I should have moved them before but I rather stupidly thought I would lose contact with them at some important moment during invasion if the telephones broke down. I have solved that by flashing lamp and wireless.'*

Instruction at the schools suffered, and staff and students spent much of the night fire-watching or putting out incendiary bombs. The time had come to evacuate and the search began for less vulnerable premises. Having the Signal School and Experimental Department co-located had brought considerable benefits, and CSS was keen that these should be retained if possible.

However this proved to be quite impracticable and the search began for new sites. Basil Willett took the Experimental Department to Lythe Hill House at Haslemere, and King Edward School, Witley (adjacent stations on the Portsmouth-London line). Broadly, Headquarters and Radio went to Lythe Hill (which had been requisitioned the previous year to provide space for the expanding department), and Radar to Witley (the schoolboys moved to the old workhouse at Hambledon nearby, which some local people thought very cruel of the Admiralty!). There were still a large number of out-stations, such as Nutbourne for aerial developments, radar at Onslow Road, Southsea, and at Eastney (moved to Witley a year later), with some 24 other small groups at universities, in industry and at sites for radio trials. On 26 August 1941 the Experimental Department was re-named the Admiralty Signal Establishment (ASE). [5]

Leydene House, near East Meon, looked a likely spot for the

[5] In 1948 the establishment was re-named the Admiralty Signal and Radar Establishment (ASRE), by which time the first buildings on the new site at Portsdown had been completed. Moves to Portsdown took place progressively over the next ten years. ASRE was again re-named, becoming the Admiralty Surface Weapons Establishment (ASWE), and eventually it became the Admiralty Research Establishment (ARE), part of the Defence Research Agency.

Map of the area, showing Leydene House

[6] See 'Life at Leydene' in Chapter 23

Standard Flashing Exercise on the Broadwalk at Leydene, 1944

The group on the left are using a Heliograph.

Signal School and CSS, Angus Cunninghame Graham, set off to investigate.

'My Commander, Laurie Durlacher, and I made an appointment to call on Lady Peel. We arrived in pouring rain and were met by a very odd looking butler who threw open a door out of the hall and said "The men have come, your ladyship". Lady Peel was one of a small section of our community who did not consider that the war should interfere with her property or her way of life. Reluctantly she took us round the house but gleefully out to the stables. She had a mackintosh but ours were left in the hall. The further round we got the more agressive she became. Laurie and I had the answer for this, for as she got ruder we got more and more polite, which was not really difficult as we had a basic sympathy for her. Eventually we raised a smile and even an offer of tea. We decided that the property would 'make do' and left the Naval Lands branch to fight the battle for which they had been trained.'

Leydene was duly requisitioned by the Admiralty and Lady Peel retired to Scotland. [6]

'We then got busy planning for the new school, but the problems were formidable as we had to go on instructing at the old Signal School to the last minute so it meant laying our hands on duplicate equipment to install at Leydene ... When we finally moved in we lost under a day's instruction which I was rather proud of!'

An advance party under Lieutenant Cullimore was sent out to Leydene to 'make ready'. Shortly afterwards a land mine was dropped near the house, but this proved to be the only sign of enemy activity for the rest of the war. Lieutenant Parker, then a telegraphist, was one of those detailed for the advance party.

H·M·S· Mercury

'We arrived as the last of the Peel family's furniture was leaving. The butler was there and he stayed around for several days ... he regarded our taking over the house as totally unnecessary. Asked about smoking, the Butler said "Her Ladyship does not allow smoking on the premises." We started by making the enormous kitchen into our Mess. Then we up-ended some long wooden tables, and slung our hammocks between the legs.'

The badge of HMS *Mercury*

The school was commissioned as HMS *Mercury* on 16 August 1941, under the command of a new CSS, Captain Gerald Warner, and in accordance with tradition, Portsmouth Motor Boat No.3520 was re-named HMS *Mercury*. (ASE then became HMS *Mercury II*, which name was given to Motor Boat No.3521).

The first contingent consisted of about 300 ratings, accommodated in a row of tents, with their dining room in what later became the wardroom in Leydene House. It was a wet summer, and the tents were not very comfortable, but by winter a row of Nissen huts had been erected, housing 24 ratings in each initially, later reduced to 14. Conditions were pretty appalling, particularly in the early winters; this did, however, make the trainees keen to get to sea! Many more temporary buildings sprang up, one of the most notable being the huge Nissen-type cinema, with a sloping floor on which many ship's company dances were held, which was built in 1943 and was to survive for exactly half a century.

HMS *Mercury* in 1956

'Divisions' are being held on the main drive. Mountbatten Block is under construction, and some 'Crescent' blocks are still to come.

After the war, it was decided that the School should if possible remain at Leydene, as it would probably be cheaper to buy the place rather than to restore it to its pre-war condition and return it to the owner. Negotiations with Lady Peel were started, but in 1949 she died, the family did not wish to take it on again, and so Leydene House and about 160 acres were bought by the Crown for £60,000. The rest of the estate was sold off, much of it to tenant farmers.

The number to be accommodated varied but occasionally was not far short of two thousand, though between ten and twelve hundred was more usual, falling to a few hundred when there were cut backs in the Navy or recruiting difficulties. The temporary buildings had to be replaced, and modern amenities provided, so a long period of rebuilding and expansion began. This is best illustrated in the aerial photographs which show how the establishment developed.

HMS *Mercury* in 1970

The new drill shed, just to the right of the crescent blocks, has been completed. The ground has been cleared for the third instructional block (Nelson) encroaching on the Broadwalk. The WRNS block (Soberton) is under construction (far left); the original WRNS Quarters at Soberton Towers were closed and sold in 1971. Still to be built, between Soberton and Nelson, are the medical centre and the P & RT centre, adjacent to the swimming pool. The Admin block would shortly be started, to replace the garage courtyard to the left of the boiler house. The large Nissen-type cinema is at the bottom right. The Droxford Road, to the right of the cinema, bends to the left and runs through the middle of the camp.

'Mercury - Roman god (Greek Hermes) son of Jupiter and Maia, was Jupiter's messenger, and patron of travellers, shepherds, traders and robbers, and god of merchandise. Many of his exploits turned upon thievery or mischief. He wore a winged cap and had wings to his feet, and could transport himself from place to place with the speed of the wind.'

Pears Cyclopaedia

Chapter Eleven

Atlantic and Arctic Convoys

'The beauty of our exploit was the timing of it ...
I think my remark "By God, we'll do a Magdeburg!"
was epoch making ...'

Signal Intelligence (Sigint) provided by the Government Code and Cypher School (GC&CS) at Bletchley Park played an important part in the naval war, not least that against the U-Boats. Amongst the Sigint sources was the naval 'Y' service, which had expanded considerably and now included an extensive shore HF DF network, and which was responsible for intercepting and exploiting German naval radio traffic. The dissemination and use of Sigint called for special security measures to avoid revealing the source, and this intelligence was passed by codeword protected messages, encrypted in special one-time cypher systems, with a very limited distribution. Any operations resulting from this intelligence had to be planned on the basis that the enemy could attribute it to other 'normal' sources of intelligence.

Enigma

It was known that the German forces used versions of the Enigma cypher machine, but progress in breaking their naval cyphers was slow until the first break-through came in February 1940, when *U-33* was sunk by the minesweeper *Gleaner* while minelaying off the Clyde, and three rotors were recovered. Papers captured from a patrol boat in April 1940 also helped, and GC&CS was able to build up some knowledge of the operating procedures for the various German keys, such as 'Home Waters', 'Distant Waters' and 'Officers-only'.

One of the aims of the raid on the Lofoten Islands in February 1941 was to capture a complete Enigma system; in the event none was found on the islands, but the trawler *Krebs* was attacked and although her machine was thrown overboard, the rotors were recovered. This enabled Bletchley to make a start on breaking the Home Waters traffic. About this time it was realised that German weather ships in the Atlantic used Enigma, and it was decided to try and obtain one of these. In May the *München*, on station East of Iceland, was captured by *Edinburgh* and *Somali*, and although the Enigma machine was destroyed, the Home Waters key for June 1941 was recovered. The *München* was towed to the Faroes, but to conceal the capture it was announced that she had sunk.

A spectacular success occurred only a couple of days after the *München* episode in May 1941 when the destroyers *Bulldog* (Escort Commander) and *Broadway*, with the corvette *Aubretia*, gained contact with a submarine which had attacked convoy OB-318, and brought it to the surface. Both destroyers prepared to ram but at the last minute Captain Joe Baker-Creswell in *Bulldog* realised that the crew were abandoning ship and there was a chance of getting on board.

Bulldog's boarding party was led by Sub Lieutenant David Balme and included Telegraphist Allen Long. They found the submarine had suffered a good deal of damage but her interior was virtually intact and there seemed to be no danger of her sinking. Long, who had thoughtfully taken a screwdriver with him, went straight to the wireless office where he noted all the settings on the radio equipment, then dismantled as much of it as he could. An enormous number of documents, including signal books, logs and charts showing searched channels leading to U-Boat bases were recovered, but the prize was an Enigma cypher machine, together with the rotor settings up to the end of June.

After some six hours *U-110* was successfully taken in tow by *Bulldog* but the weather deteriorated, she was leaking badly and eventually sank.

It was immediately realised that the captured material was invaluable and highly sensitive. The German survivors had been segregated and confined below decks so that they would not see what was going on; in fact they thought that the boat had sunk. All the ship's companies involved, as well as the survivors from sunk merchant ships who were on board, were instructed not to mention the capture, and the secret was well kept. It was not known to any of the early historians of the war at sea and only came to light some seventeen years later. [1]

At the time of the capture, the situation in the Battle of the Atlantic was desperate with ships being sunk much faster than they could be replaced. The German naval cyphers were particularly difficult to break, having more rotors than the Luftwaffe's which were the first to be cracked, and there was only a limited amount of wireless traffic on which to work. The new material helped Bletchley to decrypt the German 'Home Waters' crypto system then used by submarines, and in particular provided the settings for 'officer only' signals, while the *U-110* material included the code books which enabled them to read the special 'short' signals (*Kurzsignale*) used by U-Boats for transmitting standardised sighting messages in short bursts to reduce their vulnerability to intercept and DF.

RN Codes and Cyphers

At the outbreak of war the RN relied on the Naval Cypher, a 4-figure book used by officers, and the Admin Code, a 5-figure book used by ratings for lower classification messages. The RN thus had its own definition of cypher and code, although both were recyphered/recoded by the same process using long subtractor tables (see 'Subtract without carrying...' in chapter 22). Later the terms came to have different meanings: Cypher for high grade book or machine systems giving long term security, and code for systems designed primarily for convenience and speed but with only short term or no security.

The Admin Code was read by the Germans for the first year of the war, until it was replaced by a 4-figure system, when both cypher and code traffic became outwardly similar.

[1] *'The Secret Capture'*, by Stephen Roskill, and letter to the author from David Balme

A 4-Rotor Enigma Machine

The 4th rotor had been added to the Enigma in 1942. Helped by some breaches of security by the Germans, such as its use in error before it was in force, and in one case this being 'corrected' by repeating the identical message in the 3-rotor system, Bletchley eventually solved this at the end of 1942. Unfortunately, by coincidence the Germans had broken the British Naval Cypher No.3 early in 1942 but Bletchley, unable to read the 4-rotor Enigma, was not aware of this for some time.

The plugboard at the front is set up according to the key list, and the rotors are set similarly to the letters shown in the key list for the day. As each letter of the plain text is typed, the resultant cyphered letter in the middle panel is illuminated and this is then written down to form the cyphered groups.

Although other factors played their part, these captures, and particularly the material obtained by *Bulldog*, made a significant contribution to the eventual success of the battle against the U-Boats. Writing to David Balme in 1988, Captain Baker-Creswell said:

> *'The beauty of our exploit was the providential timing of it ... if losses in the Atlantic had gone on increasing at the same rate we would probably have had to sue for peace. In fact, I think my remark on the Bulldog's bridge: "By God, we'll do a Magdeburg!" was as epoch making as some of Churchill's sayings!'*

David Balme, and *Bulldog's* Engineer Officer, were awarded the DSC, and Telegraphist Long the DSM.

In February 1942 the Germans changed the procedures for submarine traffic, adding a fourth wheel to the Enigma, and this caused a severe setback at Bletchley. The problem was eventually resolved with the help of security breaches by the Germans, and the capture by the destroyer *Petard* of an Enigma, and valuable documents, from *U-559* off Egypt, and by the beginning of 1943 Bletchley were once more in business.

In June 1941 intelligence based on Sigint decrypts of high grade enemy cyphers was given the codename Ultra.

The Sigint war was not all one sided however. The Germans also had considerable success against the British systems, and for the first couple of years of the war were in a position to decrypt many of the convoy routeing and re-routeing signals, and thus place their submarines in the most advantageous positions. As early as 1926 a Committee had been set up in the UK to consider the use of cypher machines to replace book systems, and in the course of studying various options the Admiralty had actually instigated the purchase of two German Enigmas. Although the other services adopted what developed into the Typex machine, there was some reluctance to accept these in ships, perhaps because messages encyphered by machine tended to be longer than those using book systems, so the navy continued to rely on the manual 'subtraction' system. [2]

'Huff-Duff' and Radar

The development and rapid production of ship-borne HF DF and Radar by the Experimental Department of the Signal School was to have a dramatic effect on the war against the U-Boats. This is well illustrated by the successes of one particular destroyer, HMS *Hesperus*. Between December 1941 and May 1943 these equipments were instrumental in helping her to sink no less than five U-Boats.

By early 1941 *Hesperus*, together with some ninety other convoy escorts, had been fitted with a modified ASV RDF, known as Type 286M, with fixed aerials which required the ship to be turned in order to maximise the echo and obtain an accurate bearing. A lighter, rotating aerial was designed at Nutbourne, and ship-fitting of this set, Type 286P, began in June 1941.

Two future signal officers were on board during this period, Duncan Knight as First Lieutenant, and David Seely as a watch-keeping officer. On the night of 14 December 1941, when Knight was on watch, *Hesperus* detected a radar echo right ahead. Switching on the 10-inch projector a surfaced U-Boat was revealed, much to the amazement of those on the bridge, on the same course and already diving. Knight ran over the spot and gave her a 14-charge pattern which it seemed could not miss but proved not to be fatal; despite an all night search, A/S contact could not be gained, and the boat survived.

The experience was not wasted because a month later, when by chance Knight and the same radar operator, Leading Seaman Sheard, were on watch, an exactly similar radar echo was obtained. *Hesperus* turned towards, increased to 18 knots and illuminated a surfaced U-Boat. This one was caught completely by surprise and did not dive. *Hesperus* rammed her and engaged her with gunfire; the U-Boat heeled over then catapulted back, her conning tower hitting the ship's motor boat and flinging the Captain and his First Lieutenant on board *Hesperus*! The crew of *U-93*, as she proved to be, abandoned ship and forty were picked up. In the whaler David Seely made a determined effort to board the U-Boat, which appeared to be in good shape. However the engines had been left running slowly and seacocks opened; it proved impossible to reach her before she sank.

Hesperus was also one of the first ships to be fitted with HF DF, which played a vital role in countering the German 'wolf-pack' tactics. Lines of U-Boats would be stationed across known convoy routes, and when one made a sighting she would send a 'short signal' on HF to her Control; the information would be re-broadcast to the others which would then close, moving on the surface except when

[2] The security of the subtractor system was based on the recyphering tables being replaced frequently enough to avoid the enemy gaining adequate material to mount a cryptanalytical attack, and on the cyphering rules being strictly followed. Monty Davenport, in his contribution to 'British Intelligence in the Second World War', points out that it had not been appreciated that the volume of traffic in war would prevent these conditions being fulfilled; he suggests also that this failure can in part be attributed to the divided control of the navy's cypher organisation - DNI, advised by GC & CS, responsible for security, DSD for communications organisation, and the Paymaster Director General for cypher staff. As the war progressed, prime responsibility gradually passed to the Signal Division. (See 'Subtract Without Carrying ...' in chapter 22.)

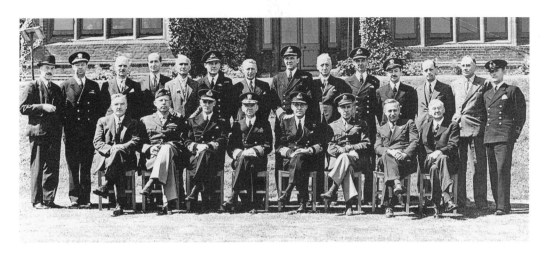

US Delegation at ASE, July 1943

Progress in many of ASE's projects were discussed, both radar and communications. The Americans were particularly interested in ASEs work on HF DF, which needed to be developed to cover the higher frequencies to which U-Boats had shifted. Photograph includes:

Front (L to R): Cecil Horton; u/k; Rear Admiral Cedric Holland, DSD; Rear Admiral Fuhrer, USN; Captain Basil Willett, Captain Superintendent; u/k; u/k; Charles Wright Director of Scientific Research, Admiralty.
Back (L to R): Sir Henry Tizard; u/k; JDS Rawlinson; u/k; u/k; Commander GF Burghard; Sir George Thomson; Captain Charles Firth; GM Wright, Chief Scientist, ASE; Commander Andrew Yates; u/k; SEA Landale; HE Hogben.

necessary to avoid detection, until the 'wolf-pack' was formed and poised to attack. Although these transmissions could be intercepted, until the arrival of HF DF equipment in ships there was no means of determining the position of U-Boats in the immediate vicinity.

In *Hesperus* Lieutenant Harold Walker, RNVR, became such an expert at interpreting the detections, that he could tell one U-Boat's transmission from another, and whether ground or sky wave; in the case of the former he could usually make a fair estimate of range, and possibly even say whether the aerial was wet or dry!

Escorting a homeward bound convoy from Newfoundland in December 1942, HF DF reported 'B-Bar - astern - 10 to 15 miles'! B-Bar was a German operating signal indicating that a U-Boat had a sighting to report urgently. *Hesperus* and the destroyer *Vanessa* raced off down the bearing and soon saw a surfaced U-Boat some miles ahead. The U-Boat dived, but after a number of attacks she surfaced, and was rammed and sunk by *Hesperus*.

In April 1943 *Hesperus* was escorting a westbound convoy which also had the escort carrier *Biter* in company. Unknowingly one of her Swordfish forced the U-Boat which had first sighted the convoy to dive and lose touch, but another, *U-191*, found herself well placed, fired torpedoes (which missed) then surfaced astern of the convoy to report. The HF DF operator picked up the transmission and *Hesperus*, with the corvette *Clematis*, moved off down the bearing and soon sighted the U-Boat on the horizon just before she dived.

Asdic contact was gained, and after a number of hedgehog and depth-charge attacks, the submarine was sunk.

Two days later *U-203* was heard transmitting, a Swordfish was despatched, sighted her and homed the destroyer *Pathfinder* who sank her. *U-108* was now the last on the scene; she attempted to signal further reports but couldn't obtain an acknowledgement from any German station. In fact the only operator to hear her was Harold Walker who, using German naval wireless procedure, answered the U-Boat's call and accepted her message 'for onward transmission'. She then ceased signalling and lost contact with the convoy which sailed on to Halifax in peace. Walker's expertise on this and many other occasions was rewarded with the DSC.

Signalman in HMS *Viscount* in the Atlantic

Viscount, one of the V and W class destroyers, was first commissioned in 1918. In August 1942 her HF DF obtained a fix, with another escort, which resulted in an attack on a U-Boat attacking convoy ON.122. In October that year she rammed and sank *U-619*, and in February 1943 was involved in the sinking of *U-69*.

In May 1943, escorting an Eastbound convoy, *Hesperus* obtained a radar contact, followed by sighting the white line of a U-Boat's wake. After a long drawn out battle *U-223* was badly damaged, but she escaped and limped home to Saint Nazaire.

The next day HF DF reports showed at least twelve U-Boats in touch, mostly astern, but suddenly one transmitted from close ahead. An accurate bearing was obtained, and as soon as the ship slowed to operating speed an asdic contact was picked up, and *U-186* was quickly sunk.

So for one ship, the early radar and HF DF equipments really earned their keep. These sets played an important part in helping the ships of the Western Approaches to hold the fort against the wolf-packs and, in due course, with the arrival of long range maritime patrol aircraft fitted with ASV radar, to turn the tide in the allies' favour.

Earlier, in 1941, Donald Macintyre in the destroyer *Walker*, escorting convoy HX112, had just picked up the crew of a torpedoed merchant ship, when another destroyer, *Vanoc*, began drawing ahead fast. Almost immediately Yeoman Gerrard said: 'She's signalling to us, sir, but I can't read it as her light is flickering so badly.' *Vanoc* was obviously ploughing ahead at full speed which would be causing her bridge to rattle and shake as the signalman tried to get a message through. The officer of the watch in *Walker*, another future signal officer, Rupert Bray, said: 'She must have sighted the submarine', and as he spoke *Vanoc* came up on R/T saying 'Have rammed and sunk U-Boat.'

While *Vanoc* picked up the few survivors from *U-100*, Walker obtained another contact, dropped a pattern of depth charges and almost immediately a U-Boat surfaced. During the ensuing gun action the boat signalled: 'I am sinking', and the crew abandoned ship. The last to be picked up, still wearing his brass hat, was the commanding officer of *U-99*, Otto Kretschmer, one of Germany's top U-Boat commanders.

Kretschmer was to surface again in some RN officers' lives - in the 1960s the author relieved Duncan Knight of the *Hesperus* as Chief Signal Officer, Allied Forces Northern Europe, at Oslo; who should be the Chief Staff Officer at the subordinate NATO Headquarters at Kiel but one Captain Otto Kretschmer.

*   *   *   *   *

Back at the Signal School 1941 had opened with good prospects for the development of radars working on much shorter, centimetric, wavelengths, necessary if small targets such as submarines low in the water or even, hopefully, periscopes were to be detected. The recently developed cavity magnetron was an essential element in this, and enabled a 10 cm set suitable for fitting in small ships to be designed.

The urgent requirement was to get it into a form in which it could be installed in a ship in a matter of days without waiting for the next refit, as had been the case with earlier sets. The answer was to design the equipment to fit into a small self-contained office, with the aerial on top, which could be hoisted on board as a unit. The early trials of a development model were so successful that it was immediately decided to make twelve 'Chinese copies' in the Signal School workshops, followed by a second batch of another twelve; in anticipation of approval, components for 150 more sets were ordered, so that commercial production could get underway as rapidly as possible.

By the end of July 1941 some two dozen escorts were being fitted with this equipment, known as Type 271, and by the beginning of 1942 a hundred production models had become available. Installation and setting up of both the Type 286 and Type 271 was carried out by a team of RNVR officers and ratings specially trained for the purpose, while Port RDF officers (later known as Port W/T Officers) were established to provide support for ships fitted with these and other unusual equipments. Sometimes known as the Corvette set, Type 271 became another vital component in the escorts' anti-U-Boat armoury, particularly valuable at this time as there was still a gap of some 1500 miles where no air cover could be provided for convoys.

King George VI outside the Signal School, 'K' Block, RN Barracks, Portsmouth, in 1941

L to R: Captain Basil Willett, Experimental Captain; George Shearing, Superintendent Scientist; Commander Harvey Crombie, Executive Officer; CL Glen-Bott, Chief Technical Adviser, (behind Crombie); HM The King; Captain Angus Cunninghame Graham, CSS.

Initially RDF operators were either telegraphists or bright young seamen, maintenance falling to senior telegraphists. In September 1940 a new specialist branch of RDF operators was introduced - Ordinary Seaman (RDF), AB (RDF) and so on, all Hostilities Only ratings - and then in May 1941 a new Radio Mechanic branch was formed to take over maintenance. RDF officers were all RNVR, either with some radio experience or a suitable degree. Early in the war the Canadians had been asked to help with the supply of technically trained people, and some twenty of the first batch were allocated for RDF training. Because of the general lack of knowledge in the fleet, these RDF officers found themselves advising on the operational use of the equipment, as well as supervising the technical aspects. Some familiarisation training for seaman officers began in 1941 with three day courses conducted at Portsmouth and Glasgow.

By 1943 the Radar Branch had expanded enormously,[2] and it was decided to relieve DSD and the Signal School of responsibility for the Branch. A new school for Radar Mechanics was set up in HMS *Collingwood*, a training establishment opened in 1939 at Fareham, and this came under the auspices of the Director of Training and Staff Duties (DTSD).

The 'Hostilities Only' system for radar operators obviously could not continue in the longer term, and two new non-substantive rates were introduced into the Seaman Branch, the Radar Control (RC) rating to man gunnery and target indication sets and carry out certain fire control duties, and the Radar Plot (RP) rating who would man warning sets and carry out plotting duties in the Action Information Centre. In a ship the RC ratings came under the Gunnery Officer, and the RP ratings under the Navigator, and their training also was in due course centred at Excellent and Dryad respectively.

Thus the Signal Branch relinquished direct responsibility for radar, although under his overall responsibility for controlling the use of the 'ether', the signal officer was still responsible for its operational use, in accordance with the electronic emission policy.

To jump ahead and complete this part of the story, in January 1944 responsibility within the Admiralty for R & D, production and fitting of all radio equipment was transferred from DSD to the newly-formed Directorate of Radio Equipment (DRE). This was in accordance with the plan to separate the policy-making functions of the Naval Staff Divisions from the 'material' functions of the Admiralty departments. DRE therefore assumed responsibility for the Admiralty Signal Establishment (ASE), which was now in the charge of Willett's relief, Captain Pat Brooking.

[2] In a Minute dated 28 September 1943, DSD says 'The Radar Branch has expanded from practically nothing at the beginning of 1940 to some 10,000 officers and men at the present time.' The number of officers was said to be 600.

'The enemy has deprived the U-Boat of its essential feature, the element of surprise, by means of radar. With these methods, he has conquered the U-Boat menace. The Scientists who have created radar have been called the saviours of their country. It was not superior strategy or tactics which gave him success in the U-Boat war, but superiority in Scientific research.'

Karl Doenitz, in a speech at Weimar, 1945

Convoy Signalmen

The lessons of the first war had been well learnt, and there was no hesitation about introducing the convoy system right from the start. Initially Commodores were provided with active service or reserve signal staffs, but pre-planned arrangements for training some 500 men specially for convoy work were quickly put in hand. The first batch of 50 new entries arrived at HMS *Royal Arthur* at Skegness in September 1939, there to be taught morse, semaphore, flag signalling and the use of the Merchant Navy signal book, *Mersigs*.

The first newly rated Convoy Ordinary Signalmen appeared just in time for the Dunkirk evacuation, where they had their first casualties. They then gradually relieved active service signalmen, first in coastal convoys and then, as the branch expanded, on the staffs of the Commodores of ocean convoys. In due course they were able to pass for Leading rate and later for Convoy Yeoman after completing courses at Chatham; by the end of 1941 most of the staffs for Convoy Commodores were provided by Convoy Signalmen.

Their war was almost entirely spent at sea, often in a rapid succession and variety of ships and oceans. Len Matthews started on the east coast and English Channel where, as Signalman and Leading Signalman he helped to run 53 convoys in 1940-41.

> *'We came under dive-bombing by Stukas and attack by E-Boats on many occasions, with shelling in the Straits of Dover as a diversion! Mines took a high toll in the Thames Estuary, and one ship I was on went down a bit quickly after encountering an acoustic mine. After passing out as Convoy Yeoman and doing four crossings of the Atlantic in HMS Highlander, senior officer of the escort, it was considered that the responsibility for communications in ocean convoys of up to 80 ships could be entrusted to a 22 year old landlubber. So I joined a typical elderly senior naval officer and stayed with him for three years.'*

Matthews' log for a twelve month period reads:

Nov. 1942   Narkunda. Troop convoy, Operation TORCH. Sunk by bombs.

Dec.   Empire Archer. Convoy to Russia. Attacked by Lutzow, Hipper. (Captain Sherbrooke, HMS Onslow, awarded VC)

Jan. 1943   Train from Archangel to Murmansk. Attacked by ski-troops.

Feb.   Daldorch. Return convoy.

Mar.   Prometheus. Liverpool to New York. Gales all the way.

Apr.   Empire Southey. Halifax to Liverpool. Icebergs, collisions.

May.   Leave.

Jun.   Letitia. Troop convoy to Sicily. Operation HUSKY. Bombed.

Jul.   Marwarri. Convoy Alexandria To Gibraltar via Tobruk.

Sep.   Markland. Gibraltar to UK. Bombed by Focke-Wulfs and attacked by submarines.

Oct.   Saluta. Gourock to Halifax. No action!

Being at the centre of the action for so much of their time, it is not surprising that the branch suffered many casualties. They also rightly earned the highest proportion of bravery awards of any service. Of the 50 Convoy Yeomen, no less than 38 were decorated, some more than once, while 41 Signalmen and Leading Signalmen were mentioned in despatches.

The Arctic Convoys

Sailing convoys through the Arctic to Russia began in September 1941. As well as the awful weather and the threat from submarines and aircraft, these convoys were also at risk from attack by German surface ships, notably the *Tirpitz* which had been positioned at Trondheim.

On 5 March 1942 *Tirpitz* put to sea with the intention of attacking convoy PQ12, although she was ordered to avoid action with superior forces. Due to fog, and searching too far south, she was ordered on 8th to return if nothing was sighted by nightfall. This was reported by Ultra within three hours, she was found and attacked by Albacores from *Victorious*, but no hits were scored; two aircraft were lost. In view of what happened three months later, it is interesting that Admiral Tovey complained about the Admiralty signalling 'detailed instructions for the handling of his forces.'

John Buckeridge, flotilla signal officer in *Somali*, escorting PQ15 wrote:

> *'The Germans operated long range aircraft which circled the convoy out of the range of our guns, homing the torpedo bombers and U-Boats on to the convoy. They were seldom able to make a surprise attack as we kept watch on their frequencies and could estimate within minutes when the attack was due, based on the build-up of their transmissions. This was a godsend as it meant that action stations need not be sounded until just before the whistle went. An interesting moment occurred when I reported to Captain D in his sea cabin that the time had come, and found that something was on fire. The 'something' was me - I was wearing a heavy kapok suit and had leant against his radiator. As the attack came in D was wrapping his flaming signal officer in a blanket.'*

Convoy PQ17, 36 ships, sailed from Iceland on 27 June 1942 for Archangel. Senior Officer of the close escort, nine destroyers and corvettes and two submarines, was Captain Jack Broome in HMS *Keppel*. Rear Admiral Hamilton in *London* led a cruiser covering force; further back, units of the Home Fleet were under the C-in-C, Admiral Tovey, in *Duke of York*. The convoy suffered attacks from German submarines and aircraft, but also from 'back-seat driving' by the Admiralty. [3]

German surface forces in North Norway included the *Tirpitz* and *Hipper* at Trondheim, *Scheer* and *Lutzow* at Narvik, and this led the Admiralty to issue a long and somewhat ambiguous signal before the

[3] The story, in particular the signal aspects, as seen from Keppel, is covered in detail in Broome's book *'Convoy is to Scatter'*, published after a long and well publicised libel case (which he won)

convoy sailed concerning the control of the movements of British forces. The signal read, in part:

> '...*As Admiralty may be in possession of fuller and earlier information of movements of enemy surface forces than our forces will be and as you may not wish to break W/T silence it appears necessary for Admiralty to control movements of convoy as far as this may be influenced by movements of enemy surface forces.*

> '*(This) will not prevent either C-in-C HF, CS1, SO of escort or Commodore of convoy giving such orders regarding movements as local conditions may necessitate.*

> '...*Admiralty may be unaware of weather conditions and even though Admiralty may give orders for course (of convoy) to be reversed it is at discretion of SO present with convoy to ignore the Admiralty order ...*

> '*Should the passage of the convoy be barred by a force including Tirpitz in good visibility and to eastward of Bear Island there will be no alternative but to reverse course of convoy, anyhow for a time. This action may be taken by*

North Norway and the convoy route

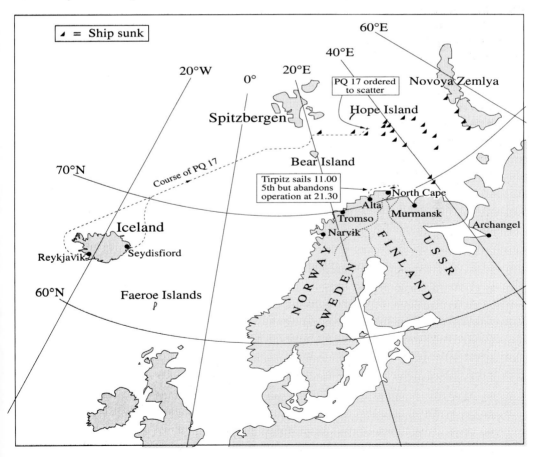

Admiralty, but if necessary C-in-C HF or SO of cruiser force or SO with convoy may give this order.

, *'Once convoy is to eastward of meridian of Bear Island circumstances may arise in which best thing would be for convoy to be dispersed ... It is at the discretion of either C-in-C, SO of cruiser force or SO of escort of convoy to give this order. = 0157B 27 June.'*

The Admiralty was trying to be helpful, and certainly would receive intelligence not known to forces at sea, and for this reason it was normal for convoys to be routed or re-routed from shore. Those at sea would be reluctant to break W/T silence, at least until it was clear that they had been located by the enemy. However this signal went further, floating a large number of possibilities and options particularly in the realm of 'command and control', and opening the way for the Admiralty to order what could amount to 'tactical' manoeuvres.

On 3 July, by which time the convoy was passing to the North of Bear Island, air reconnaissance showed no German ships in Trondheim and the Admiralty assumed they had moved north with the intention of attacking the convoy. *Scheer* and some destroyers had in fact already reached Altenfjord (*Lutzow* and three destroyers had run aground near Narvik, and took no further part).

By now the convoy was being shadowed by both aircraft and submarines. Broome commented in his report of proceedings:

'Having been used to snatching at slender threads as regards HF and MF DF with Atlantic convoys, and making the most out of generally a very few interceptions, PQ17 was found to be a very different problem. We were almost suffocated with a continual stream of high and medium frequency information from Admiralty and our own instruments. I was well aware of the fact that the convoy was being shadowed ... and on the whole this abundant confirmation was little use to me.'

So far Sigint had not been much help in tracking German surface ships, but late pm on 4 July Bletchley reported that *Tirpitz* and destroyers had arrived at Alta at 0900 that morning, the destroyers being ordered to fuel at once. This was passed on to C-in-C HF in an Ultra signal at 1918B.

At 2011B 4th July CSl signalled *Keppel*: 'Convoy is to steer 045 degrees until further orders', and followed this at 2040B with one referring to the 'proximity (of) surface forces', no doubt as a result of the Ultra signal of 1918B (which was in Flag Officers cypher and thus could not be read by *Keppel*). An Admiralty signal originated at 2111B to CSl and the escort read: 'Cruiser force withdraw to westward at high speed.'

This signal had not been seen by Broome before the arrival of the following from Admiralty: 'Owing to threat from surface ships convoy is to disperse and proceed to Russian ports = 2123B/4.''

This had clearly been triggered by the Ultra information. Although

Godfrey Winn was in an AA ship, the Pozarica. One morning a ship in the convoy began acting strangely. 'At first sight all of us on the bridge viewed with dismay and bewilderment as an American 'liberty' ship hauled down her flag. It was the Yeoman who first saw the downward fluttering of the flag out of the corner of his eye, and shouted out at what was happening. Then someone else shouted 'Look - they can't take it'. Were they surrendering? Then, in place of the flag hauled down, a new stars and stripes was being run up to the masthead - the new one looked twice the size. Then my eyes travelling beyond, up and down the columns, registered that all the other liberty ships, whose numbers dominated the convoy, were doing the same. Suddenly, it dawned on us: it was the 4th of July!'

Quoted in Winn's book, *'PQ 17'*

*From: Senior Officer (of escort)
Submarines*

*To: Keppel
'In the event of attack by
heavy enemy surface
forces propose to remain
on the surface'*

From: Keppel

*To: Senior Officer Submarines
'So do I'*

'Make Another Signal',
by Captain J E Broome

there was no further information on the German movements, the Admiralty Operational Intelligence Centre (OIC) considered that, although the force could have been ready to sail by about 1200, there was no indication (eg from W/T traffic) that it had done so. Asked later that evening by the First Sea Lord if *Tirpitz* was still in harbour, the OIC said that although an absolute assurance could not be given they were confident she was. In the face of this negative information, Pound decided that *Tirpitz* was likely to have sailed to attack the convoy as soon as the destroyers had fuelled. Broome commented:

> *'These signals, made inside half an hour, changed PQ17 from
> a convoy with its chin well up, into a shambles. My small
> communications staff was now at full stretch, the CPO Tel in
> charge, and the Doctor thrashing the cyphers. Had we gone
> into action would our Doc have been able to de-cypher with one
> hand and amputate with the other? I wouldn't put it past him!'*

It is tempting for an originator to think that his signal will be seen by the addressee almost as soon as he has dictated it. Realistically of course time is taken to encypher it, and it may have to take its turn with signals of higher precedence; unless the addressee is in company the message will have to be passed ashore for re-transmission on the appropriate broadcast. The reverse process at the receiving end will also take some time. Broome again:

> *'Signals repeated to us (for information), whatever priority
> and cypher, would queue for distribution after signals
> addressed (for action) to Keppel, and might not be seen by
> me for some time after receipt.'*

Admiralty's 2111B to CS1 was not seen by Broome until after the next signal which arrived with a shattering impact:

> *'From Admiralty: My 2123B/4. Convoy is to Scatter =
> 2136B/4.'*

Diagram from *'Mersigs'* of
the Scattering procedure

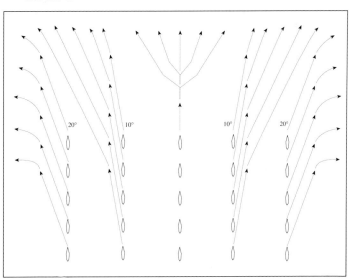

Scattering a convoy is a last resort, in the case of attack by a superior force, when it is considered that more ships will survive if scattered over the ocean than if left concentrated. The decision is of course irrevocable, since it would be virtually impossible later to round up the ships and reform the convoy. Broome could only assume that the threat was imminent. 'By imminent I mean that the surface forces are in sight. We were all expecting therefore to see either the cruisers open fire, or to see enemy masts appearing over the horizon.'

Leading Signalman Elliot noted as he bent on the red and white pendant that 'The Captain was a very angry man'. The signal was repeated to the Commodore by light and R/T, but he was reluctant to believe it and kept his pendant at the dip until *Keppel* had pulled alongside and Broome explained the situation, so far as he understood it.

Broome then formed up the destroyers and joined the cruisers ready to do battle, leaving the rest of the escorts to make their way independently to Russian ports. The cruisers and destroyers steamed away at high speed through the night. Nothing happened. It turned out that CS1 was equally in the dark, there was no sign of the enemy, and it was too late to send the destroyers back to attempt to assist ships ex-PQ17, by then scattering over the Barents Sea some four hundred miles away.

Tirpitz, Scheer, Hipper and destroyers did eventually sail from Altenfiord at 1100 on 5 July, over twelve hours after the convoy had scattered. Until then the Germans thought that the Home Fleet, including a carrier, could be within striking range, and the German High Command did not wish to put the force at risk. They made only a short sortie before being recalled at 2130. In any case, the convoy having scattered, it was best left to the U-Boats and aircraft to pick off the ships one by one. Thirteen ships, including two rescue ships, eventually reached Russia.

This was one of the less happy episodes of the war. Despite the plethora of signals from the Admiralty, senior officers and ships were not fully informed of the true picture or the reasons for many of the instructions and decisions (the restrictions imposed on the release of Ultra material no doubt played their part in this). Although it is impossible to say what would have happened if the convoy had not been scattered, the normal rules should have been followed, the decison being left to the man on the spot (as indeed had been inferred from the last paragraph of Admiralty's 0157B of 27 June).

Broome concludes his account, understandably: 'Radio came half a century too soon for PQ17'.

On 31 December 1942 a German surface force consisting of the pocket battleship *Lutzow*, heavy cruiser *Hipper*, and six destroyers attacked a convoy of fourteen ships, JW51B. In what became known as the Battle of the Barents Sea [4], four of the six escorting destroyers, led by Captain Sherbrooke in *Onslow*, fought a brilliant action in which they held off the enemy until the covering force of two cruisers could arrive. One German destroyer was sunk, and the British lost one destroyer, the *Achates*, and the minesweeper *Bramble*, while *Onslow* was severely damaged. The latter's wireless office suffered and became unduly hot

Captain Jack Broome and Rear Admiral Roy Foster-Brown. Broome devised a TV series *'Sea War'* which was narrated by Foster-Brown and shown on Southern Television in 1960. As well as writing several books, including *'Make a Signal'* and *'Make Another Signal'*, for a period after the war Broome edited *'The Sketch'*, a magazine somewhat similar to *'The Tatler'*.

[4] This action is described in detail in the book *'73 North'*, by Dudley Pope

from fires in the messes underneath, but PO Tel Frank Lovett repaired the mains supply and also got the main transmitter back into action, while Leading Tel Donald Grant did his best with the damaged aerials.

But, as usual, radio conditions were difficult, *Onslow's* aerials were severely iced up, and she had difficulty in getting through. An alert operator in HMS *Anson*, flagship of Vice Admiral Fraser, then second-in-command of the Home Fleet, which was off Iceland, heard a weak signal from a ship trying to raise Scapa W/T. Realising she was trying to transmit an enemy report, he called the PO Tel who telephoned the staff signal officer, Lieutenant 'Teddy' Poulden. 'I authorised the wireless office to transmit to Scapa W/T the contents of the enemy report and to continue to relay any such signals until they were confident that Scapa was hearing the originator direct. As soon as I had done this, I reported to the Captain that I had authorised an emergency breaking of radio silence. He instantly concurred.' Not many months out of initial training, the operator had, Poulden noted, 'acquired the sixth sense - the 'feel of the ether' - found only in very few telegraphists of great experience.'

The convoy got through to Russia without loss, but Sherbrooke, who was awarded the VC, achieved more than he knew. Hitler had for some time felt that the big ships 'idly lying about and lacking any desire to get into action ... were utterly useless' (ignoring the fact that he himself had ordered no risks to be taken). He became increasingly angry at failing to receive any news of the action for 36 hours; he was told that this was due to the failure of landlines and poor W/T conditions, but in fact Admiral Kummetz in *Hipper* considered that he hadn't anything urgent to report, and the signals he did originate were held up because the ships had not received the January cypher tables!

Even more furious when he did discover what had happened, Hitler ordered all battleships and cruisers to be paid off in order to strengthen the submarine campaign, and release resources for the Army. Later *Tirpitz, Scharnhorst* and one or two others were re-prieved, but most ships never left port again, and the building of new surface ships ceased. Within a month Admiral Raeder had resigned, to be succeeded by Admiral Doenitz.

Thus the Battle of the Barents Sea marked an important turning point in the naval war, especially in the Arctic where the losses steadily reduced. Some forty convoys altogether were sailed to Russia, and although the overall loss rate was greater than in other areas, of the 811 merchant ships sailed, 720 arrived safely.

*   *   *   *   *

Those who served at the headquarters of Allied Forces Northern Europe, AFNORTH, at Kolsas, near Oslo, may well have come across Bjorn Rorholt, one of those Norwegians who kept the British informed of German naval movements during the war. In the 1960s he was the Chief Signal Officer to the Chief of Defence, and thus the Norwegian opposite number to the British CSO at Kolsas.

When Norway was occupied in 1940, Rorholt was an Army cadet, having studied radio at Trondheim Polytechnic. He operated a clandestine radio net in Oslo until this was detected by the Germans in September 1941; his house was surrounded but he managed to shoot his way out and escaped to Sweden and then to England.

Middag at Gaustatoppen, 1965

Bjorn Rorholt, Chief Signal Officer to the Chief of Defence, Norway (centre), talking to the author (left) who was then Chief Signal Officer, AFNORTH, and General Henrici, German Army, Chief Signal Officer at SHAPE.

The radio station on Gausta Mountain, near Rjukan, west of Oslo, is reached by a steep tunnel up through the mountain.

In January 1942 he agreed to return to Norway, despite the fact that there was a price on his head, in order to organise local agents to report on the movements of German ships, in particular the *Tirpitz* which, as we have seen, posed a serious threat to allied shipping and especially to the convoys to North Russia. Taking three transmitters with him, he embarked in the fishing boat *Arthur*, skippered by Leif Larsen, and was dropped at one of the outer islands from where he made his way by the regular passenger steamer to Trondheim.

Contacting various friends, they decided to set up the transmitters in the town, at Foettenfjord where *Tirpitz* was normally berthed, and at Agdenes at the mouth of Trondheim Fjord. Agdenes was inside a military zone, but Rorholt posed as an insurance salesman and gained access to one Magne Hassel who agreed to help, and whose house had a clear view down the fjord. Hassel didn't know morse, but a simple code was devised which he could use to signal the movements of the *Tirpitz*.

Rorholt then gathered together half a dozen other Norwegians, and sent them for wireless training to England by means of the 'Shetland Bus', a regular service of fishing boats which carried agents and equipment between Norway and England. Then he set up another radio network based on Oslo.

Agent information helped the RAF to mount three attacks on the *Tirpitz* at Foettenfjord in March and April, but she was not damaged, nor was the *Hipper* which had arrived during April. This information was duly relayed by Rorholt, shortly before he walked into Sweden and so back to England.

In April 1944 aircraft from Victorious and three escort carriers attacked Tirpitz in Kaa Fjord, scoring over a dozen hits with bombs, causing heavy casualties, and putting her out of action for some months. Three Barracudas were lost. Two further Fleet Air Arm attacks in July and August were unsuccessful, though one armour-piercing bomb hit but failed to explode, and several more aircraft were lost. She was finally capsized after the second of two attacks by RAF Lancasters with 12,000 lb bombs in November 1944.

Later in 1942, Leif Larsen and the *Arthur* were again involved in operations against the *Tirpitz*, when they towed the two human chariots which were to attempt an attack on *Tirpitz*. In fact these two broke adrift and were lost in bad weather which sprang up suddenly while on the last lap of the journey up Trondheim Fjord, only a few miles short of the target.

The *Arthur* had to be scuttled, and the crews set off overland for Sweden; except for one of the chariots' crew who was captured and subsequently shot, the rest escaped over the frontier to Sweden and returned to England. In September 1943 *Tirpitz* was attacked by midget submarines (X-craft) at Kaafjord, near Alta, in North Norway. Two of the craft were able to get through the nets surrounding the ship and laid their charges, with the result that *Tirpitz* was badly damaged and put out of action for several months.

North Cape

1943 culminated with the last battleship action fought in European waters. Russian convoys, suspended for the summer, had been restarted later in the year. The Germans had strong naval forces in northern Norway, but the *Tirpitz* was out of action and the *Lutzow* had been withdrawn to the Baltic. This left *Scharnhorst* and a number of destroyers based at Altenfjord.

Admiral Sir Bruce Fraser, now C-in-C Home Fleet, was convinced the Germans would sooner or later try to attack a convoy, and this view was supported by intelligence indications. The first two convoys of the new cycle got through safely. Knowing that the Germans had sighted the next, JW-55A, Fraser took his covering force right through with the convoy which arrived at Murmansk without any losses.

By the time RA-55A (the return convoy) sailed from Murmansk on 22 December, with *Belfast* (CS1 - Rear Admiral Burnett), *Sheffield* and *Norfolk* (Force 1) in support, the next outward bound convoy, JW-55B, was on its way. Fraser in *Duke of York* with *Jamaica* and four destroyers (Force 2) called at Akureyri in Iceland on 23 December to fuel and for a final briefing before sailing to follow JW-55B.

The Fleet Signal Officer was Dicky Courage, the Fleet Wireless Officer Peter Dawnay, and the Commissioned Telegraphist on the staff Jan Webber. Courage missed the briefing in order to conduct a final signal exercise on VHF, using operational callsigns, codes etc., accepting the small risk that this might be intercepted by the Germans. This meant opening sealed orders: '...it was important that the signal staff should be familiar with the race card before the actual race took place', as Courage put it. 'The internal coding exercise ended up with "Make to Admiralty - *Scharnhorst* sunk". I was somehow certain we should be making that signal in due course.'

Fraser, mindful of the problems that had arisen with the PQ convoys the previous year, had determined that he would, if necessary, break W/T silence to ensure that the British forces were aware of each other's movements. He did so at 1325 on the 24th, having become worried at the distance separating JW-55B from the supporting forces, to tell the convoy to reverse course for three hours. In the prevailing weather this manoeuvre wasn't practicable, but a reduction in speed more or less achieved the desired result. Fraser broke silence again twelve hours later to order the homecoming convoy to head further north and transfer some of its escort to JW-55B. This signal was intercepted by the Germans but was mis-interpreted, and although air reconnaissance had sighted Force 2, it failed to report the presence of a battleship.

The Germans were indeed planning a sortie against this convoy, and *Scharnhorst* with six destroyers sailed on Christmas Day, Doenitz having signalled: 'Attack and destroy the convoy to alleviate the struggle of your comrades on the eastern front'. Some hours after sailing *Scharnhorst* broke wireless silence to report that she was entering the operational area; this transmission, and the earlier sailing signal, were intercepted and at 0217 on 26 December Admiralty originated an Ultra signal to say that *Scharnhorst* had probably sailed at 1800A/25 December. This was followed by their 0319, a 'cover' appreciation for the benefit of non-Ultra recipients: 'Admiralty appreciates that *Scharnhorst* is now at sea'.

By this time, RA-55A was well to the west of Bear Island and apparently undetected, while JW-55B was some fifty miles to the south of the island but had been shadowed consistently. If the Germans were going to attack, clearly JW-55B would be the target. Force 2 was still some 350 miles to the south west of the convoy, and Force 1 was some 150 miles to the east. Dawnay recorded:

> 'The C-in-C at once wished to divert the convoy to the northward and also discover the exact position, course and speed of Force 1 and the convoy; since the safety of the convoy was his primary object, he decided to break silence and risk revealing the presence of a heavy ship. The question of the precedence to be used on the diversion signal was a difficult one. Speed was essential if the diversion was to be of any use, and the delay in transferring the message from 'ship-shore' to the broadcast had to be taken into account; on the other hand we did not want the enemy to suspect that we knew he was at sea. We decided to use 'Emergency' in keeping with our primary object. I well remember the feeling of impatience waiting for these two messages to come out on the broadcast, and satisfaction as they were quickly and accurately broadcast, followed by the replies from CS 10 and the Convoy Escort Commander with little delay'.

Peter Dawnay,
when Captain of the Signal School,
1952-54

Force 2 steamed on eastwards at 27 knots in the Arctic darkness with an enormous following sea. Things were beginning to fall a little flat when at about 0840 Force 1 gained a radar detection; a few minutes later *Belfast* reported 'Enemy in sight', and the cruisers opened fire. Dawnay again: 'It became apparent that *Belfast's* enemy reports on Fleet Wave (210 kHz) were not being received by Scapa W/T and

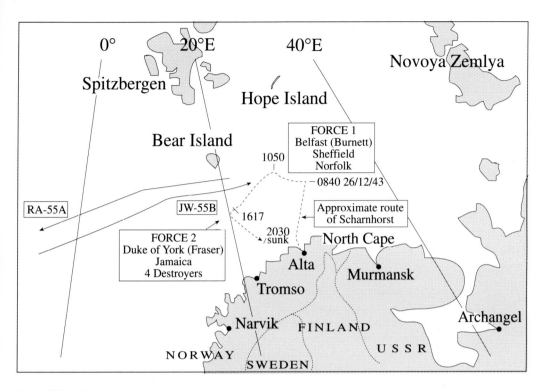

Battle of North Cape,
December 1943

were not coming out on the broadcast. As we had ourselves been transmitting on HF, I ordered these reports to be re-transmitted to Whitehall on ship-shore. Before doing so I asked the C-in-C, but found that he was so engrossed in the tactical situation that thereafter I took all decisions of this nature myself'. This decision was justified when it became evident that Force 2 was already being shadowed by enemy aircraft.

In a short engagement with the cruisers *Scharnhorst* was hit and had her radar damaged, but her superior speed told and the cruisers lost touch. She then tried to work round behind the cruisers to get at the convoy, but was intercepted again about two hours later. After another short engagement in which *Norfolk* was damaged, *Scharnhorst* broke off, sent her destroyers home, presumably because of the weather, and set off SSW pursued by the cruisers, thus giving Force 2 a good chance of intercepting her.

Meanwhile Dawnay was finding the Remote Control Office (RCO)[5] somewhat inconvenient. 'To get to the Plot from the RCO to talk to the admiral I had to go out on to the bitter and dark wing of the bridge, where of course I was blinded, and then through five doors in all, via the admiral's bridge to the Plot. (Afterwards I had the trap hatch between the RCO and the Plot enlarged so that I could climb through it)'. Courage described the weather as very rough indeed with flurries of snow and, except for about two and a half hours around midday, pitch dark:

[5] The RCO, so-called because it was remote from the main wireless office, was a small wireless office adjacent to the bridge from which vital circuits, all morse in those days, could be controlled.

145

> *'Our destroyers had a job to keep up with Duke of York who at full speed was plunging under the huge waves of a following sea which made her look like a submarine just breaking surface. A number of close-range AA weapons which had been fitted on the foc'sle were torn from their mountings and water poured into the messdecks through the rivet holes. On the totally enclosed admiral's bridge all was calm and comfortable with the C-in-C puffing at his pipe, quietly confident.'*

At 1617 *Scharnhorst* was detected by *Duke of York's* radar at about 22 miles. Fraser didn't want to alert *Scharnhorst*, so allowed the range to close to about six miles before ordering *Belfast* to illuminate and then allowing *Duke of York* to open fire, apparently achieving complete surprise. Courage again:

> *'It was a dramatic moment, especially as the C-in-C nearly became a casualty. A large 'kitchen' clock was hung on the bulkhead of the Admiral's bridge - essential in connection with changes of course when zig-zagging. Normally before a full calibre firing such items are taken down but in the long drawn out run-up to the action this had been overlooked. With the first salvo it fell with a loud crash between the C-in-C and myself. That was our most dangerous moment, and also the only time either of us saw the Scharnhorst. The C-in-C then went back to the Plot while I remained outside in the darkness and could see nothing except the splashing of Scharnhorst's shells which seemed to be much too close for comfort.'*

Dawnay had sent out the first enemy report at full power on Fleet Wave to Scapa:

> *'Would we get Scapa at this range or fail like Belfast? It was with profound relief that I heard Scapa give us the 'R' for the message. The roar and concussion of the first 14-inch 10-gun broadside occurred just as this enemy report was being transmitted, and although the Leading Tel on the key was, as usual, nearly shot off his chair, I shall never forget the calm manner in which he continued as if nothing had happened.'*

On the bridge, Courage remembers seeing the two large battle ensigns which the Signal Boatswain, Harold Kelly, had broken out at each masthead as the first salvo was fired - 'an inspiring sight when illuminated by the flash of our guns'. Then he heard what sounded like the aerials being shot away and shouted the news down the voice-pipe to Dawnay, but a quick trial showed that they seemed to be still in good order. (Both masts had in fact been hit, one tripod being severed and some W/T and radar aerials damaged; Webber and the radar officer, Lieut H Bates, RNVR, managed to make temporary repairs, the latter climbing halfway up the mast at the height of the action in a freezing gale).

Force 1 joined in just before 1700, but *Scharnhorst's* superior speed was telling and after twenty minutes the cruisers were out-ranged.

At 1723 Fraser signalled to Burnett: 'Steer south to get between enemy and his base'. *Duke of York* continued firing as the range increased but at about 1830 it became apparent that *Scharnhorst's* speed had been reduced - she had been hit and a broken steam pipe temporarily reduced her speed to ten knots. This enabled the four destroyers - *Savage, Scorpion, Saumarez* and the Norwegian *Stord* - to close in and attack her with torpedoes.

In the RCO things had risen to a crescendo:

> *'One had no time to think of the enemy's shells which could be heard whistling overhead and exploding with sharp cracks. Our own broadsides became less noticeable, as did the rough sea. Quick decisions had to be made, and with a backlog of coding and decoding in the small RCO, when an urgent signal for CS10 was handed in from the plot I ordered it to be made in plain language as it could not help the enemy even if he read it. Having broken the ice, we used P/L from time to time when appropriate.'*

No one actually saw the *Scharnhorst* sink - she just disappeared from radar screens. When destroyers reported picking up survivors, Courage was at last able to originate the signal: 'Admiralty from C-in-C: *Scharnhorst* Sunk - 262100'. Dawnay remembered:

> *'I had great difficulty in getting the signal through and eventually got Iceland to take it - just two groups of Fleet Code. Then came a busy hour of signalling, clearing up the mess and giving instructions what to do and where to go. By this time the Duke of York was steaming by herself at high speed for the Kola Inlet; with U-Boats about, she had been hanging around for quite long enough. Having transmitted the last orders I re-imposed silence on MF, and comparative peace reigned once more'.*

But the problems faced by Courage and Dawnay were not over:

> *'A situation dreaded by all signal officers arose; Admiral Fraser wished to talk to Admiral Burnett on the R/T. Neither had received any training whatever in how to use this method of communication'.*

Unable to persuade the C-in-C to desist, Dawnay embarked on a lesson:

> *'First Sir, you press this thing when you wish to speak; when you have finished, you say "Over" and release it, and listen to Admiral Burnett. Finally, you must use callsigns or you will make it too easy for the Germans. Yours, Sir, is WIGLEY, and Admiral Burnett's is REMBRANDT. Then the trouble started. "WIGLEY? Who gave me this ridiculous name? You?"'*

Meanwhile Admiral Burnett was happily in ignorance of the fact that he was about to be summoned to the microphone, nor did he have the benefit of instruction from the Fleet Wireless Officer.

Courage again:

> *'In Duke of York we heard only one side of the conversation,*
> *which went like this: "Bob, is that you? Bob, Can you hear*
> *me?" ("Say 'Over' and release the handle" from Dawnay).*
> *"Bob, are you clutching your thing? I'll send you Jamaica.*
> *I'm off to Russia, follow me when you can" ("Out!" from*
> *Dawnay). It may have done more good than harm - it was*
> *clear that even 'very senior officers' must be properly*
> *trained in this double-edged means of rapid communica-*
> *tion. It also made us all laugh.'*

In Murmansk Courage was on the Quarterdeck at about 0200 when a large black motor boat drew alongside. Out stepped two Russians carrying parcels. They told the Officer of the Watch that they wanted to see the C-in-C in person. Nothing would dissuade them, so the poor Flag Lieutenant, Vernon Merry, was hauled out of bed. The Russians had express orders from the Supreme Soviet to present the C-in-C with a large fur hat and an enormous fur coat. The Admiral had to turn out and drink a glass of whisky with them, and the Flag Lieutenant then had to give them a conducted tour of the ship! At 0400 they all finally got to bed.

In 1984 a plaque commemorating the battle was unveiled at the North Cape tourist centre by Admiral of the Fleet Sir Henry Leach and Vice Admiral Skule Storheill of the Royal Norwegian Navy. Storheill commanded KNM *Stord* during the battle, and Leach was a sub-lieutenant in *Duke of York*. Admiral Storheill was recalled to active service for a period in 1984, flying his flag in KNM *Narvik* for the D-Day fortieth anniversary ceremonies, and the North Cape unveiling.

*   *   *   *   *

Back at Scapa, the need arose to carry the Despatches to London. Courage being a noted horseman, it was suggested that he should take them and arrive at the Admiralty on horseback. The C-in-C thought this a splendid idea, and arrangements were made for Courage and the Master of the Fleet to fly down to Hendon, and then rendezvous at Charing Cross with the Metropolitan Police who would have suitable white horses ready. 'The horses must arrive steaming, better pour some hot water over them', said Fraser.

But the flight was diverted to Hornchurch due to fog, the ride was cancelled and the pair eventually arrived at the Admiralty late in the evening. Courage was relieved: 'I was in no state to ride a sharp two furlongs across Trafalgar Square in the blackout!'

Chapter Twelve

Combined Operations

*'I can't sit still and see things done in an antiquated and
unprogressive manner ... the VA resents that I should
have any ideas, especially modern ones,
on any subject but signals.'* [1]

Bertram Ramsay,
Flag Lieutenant in Dreadnought, 1914

I
n May 1942 Ramsay found himself appointed as Flag Officer
Expeditionary Force to plan the naval side of the projected
invasion of France, then known as ROUND UP, and an alternative,
the capture of the Cherbourg peninsula (SLEDGEHAMMER), both
subsequently put in cold storage. He had already worked closely with
Generals Brooke and Montgomery, with whom he got on well, in
preparing for a possible German invasion, and it was not surprising
that he was diverted later in the year to plan Operation TORCH, the
landings in North Africa. An old friend, Andrew Cunningham, was
back as C-in-C Mediterranean, Commodore Royer Dick being his
Chief of Staff again, and Commander Laurie Durlacher Cunningham's
Signal Officer.

The naval aspects of TORCH went well and, now that he seemed
to be the expert in planning such operations, Ramsay soon found
himself dealing with the next, the invasion of Sicily (Operation
HUSKY), for which he was designated as the Eastern (British) Task
Force Commander. Once Monty was free of chasing the Germans out
of Tunisia he was able to concentrate on the HUSKY planning with
Ramsay, their views usually coinciding, so that Ramsay sometimes
found himself at odds with Cunningham, who also had strong views
but not necessarily the same ones. After one briefing, Mike Villiers,
Ramsay's Signal Officer, said that 'Monty, in a brilliant presenta-
tion, referred throughout, either consciously or unconsciously, to
'General Ramsay', which went down very well with the Army!'

The HUSKY Task Force was divided into three Task Groups,
Rear Admirals Troubridge in the headquarters ship *Bulolo*, McGrigor
in *Largs* and Vian in *Hilary*. The weather was not good, but improved
during the night, and again surprise was achieved. Ramsay's part was
soon over and he left for home. Monty wrote:

[1] Diary, August 1914
Churchill College Archives

> *'We missed you sadly when you had gone ... You understand us soldiers and you know more about the land battle than any other sailor.'*

On 23 October 1943 Ramsay was appointed as the Allied Naval Commander Expeditionary Force (ANCXF) for the allied invasion of Europe (OVERLORD) in the rank of Admiral, and early in 1944 nearly five years since being reemployed, he was restored to the active list.

*   *   *   *   *

Meanwhile, Commander Reggie Paul moved from the Combined Operations staff in the summer of 1943 to become Chief Naval Signal Officer for the planning of Operation NEPTUNE, the Naval part of OVERLORD. At that time the general cover plan made no mention of radio, but it was evident that the wireless and radar organisation needed building up in a way which avoided pointing to the intended area of operations, which meant planning for both genuine and deceptive activity.

Paul's previous experience had been invaluable; in 1940 he had been involved in planning the Dakar expedition, Operation MENACE, and although the projected amphibious landing never took place, it highlighted the lack of suitable resources, adequate combined procedures or any practical experience. The chain of command had been unclear until late in the day, and it was difficult to establish exact responsibilities for the various forces involved, which made it difficult to produce a sensible signal organisation. Although the Naval and Army Commanders had at least been introduced to each other, an uncertain element was provided by General de Gaulle who hardly came into the planning at all. When things began to go wrong he had to be consulted about every step, but as he was in a Dutch liner lost in the fog at the time this was not easy.

The Dakar operation raised the question of the provision of suitably equipped Headquarters ships. The Dutch liner used in MENACE had been organised by the Free French over which the British exercised little control, and the naval HQ ship was the battleship *Barham*, provided with some extra equipment, to which the Admiral and staff transferred only a day before sailing. Paul commented that since then he had recommended against the use of warships as headquarters ships, and certainly not to let them be used for bombardment: 'Nobody can run an amphibious operation from a ship firing eight 15 inch guns'. In contrast, in Operation NEPTUNE there were to be twenty three specially fitted HQ ships.

In 1942 Paul had joined the Combined Operations Staff under Admiral Mountbatten, with Captain Micky Hodges as the Chief Signal Officer. Experience was gained with Commando raids in Norway and across the Channel, and tri-service procedures were developed at the Combined Signal School, HMS *Dundonald II*, at Troon, in charge of Commander Ian Robertson.

The French battleship Richelieu was in Dakar, and had been attacked two months earlier by Hermes' Swordfish, which scored one torpedo hit, causing minor damage. In MENACE Ark Royal flew a number of Free French airmen ashore to make contact with the authorities, but they were taken prisoner.

Barham was hit and the battleship Resolution torpedoed, and an attempted landing by the Free French was repulsed. The operation was then called off. Later in the war, Richelieu joined the Allies, serving with the Eastern Fleet.

Here the first Bombardment Units were formed, composed of a mixed bunch of soldiers and sailors, whose prime task was to call for effective gunfire support from ships during an opposed landing, before the Army's own artillery had been landed.

Royal Artillery Officers were trained to be Forward Observation Officers (FOO), or Army Liaison Officers (ALO) on board ship. Two Telegraphists and a Signalman were usually included in the FOO's party, with an 18M radio (later Type 68) and an aldis lamp, plus telephone lines for communicating within the party.

After the port of Diego Suarez had been captured, one of the FOO parties, with Telegraphists Bradshaw and Shaw, was ordered to move about fifteen miles along the coast. Their trucks broke down in the rough jungle terrain so Bradshaw went off to look for a canoe; he returned instead with the French Admiral's barge belonging to a sloop which had been attacked by the destroyer Laforey. They found the barge well stocked with wine, chocolate, cigarettes and ham.

Their first operation was the capture of Diego Suarez, Madagascar, in May 1942. The HQ ship was the *Winchester Castle*, three FOO parties were landed with the Commandos and Army units, and six ALOs were in the bombarding ships, *Ramillies*, two cruisers and three destroyers. Diego Suarez was captured within two days with few casualties, but French resistance continued in the rest of the island which was not finally surrendered until November.

Paul described the operation as 'primitive but effective, though there was still much to learn.' The *Winchester Castle* had been fitted with additional radio equipment but was still not really suitable. The staff therefore pressed for the conversion of a special ship, and were allocated the *Bulolo*, about 5,000 tons, which was ideally suited to the purpose. Paul co-ordinated the planning of the communication requirements and supervised the ship fitting, and within about three months they had a cross between a flagship, a Divisional HQ and an RAF Group Operations Room, with communications to match.

The *Bulolo* drawings had been passed to the USN who used them as the basis for their ships, usually larger and even more elaborately fitted copies, while at home *Bulolo* was followed by *Largs*, *Hilary* and *Lothian*. At the same time experience had shown that there was a need for smaller and more nimble HQ ships to control the groups which constituted the assault force. The prototype of this was a Hunt class destroyer, of which two took part in the Dieppe raid; later

HMS *Bulolo*

The first specially fitted Headquarters ship.

specially fitted frigates were used. Also required were Fighter Direction ships, with special radar as well as radio, for which the need had become apparent with TORCH and HUSKY. For NEPTUNE LSTs were adapted, becoming in effect floating RAF Sector ops rooms. Various other craft, such as ML 'navigation leaders' had to be fitted with an increased scale of radio and radar. Radio aids, largely provided by the RAF, were needed for making accurate landfalls, earlier operations having indicated that slow moving landing craft could have difficulty in the fast moving Channel tides.

Robert Phillimore, who had been involved in the TORCH planning, became the signal officer in *Largs* for the operation:

> *'Her conversion was barely complete when we sailed from Greenock, and the bunk-house for staff officers at the back of the bridge was so unfinished that we had to protect ouselves from the weather with umbrellas.'*

The landings achieved almost complete surprise, despite the very large convoys which had to be assembled in both Britain and America, and routed through the Strait of Gibraltar to arrive at the time planned weeks in advance - an achievement primarily due to the strict security arrangements that had been built in to the plan.

For the TORCH landings the main innovation was the use of a special Bombardment Calling Wave, linking all ships concerned. Previously 'attachments' had to be made on Fleet Wave but traffic levels often resulted in long delays before the request got through. The new scheme was a considerable success, the headquarters ships receiving much more information from shore, and it was subsequently adopted as standard practice.

In Operation HUSKY no less than 64 BLOs and FOOs were involved, together with over 100 naval ratings and other ranks. Later, during the invasion of Italy, one party was captured. Telegraphist Brice recalls:

> *'It happened on a hillside a few miles north of Salerno whilst trying to demolish an enemy pillbox with cruiser fire ... with about 30 men from the Yorks and Lancs we were sur-rounded. While we were lying in a field guarded by busi-ness-like machine guns, another party of prisoners arrived, amongst them Tels Backhouse, Woolrich and Signalman Robertson. We were taken by lorry to Rome, then by cattle truck to Stalag 7A at Moseberg, near Munich, and finally to Stalag 88 near the Polish border. There we found Sigs Jackson and Greenhill, both victims of the Dieppe raid.'*

OVERLORD

Planning for an operation of this magnitude tends to start well before the Command have made up their minds what they want, or what the chain of command will be, and without most of the Commanders or forces having been designated. However a Combined Headquarters was built, or rather dug into Portsdown Hill at Fort Southwick, in 1942, largely on the initiative of the Combined Ops staff; others followed at Dover and Plymouth. In the event, Portsmouth was the one wanted, Plymouth was extremely useful as a rear headquarters for the US Task Force, and Dover served primarily for cover purposes. Each was fitted out with a vast amount of radio and line telecommunications equipment, while a correspondingly large and complex telephone and telegraph system grew up in the South of England, and miles of submarine cable were manufactured ready for laying across the Channel.

In the end the CHQ at Portsmouth proved much too small and it became clear that the Joint Cs-in-C would have to stay out of it; thus the Air Force remained at Stanmore, and ANCXF took over Southwick Park, borrowed from the Navigation School, while 21st Army Group headquarters squatted in the grounds.

Signal planning was co-ordinated by the Combined Signal Board, on which Paul and his US Deputy sat. Their colleagues were one or two star officers who, as Paul said, 'unlike myself, were in a position to go home after each meeting and toss the details to enormous expert staffs'. Paul had a staff of six, most of whom lacked experience of combined operations and also of the Whitehall machine. It wasn't possible to delegate much to the Task and Assault Forces because of the necessity for all to use standard procedures and common radio plans so that, for instance, ships might sail from any port to any beach, and those in support, such as bombardment ships, could be attached to any assault force whether British or US.

Vice Admiral Sir Charles Mills, then on Paul's staff, recalls that 'Dafty' Robinson, whom we came across earlier, was recruited to set up an experimental VHF 'Forward Scatter' system, which he thought would achieve some 90 miles, just enough to provide cross-channel voice communications. This was 'state of the art' stuff, intended partly to relieve the almost insatiable demand for telegraphists, and it developed into what became known as the 'South Coast Radio Scheme', providing duplex voice facilities in the 85-95 MHz band between headquarters and, after D-Day, across the channel to headquarters in France. With directional aerials giving some security, it was considered acceptable to use plain language. For the advance eastward, terminal equipment was fitted in vehicles, so that it was still possible to maintain contact with the relevant headquarters.

Mills had to deal with the provision of crystals for the many VHF radios involved; a special combined-ops signal depot near Staines dealt with the grinding and distribution of the crystals required, for example, for ship/air gunfire support communication; with the inevitable last minute changes and additions to the signal plans just before D-Day, couriers were being sent all over the country with crystals to catch ships before they sailed.

By November 1943 the manning implications were becoming clear and the Admiralty was presented with a bill for 3,300 additional

Commander Dicky Wells

Wells was Signal Officer to Admiral Vian, Naval Commander Eastern Task Force, joining the planning staff just before Christmas 1943.

'My opposite numbers were a Colonel and two Captains of the Royal Signals, and a Squadron Leader, RAF. At the first meeting after Christmas they had turned into a Major General, two Brigadiers and an Air Commodore! The Navy always does seem to make do with fewer officers of lesser rank than the other services.'

communication ratings - about three times the normal total for a large fleet. This meant an enormous additional training programme, with the Reserves and WRNS meeting a large part of the requirement, and seamen and other non-specialists being given enough training to cope with the limited needs of small vessels such as landing craft.

The communications plans for the assault forces had to be exercised, and this had to fit in with the general cover plan. The characteristic communications of an amphibious force could not be concealed, and the Germans would undoubtedly be attempting to monitor them. Five assault forces, three British and two American, had to be worked up, and eventually assembled on the South coast, without revealing the likely invasion area or the date.

The first step was to fabricate the bogus and 'ethereal' assault forces. A mobile Joint Deception Unit was attached to each real force, and when it wasn't deceiving, the unit was usefully employed vetting the wireless security of its force which it got to know well, as no doubt did the Germans. Its transmitters were assimilated with those of the real force to a degree that it was hoped would withstand technical analysis.

The next step was to create some bogus forces and it was decided, as Paul put it, 'to pop a Division into Boulogne and another into, say, Fécamp'. These bogus assault forces were composed of flotillas of HDMLs, each bulging with radar jammers, and with 'Moonshine' RCM (Radio Counter Measures) sets borrowed from Bomber Command, the function of which was to return multiple echoes to any radar fitted aircraft. They would also tow balloons fitted with large reflectors to simulate the radar echoes of large ships. RAF Lancasters had the job of dropping packets of window from a low level, to produce many more ship-like echoes, the whole 'package' being designed to simulate a speed of advance of about eight knots. At the same time, the MLs would make the right wireless noises associated with a Divisional assault force at sea - fortunately fairly limited.

The RCM plan required a high proportion of the enemy radar and 'Y' stations along the French coast to be knocked out in advance, avoiding any emphasis on the actual assault area. Fortuitously, largely at the instigation of Dr R V Jones, then ADI (Science) at the Air Ministry, the Admiralty Signal Establishment had spent a good deal of time and effort compiling the technical details of some 200 of the German coastal radar stations, and this was then supplemented by the Naval 'Y' service, and by RAF and RN intercept flights. This information was essential in order that ASE could develop and arrange production of the jammers to be fitted in large numbers in ships and landing craft; work went on at ASE in nissen huts and potting sheds and resulted in the Type 91 which could cover the appropriate frequencies. There was a worry that the Germans might develop a centimetric radar which the Type 91 could not deal with, but happily they did not believe this was practicable until they captured an RAF H2S radar, complete with magnetron, but this was too late for them to produce their own version by the time of OVERLORD.

Force G, headquarters in Bulolo, was divided into two assault groups, G1 (HQ ship Nith, signal officer Donald Forrest), and G2 (Kingsmill, Peter Howes). Forrest remembers that amongst the mass of new radio equipment, 'one unique item to appear was a suitcase transceiver developed for secret agents. As the rear HQ (in a block of flats at Southampton) had no equipment, this gave rise to the idea of setting up a link with the Nith and Kingsmill; we had been allocated spare frequencies, and some of the WRNS cypher officers were ex-telegraphists.

What it was for was not entirely clear, but it soon proved very useful for ordering such important supplies as clean stiff collars! After a few days the 'Y' service began to take an interest and silence was imposed, though listening watch continued. Howes, second only to Dicky Courage as the navy's pre-eminent horseman, was not deterred from transmitting instructions to place a bet on the Derby. The horse backed was appropriately named Ocean Swell, and it won!'

American jammers were also provided in large numbers, others were allocated by the RAF, and eventually a total of some 800 assorted RCM sets were fitted in ships and craft. The small ships also had to be supplied with special shells and rockets to allow the regular deployment of 'window' all over the seascape during the assault passage.

Some six months before D-day two main deception plans were put into operation in the UK - FORTITUDE NORTH and FORTITUDE SOUTH. The former was designed to simulate a threat to Norway and included the 'training' of two spurious joint assault forces in the Clyde area where it was unnecessary to bother about visual simulation so that radio activity only was involved. This appears to have helped to keep the Germans guessing - they actually reinforced Norway with two divisions in May 1944.

The main deception effort, FORTITUDE SOUTH, was concentrated on the east coast, the aim being to pose a major threat to the Low Countries. For this, three bogus amphibious forces were laid on, their training pattern being designed to match that of the real assault forces, but sustained for some time after D-day so as to continue this particular threat. These forces included a mass of shipping (which was assembling on the east coast for Channel activities in any case), a large and 'noisy' HQ ship berthed at Harwich, dummy canvas landing craft in creeks and estuaries, air activity, and a great amount of wireless traffic.

For the invasion proper, some 7,000 ships and craft had to be concentrated along the South coast, many arriving from the United States, so naval wireless traffic was adjusted artificially from the beginning of the year to avoid peaks and troughs of activity, with a gradual lessening of radio activity as D-Day approached. By mid-May, the ASE team had been deployed to help with the massive installation, testing and tuning programme, mainly of the US jammers and some other late arrivals, having first trained the leaders of each installation party. By then most of the Type 91 jammers had already been installed in the larger RN ships.

From time to time a few days wireless silence was imposed on the various forces under training. The idea was to get the Germans used to these breaks, and the programme was arranged to result in a 'quiet' period at the time when forces would be embarked and unable to use radio. The deception units were then able to take their place, moving back to the east coast to continue their part in the FORTITUDE SOUTH deception plan.

There were some forty German radars around the assault area, of which about half had been put out of action by the RAF. At 2130 on D-1, although there was no apparent evidence that the assault forces had been detected, the RCM barrage opened as planned, despite the risk of alerting the enemy, since the leading minesweepers would be coming within range of those radars still operating. Although the Germans did briefly detect a minesweeper some eight miles off Arromanches at about midnight, the HQ at Cherbourg took no action.

Vian and his staff were embarked in HMS Scylla. 'The crypto load was very heavy but there was no room onboard to accommodate any more cypher officers,' said Wells, 'so we devised a scheme whereby a dozen or more came over every other day in the MGBs which carried out anti-E-boat patrols round the anchorage; they worked hard for 48 hours, then returned to Portsmouth, having been relieved by another lot. During one of these changeovers I received a basket of strawberries from my wife, which Dicky Courage had thoughtfully sent over!

'My brother Walter was the Beach Signal Officer, Force G; they had set up their HQ in a farm house near Ouistreham and engaged the services of the ex-chef to the President of France. Visitors were guaranteed a five star meal!'

On D-Day itself, the Germans again misjudged the situation, considering the weather too bad for an invasion, and relaxing their air and sea patrols. At the same time they were satisfied from radio intercept that the assault forces were still exercising in harbour and, as had been hoped, were not sure that Normandy was the principal assault area, being more worried about north east France and the low countries. Here the 'bogus' forces directed at Boulogne and Fécamp fetched up off-shore at about 0400 in a flurry of searchlight and air activity, having drawn off many of the night fighters in Northern France, to the benefit of the aircraft striking at targets in Normandy, and causing some confusion at von Rundstedt's headquarters.

Beach Signal Units and Gunfire Support

A number of RNVR officers who had qualified as Observers in January 1944 found themselves diverted to temporary invasion duties and were trained at HMS *Mercury* to take charge of Beach Signal Units. 'We used experimental VHF radio sets to reduce the possibility of interception,' recalls Alex Davis, 'practising setting up the equipment and transmitting messages on the flatlands around Chichester Harbour. Training continued with landing practice on Isle of Wight beaches.'

Each of the British beachheads, Gold, Juno and Sword, were divided into Red and Green sections, a unit of one officer plus seven being allocated to each.

The beach-head and bombarding ships

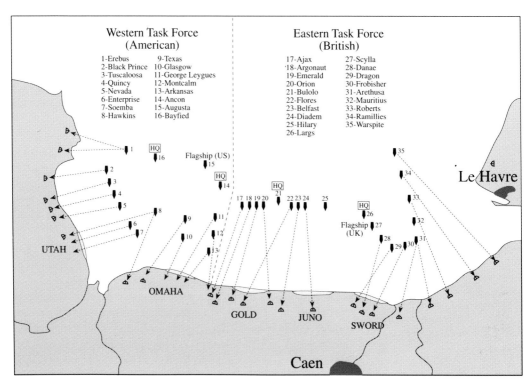

Telegraphist Penny was in the first party to get through to Caen, and in some eighty shoots between D-Day and the attack on Walcheren seems never to have failed to get through to his ship on the 68 set. Awarded the DSM, the citation says:

'Operated his set in a forward position north of Caen under continual mortar fire, thus ensuring effective supporting fire from HMS Rodney, and together with his FOB was the first OP party to bring down fire at a critical juncture of the battle, operating his set over a distance of 18 miles.'

'Equipment consisted of a handcart with a low power shore-to-ship transmitter which went ashore with the assault parties; a 30-cwt truck with a more powerful transmitter landed during D-Day; and a 3-ton truck with more sophisticated equipment which followed three days later.

'We sailed in LSTs, and were then given our sealed orders. Our vehicles were fitted with water-proofing and extended exhausts to enable them to drive through deep water to the beach. Once on the beach we reported to the Naval officer in Charge, linked our equipment by landline to the Army, and looked for high ground for our dipole aerials. When we first got through, it was an exciting event. When the 3-ton truck arrived, we were joined by a small Marine unit led by a sergeant for our defence, and a technical sub-lieutenant to keep the equipment operational.'

Some 42 FOOs (now renamed FOBs) and 78 ALOs (now called BLOs!) took part, together with their communication teams, to cope with 84 bombarding ships. Most of the BLOs joined their ships well before D-Day, thus in some cases finding themselves escorting Atlantic convoys.

As the advance progressed, intermediate wireless stations were set up and a Mobile Bombardment Control Unit (usually known as the Mobile Bath Unit) came into being, fitted for W/T and Voice communications with bombarding ships, FOBs and spotting aircraft.

*   *   *   *   *

In his Despatch on the operation, Admiral Ramsay commented:

'As our forces approached the French coast without a murmur from the enemy or from their radio, the realisation that once again almost complete tactical surprise had been achieved slowly dawned. This astonishing feat cannot be explained by any single factor and must be attributed in part to all of the following: the miscalculations of the enemy; the high degree of air superiority which drastically reduced the enemy's air reconnaissance; the bad weather which caused the enemy to withdraw his E-boat patrols to Cherbourg; and finally the radio counter-measures employed by our forces which, coupled with the diversions against Pas de Calais and Cap d'Antifer, left the enemy in doubt as to the points at which we could land even when he had become aware that the invasion was in progress.'

The East Indies - Operation ZIPPER

For naval operations in support of the Burma campaign, and then the invasion of Malaya (Operation ZIPPER), Bombardment Units were also required and training was undertaken in the signal school at HMS *Braganza*, Bombay.

For ZIPPER, the cruiser *Royalist*, flagship of AC21, commanding the half dozen carriers taking part, had had her 'Q' turret removed to make way for a fighter control room, fitted with enough radio equipment to control the fighter cover for the two-Division operation.

Eric Lowe was the squadron wireless officer. 'At a late stage in the planning the Army realised that as it advanced inland it would lose touch with the ships, and it was decided to replicate the necessary communications in vehicles which could follow Corps HQ and thus provide communications between the Naval Air Commander at Corps HQ, and the ships and their aircraft.' This requirement arose because, unlike previous landings where support was required mainly in the area of the beachhead, ZIPPER envisaged the army having to fight its way through many miles of difficult terrain before airfields could be captured and land-based facilities set up.

Thus Naval Party 2441 was established 'at the rush', to form what became known as a Mobile Support Control Unit. Lowe found himself in jungle green, with Mr Pick, Warrant Tel:

> 'a colourful character who dressed like an army despatch rider, and who stitched the equipment together in containers and caravans as it arrived, assisted by Italian POW engineers. There were twenty or so large vehicles, and some 20 miles of remote control cabling. Chief Tel Williams trained and organised the telegraphists, and the army taught the stokers how to handle the heavy trucks. We stripped a BI passenger ship of its electrical generators, the only suitable AC power source we could find for our RAF ground to air VHF transmitters. They produced enough power to light a small village, but not being ruggedised, were a constant source of trouble.'

In the event the landings took place just after the Japanese surrender had taken effect, and were unopposed. Nevertheless, the MSCU was deployed ready for action in case of trouble. Kent remembers the mudflats near Port Swettenham chosen for the main landings proved less than suitable:

> 'The MSCU landed north of Morib beach and our LCP hit a sandbank 200 yards from shore. But we established communications with Bulolo (the Force 'W' HQ ship) after occupying an ex-Japanese camp. A large number of Chinese and Malay communists came out of the jungle to meet us and offer help; they told us that all Japanese soldiers had been told to make their way to Singapore, which was comforting!'

Lowe commented:

> 'I am not sure that the MSCU would have coped with the full weight of traffic envisaged whilst maintaining mobility in combat conditions in the Malayan rain forest. The biggest problem turned out to be to get the VHF antennae above the tree canopy - our masts were not designed for the job and we never really solved that problem.'

For one bombardment demonstration for VIPs, the invitation read: 'Officers are advised to bring their own glasses.'

On subsequent occasions the word 'binoculars' had to be used instead.

Harry Kent, one of the telegraphists, remembers that during their training 'we were instructed not to take notes but to memorise frequencies, and become expert at the clock code system for selecting targets. Our uniform consisted of a jungle green bush jacket and trousers, with an Australian type bush hat, plus a monsoon cape with enough room on the back to carry a Type 18 which had a voice and morse capability.'

Chapter Thirteen

The Far East
and the British Pacific Fleet

*'I have high hopes for your success with typewriters...
female instructors could speed things up...'*

With the war in Europe drawing towards its close, the decision was taken to strengthen our Naval forces in the Far East in order to play a significant part in the war against Japan, not least so as to safeguard our position and interests in the area after the war.

Admiral Fraser hoisted his flag as C-in-C British Pacific Fleet in HMS *Howe* on 22 November 1944, although the fleet as such still hardly existed. Dicky Courage was again his Fleet Communication Officer, the new title reflecting the fact that he combined the jobs previously done by separate Fleet Signal and Wireless Officers; experience in the Home Fleet had shown that since the fleet could be manoeuvred by either V/S or W/T, or a combination of both, it was essential to have one senior Signal Officer responsible for both.

Courage was sent on ahead, via Washington where he met the US Naval Signal people, and then to Pearl Harbour. In early December Admiral Fraser visited Admiral Nimitz to agree on the part to be played by the British Fleet. A fundamental question was how the two navies were to inter-communicate; should the British continue to use the RN books and procedures, with liaison teams exchanged to interpret them to the Americans, and vice-versa, or should the British adopt the American systems, lock, stock and barrel?

The First Sea Lord, Andrew Cunningham, was against 'going American' so the Admiralty argued that the RN system should be used, mainly on the basis that 'ours is much better'. Courage quickly realised that this wouldn't work; the British Fleet would never be able to play a properly integrated role unless US books were adopted. In any case the precedent had been set by the adoption of British books and procedures by American ships operating with the Home Fleet. Fraser agreed, made the case strongly to the Admiralty, and obtained approval.

The American Fleet Signal Officer, 5th Fleet, 'Red' Armstrong, was most helpful and immediately set in train the mammoth task of supplying the large number of books needed, with the offer of whatever other help might be required. For the British the decision meant not only learning a whole new set of signal books, procedures, and flags, but a new phonetic alphabet, and in particular the ability to read the US morse broadcasts which ran at 25 words per minute. This was too fast for pencil and paper, so there was an urgent need to train our telegraphists to morse-type. On the crypto front, the RN were about to introduce the Typex machine, while the Americans were fitting CCM; the decision here was for US Crypto liaison teams with CCM machines to embark in British flagships. On the radio side, the Americans manoeuvred by VHF radio, principally the TBS, which again had to be procured and fitted in British ships.

By the end of 1944 5 fleet carriers, 2 battleships, 7 cruisers and 22 destroyers had been allocated to the BPF. The main headquarters and supply base was Sydney, where the fleet gradually assembled. The headquarters built up to a sort of miniature Admiralty on the other side of the world, and for obvious reasons had to take direct control of such things as local drafting and appointments, rendering periodic reports to the UK showing where people were actually serving. After a few months the total number of signal officers, RN, RAN, RNVR, and WRNS on the station totalled around one hundred.

By the end of January 1945 things were moving but were still somewhat fraught. Armstrong wrote to Courage:

> '*I am grateful for the advice you are sending me, but God and his angels only know when I shall be able to supply you with coherent advice on what to do next ... CENTCOM 2 (the communications plan) as revised, corrected, amended and aborted, seems fairly firmly set ready for our (joint) use ... urgent airmail delivery of a large supply for you has been hastened. Not all of us have CCM as yet but I do not anticipate much longer delay even by those masters of procrastination, the Registered Publication Section. I have high hopes for your success with the typewriters. Perhaps if you could get in some female instructors this could speed things up immensely*'.

Despite pleas to the Admiralty, neither morse-typing trained telegraphists nor typewriters were forthcoming from the UK, so the idea of using female Australian typing instructors was taken up, a cinema was hired as a classroom, typewriters were commandeered, and this programme got underway with surprising success. Replying to Armstrong, Courage wrote:

> '*The Communicators in the Fleet are, on the whole, delighted that we have adopted your books and are great admirers of CENTCOM 2. There are reservations - frankly, we prefer our DG (Delivery Group) system and are sorry you have not got the same. We also consider your Honolulu*

broadcasts try to handle too much traffic. The Liaison teams have arrived - I do not expect that we will require them after our first operation with you. No coffee and no iced water brings them near to mutiny; however a little Scotch occasionally keeps them sane.'

It took some time for the new fleet to build up but an early arrival on the station was CS4, Admiral Brind, in *Swiftsure*. His SCO and Flag Lieutenant, Edward Ashmore, commented that a lot of what he had learnt on his long course now had to be discarded:

'Hard though this was for me, it was much harder for those longer qualified and more practised in the British art of signalling at sea and especially for the Signal Boatswains and Warrant Tels who were experts in their trade in the old ways'.

The BPF's operating area

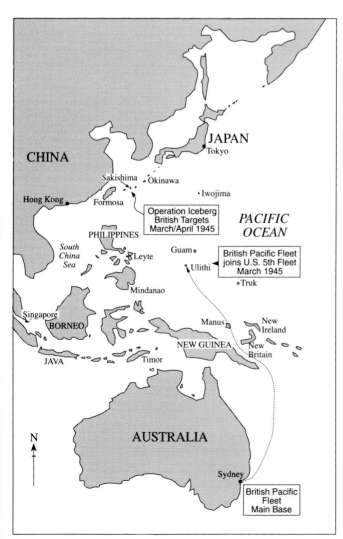

Swiftsure was quickly sent North to Ulithi where Admiral Spruance and the 5th Fleet were gathered pending their next operation. Ashmore's brief was to familiarise himself thoroughly with the US methods of signalling and manœuvring and to report any likely difficulties; he had a set of US publications to study on the way up so was not entirely unprepared for the meetings with Armstrong and his team.

'Arrival at Ulithi was unforgettable, with the coral atoll crammed with ships. People were flashing at us from all directions - we couldn't take in them all. One I remember was "Welcome from the signal gang of USS Colombia", another "Hello Swiftsure - where is the other half of the British fleet?"'

'Red' Armstrong invited Ashmore to attend a meeting of the communicators of the carrier force, some fifty officers, of whom he was clearly the youngest and most junior.

'We were given trunkloads of operation orders and the American signal books, notably their General Signal

161

> *Book and something called PAC70B which I had to absorb*
> *and teach my staff about while on passage. All kinds of things*
> *were different, even the phonetic alphabet - my third!'*

Because of the absence of a serious submarine threat conventional screening systems had been discarded; circular screens, arranged about an axis centred on some point in the middle of the formation, which might or might not be occupied by a ship but round which the heavy units would be disposed, had been adopted. 'Rotating the axis' became a manoeuvre to conjure with but station keeping was less exacting than in the more conventional formations. A USN Captain had taken passage in *Swiftsure* to Ulithi:

> *'He was the greatest possible help to me as, reading through*
> *the books, I came upon points that defied my comprehension.*
> *The weather was lovely and the British were in their white*
> *shirts and shorts. This became a strong bone of contention*
> *with the Americans who wore khaki and felt that the white*
> *would make us the more visible at night to the Japanese who*
> *were renowned for the strength and optical efficiency of*
> *their binoculars as well as for their general alertness!'*

However a proposal to shift to khaki was turned down, although one or two officers serving with the Americans did wear it - Michael Le Fanu, liaison officer to the US Fleet Commanders also sported a baseball cap, except when meeting British Admirals!

From Ulithi *Swiftsure* was sent to Manus in the Admiralty Islands which was to be the forward base for the British Fleet. As no British broadcasts had yet been opened up, the ship had to read the American 'Fox' as they called the broadcast. This was alive with information, most of it irrelevant to the immediate needs but it also carried essential messages, and the only way of sifting it was for the Signal Officer to scan every message, there being no other qualified filter.

It was learnt that the British ships were to operate as an integral component of the American Pacific Fleet, and this introduced them to the novel but eminently practical Task Force system. The US Fleet consisted of a number of Carrier groups, each about the size of the British contingent, operating under alternate Fleet Commanders, Spruance commanding the 5th Fleet, and Halsey the 3rd. One Admiral and his staff conducted an operation while the other, back at Pearl, planned for the next. The British component became Task Force 57 (TF57) when Spruance was in charge, and TF37 under Halsey. The Task organisation allowed for the force to be divided into groups, e.g. TG57.l, TG57.2 and so on, and further sub-divided into Units (e.g. TU57.1.1). The senior officer would be designated, for example, Commander, Task Group 57.1 (CTG 57.1), CTU 57.1.1, and so on. Ships were allocated and re-allocated as necessary, so that the fleet organisation could be extremely flexible. The system was subsequently adopted by the British and, in due course, by NATO.

Lieutenant Commander John Ellis was the Signal Boatswain on CS4's staff. 'We had been the first class at the Signal School to be instructed in the American methods of signalling and manœuvring; we found these very easy to pick up - after all it is much simpler to understand TURN and CORPEN than BLUE and WHITE and RED! I had some interesting experiences, for example being invited onboard a number of US warships to absorb their operational and communication methods. I found to my delight that, whereas in the RN you could expect a cup of this or that, in the USN you could have a full meal of this and that at any time of day or night!'

The Task Force system didn't supersede the traditional Squadron and Flotilla organisations, which still had a place in the command structure especially for administrative purposes; a Squadron could also be designated as a Task Unit, for example, or as part of a Task Group; or it could be split up with individual ships being detached to different parts of the Task Force. Thus the two systems could quite happily co-exist. The normal manœuvring rules applied whatever the particular designation.

Back in Sydney, Dicky Wells was one of a large number of signal officers and ratings flown out at Courage's urgent request. While waiting to get to sea as SCO to Rear Admiral (Destroyers), he had the task of compiling a 'child's guide' to the American books and procedures, which was then used in the intensive training undertaken both at the Australian Naval Signal School at HMAS *Cerberus* (Flinders Naval Depot), and in the ships of the fleet as they arrived in Australian waters.

Meanwhile on 4 February Rear Admiral Vian, Commanding the 1st Aircraft Carrier Squadron, with Peter Hankey as his signal officer, had arrived at Fremantle with the main body of warships. They moved on to Sydney by the middle of the month, where Vice Admiral Sir Bernard Rawlings hoisted his flag in HMS *King George V* as Second-in-Command of the BPF, with James Stopford as SCO. A fortnight later the Fleet moved up to Manus in the Admiralty Islands, which was to be their intermediate base, with Leyte in the Phillipines as the advanced base. The climate at Manus was unpleasant; Admiral Rawlings in a report to the Admiralty expressed his bewilderment regarding 'under what circumstances and by whose whimsical conception these islands should have been named in honour of Their Lordships'.

With the need to support the Fleet over the vast distances involved in Pacific operations, it was necessary to copy the Americans and form what became known as the Fleet Train. This 'armada' of tankers, supply ships and repair ships was treated as a naval force, under the command of Rear Admiral Fisher in HMS *Montclare*, with Fred Stannard as SCO. Full naval manœuvring and signal procedures were used. By July the total number of ships in the Fleet Train totalled over 90, flying a variety of ensigns, British and foreign.

The BPF took part in Operation ICEBERG, the assault on Okinawa, in April and May 1945, and in June the newly arrived *Implacable*, temporarily Admiral Brind's flagship, launched carrier-borne attacks on the island of Truk. It was soon found that the scale of radio equipment fitted in British ships, especially VHF, was inadequate, and it was only the loan of US sets that allowed the essential circuits to be manned. The Americans themselves were none too well off in this respect.

The extensive use of R/T by the Americans was something of a surprise to the British, used to the more formal signalling methods of W/T and flags; the latter of course were not very suitable for

Captain RFT Stannard

SCO to Flag Officer Fleet Train in the BPF. From 1955-57 he was DSD, and then Director of the London Communications Security Agency.

manœuvring the large and widespread formations that made up a task force. There tended to be so many ships on the Tactical Net, and the British regional accents so difficult to interpret, that it was often necessary, for example when in charge of a replenishment, for a signal officer to control the net. This also became the practice in the combat area and Ashmore well remembers, as a Kamikaze was approaching Vian's flagship, 'hearing David Milford Haven's voice on the TBS going ever faster to get his message away before the enemy hit her deck and burst into flames'. David Seely, SCO of the 27th DF, serving temporarily in HMAS *Quickmatch*, found Australian operators useful as they could usually be understood by both British and Americans!

For air defence, in particular, complete reliability and flexibility of communications was essential, but was simply not attainable. There were too few sets, breakdowns all too common, and the process of tuning HF transmitters was vulnerable to interception. Admiral Rawlings reported that 'Whereas in the matter of Radar Equipment, the superiority of the Americans was only a matter of degree, and the British had little difficulty in maintaining a tolerable standard of warning, the communications were a constant anxiety and at all times threatened the organisation with complete breakdown.' [1]

[1] Report by VA Second-in-Command, BPF - quoted in Naval Staff History

After a break in Sydney, the fleet moved up for attacks on the main islands of Japan. At the beginning of August part of the fleet had joined up with American battleships and cruisers to bombard the forts at the entrance to Tokyo Bay, but on 5 August this was cancelled and ships were ordered to be clear of the area; the next day the first atomic bomb was dropped on Hiroshima. Three days later after the second bomb had been dropped on Nagasaki the flag signal 'Cease hostilities against Japan' was hoisted in the British Fleet. Just as the signal was executed, a Kamikaze splashed into the sea three hundred yards astern of *Victorious* . For a time the fleet remained under continuous air attack, giving rise to Admiral Halsey's well known signal to the effect that attacking aircraft were 'to be shot down in a friendly manner'.

One of the most important aspects of the BPF's operations with the Americans was the tremendous co-operation, and growing respect for each other's achievements, in the communications field. The extensive use by the USN of Voice on tactical nets, relaxed procedures, high speed morse broadcasts, and the development of tactical communications and manoeuvring procedures suitable to the operation of forces built around large aircraft carrier groups spread over considerable distances, were new to the British. For their part the Americans came to respect the RN communicators' high degree of radio discipline, precise and succinct message drafting, the professional competence of signalmen and telegraphists, and the fact that the British signal officer was very much a member of the operational staff, with a close relationship with his Admiral, and overall responsibility for all aspects of the fleet's communications.

The successful integration of the two fleets produced the confidence and friendly relationships between Communicators which laid the foundation for the close Anglo-US liaison in the communications field which was maintained and developed after the war.

In mid-August the main body of the British Fleet departed for Sydney but *King George V, Duke of York* and some others entered Tokyo Bay, passing the forts they were to have bombarded which were now flying white flags. Courage and Ashmore were present at the surrender ceremony on board USS *Missouri*.

> *'That evening, Admirals Halsey and Wilkinson attended an impressive sunset ceremony held by Admiral Sir Bruce Fraser on board flagship Duke of York, anchored not far from Missouri. The flags of all the Allies, flying from the signal yards, were handsomely lowered in unison as the massed bands from all British ships present played the music of the sunset hymn. Nothing could have been more appropriate to the occasion ...it made sailors feel that their navies had achieved something more than a military victory.'* [2]

[2] Samuel Eliot Morison,
'A History of United States Naval Operations in World War II'

*   *   *   *   *

Rear Admiral Servaes had arrived on station flying his flag in HMS *Bermuda* just in time to take part in the last carrier-borne operations. Before the formal surrender he was then engaged in the operation to repatriate allied prisoners of war and internees (RAPWI), going first to Formosa with the carrier Colossus, two destroyers and a New Zealand hospital ship. Duncan Knight, SCO and Flag Lieutenant, commented that they were:

> *'not empowered to accept the surrender of the local forces as this was to be an American 'sphere of influence' ... the Japanese C-in-C arrived wearing sword and medals, conspicuous amongst which was the Allied Victory Medal of World War I. He was not received with Guard and Band!'*

Later, at Shanghai, *Bermuda* was allocated No.3 buoy; No 1, traditionally reserved for the British flagship, was occupied by an American warship. 'This brought home to us the fact that the sun had set on the era of British supremacy on the China coast. The communications staff was run off its feet, having to maintain contact with Hong Kong (C-in-C BPF), Chungking (British Embassy), Kure (British Forward Base) and several US authorities.

> *'We got on well with the USN - indeed we largely depended on them for radio spares, signal stationery and many other things. We grew to realise that ours was not necessarily the only way, or even the best way, and that they were trained and equipped to maintain a fleet at sea in a forward area for long periods, which we certainly were not. In one respect however we did have the edge over the Americans - the Fleet*

Amenities Ship Menestheus. A converted Blue Funnel freighter with a purpose built theatre, she had a resident professional concert party, English pub with home-brewed beer, and a range of shops including Gieves the tailor. All staff were in uniform, including those in Gieves who appeared as RNVR Special Branch Sub-Lieutenants!'

Meanwhile Rear Admiral Harcourt, commanding the 11th Aircraft Carrier Squadron of light fleet carriers, which arrived on station just too late to take part in operations, with John Parker as Flag Lieutenant and SCO, had been despatched post haste to re-occupy Hong Kong.

There was an urgent need to re-establish a communications facility, and Parker asked for some of the WRNS (Ce) officers, now under-employed in Sydney, to be sent to Hong Kong to set up a Comcen, under the redoubtable Communication Lieutenant Jackie Condon. David Seely was now in *Kempenfelt*: 'I accepted the surrender of Stonecutters Island, though from nobody, as the Japanese had already disappeared!' There was no serviceable equipment at Stonecutters, and for the time being HMS *Montclare* acted as the Communications Centre at Hong Kong. Peter Keith Welsh, Assistant SCO in *Montclare*, remembers that Stonecutters was overgrown and rat-infested. He and his staff set about re-establishing it as a transmitting station by borrowing equipment from ships and repairing what they could, and managed to set up some radio links. In the course of this, they came across the old Fixed Service operator's log - his last recorded message was the operating signal for 'Am closing down until further notice.' Once on the air, 'Cancel my so-and-so' was the first message to be transmitted. They were also told to provide facilities for the BBC to report on the Surrender ceremonies:

'To decide on the most effective frequency, we transmitted on a selection, asking for anyone who received us to report on the strength and quality of our signal. We were still getting replies weeks after the ceremonies were over!'

Seely moved on to be the Signal Officer to the Naval Element of the occupation force in Japan at Kure. The HQ was in a converted Glen Line ship which had embarked a 'Momonster', a major wireless station designed for setting up a naval air station. This had to provide a broadcast, ship-shore circuits, fixed service to Hong Kong, and a

Jack Pennington, was a telegraphist at Stonecutters in 1941, where they employed Chinese tea boys and cleaners. One particular lad seemed to be a cut above the rest, but disappeared at about the same time as a confidential document was found to be missing, although the two events were not connected at the time as the boys were always coming and going. When Hong Kong was overrun by the Japanese, Pennington was taken prisoner. Lined up on the parade ground, the communicators saw a large limousine approach. Out stepped a small Japanese officer who walked down the line. Stopping to look at Pennington he smiled and said: 'Remember me Mr Pennington, and all that commotion over the missing document? Well, I took it!'

500 kHz merchant shipping channel, as well as all the facilities for a naval base. The kit did not include an MF transmitter of sufficient power for 500 kHz, but an American TED was acquired at the cost of two bottles of whisky, as the stores depots had conveniently just been told to tear up their records and start a new 'bottom line' in January 1946!

The station had hardly got going when they were ordered to take all British and Australian Army traffic as well, as the Army had failed to provide their own communications. The fixed service rapidly became seriously overloaded, so Seely got approval from George Ram, the senior RN signal officer in Japan, to send all Deferred and Routine traffic to Hong Kong by sea mail!

> *'Then came the final straw, a signal from the Australian Force Commander about the passage of his wife and furniture marked Flash Top Secret! Being unaware of the Army practice of relating precedence and classification to rank, I downgraded it to Routine Confidential and sent it by post!'*

Seely escaped any repercussions as shortly afterwards he broke his back in a motor accident, having been run off the road by a Japanese lorry.

The Signal Division - 21 June 1945

Front (L to R): Cdr (Sp) GE Hughes RNVR, Cdr (S) WGS Tighe, Cdr WS Handcock, Cdr JH Bowen, Capt CL Firth, Rear Adm LV Morgan (DSD), Capt HF Layman, Capt NB Deare, Cdr NJ Wagstaff, Cdr (Sp) LH Cox RNVR.
Centre (L to R): L Wren JM Pesshall, Cdr JCG Martin, Mr HFT Brown, Lt RH Buxton RNVR, Lt Cdr E Lloyds RNVR, Sig Lt Cdr WR Paris, Lt Cdr C Bancroft RNVR, Lt Cdr TL Lace RNVR, Lt UG Huggins RNVR, Lt H Mee RNVR, Lt Cdr JAC Henley, Lt Cdr HJ Patten RNVR, Lt Cdr LPC Warren RNVR, Cdr PH Matheson, Lt Cdr RW Briggs, Lt CAJ Graham-Watson RNVR, L Wren E Twomey.
Back (L to R): Wren BP Jefferies, Mr SR Thorpe, Mr SWH Salter, 1/0 LD Noble, 1/0 P Ahern, Lt Cdr EF Kay RNVR, 2/0 B Baily, 2/0 MG Davies, Elect Lt D\Cdr WD Sutcliffe RNVR, Lt (S) JS Dixon RNVR, Lt NA Watkins RNVR, Elect Lt RC Lang RNVR, CYS EG Guy, Lt FWC Pitt RNVR, Lt WBM Dempster RNVR, Wren M Edwards.

Signal!

Chapter Fourteen

New Signal Books
and the Korean War

*'When in any project for signals they appear intricate and
difficult to comprehend you may be sure they are faulty;
what is good must be clear and simple.'*

Kempenfelt, 1781

I t used to be said that the Signal Branch liked to change the books
as soon as admirals and captains had come to know as much
about them as their signal officers. Certainly, the books seemed
to be changed or amended pretty frequently, although of course this was
due to advances in tactical thinking, new weapons and sensors, and
therefore new requirements for signalling the appropriate instructions.

Immediately after the war it was clear that the British books
needed to be up-dated to reflect war experience, and particularly that
gained in operating with the Americans in the Pacific. Cooperation
with the US Navy had developed into a unique and on-going 'special
relationship' in the communications and intelligence fields. The
wartime Combined Communications Board (CCB) [1] continued in
being, and played an important role in the post-war period in the
development of measures to ensure 'inter-operability' at sea between
allied navies. Liaison between the RN and USN became very close,
so that the British Naval Staff in Washington, unlike any other Navy
(or Service) had their offices actually in the US Naval Headquarters.

In the UK a Signal Books Committee was set up, suitably chaired
by Admiral Sir Patrick Brind with recent experience of operating
with the US Navy, and who had endorsed recommendations that
many American procedures should be adopted by the RN. The
principal signal officers on the committee were Captains Keith
Campbell-Walter and Peter Reid, with James Stopford, 'Dusty'
Dunsterville, and for a time a Canadian, Commander (later Vice
Admiral) John O'Brien, all with appropriate experience.

As their Pacific Force had converted to US books and tactical
doctrine towards the end of the war, the Canadians decided to stay
with US methods in peacetime; O'Brien was therefore instructed to
ensure that whatever the Committee produced, it should be as

[1] The early days of RN-USN liaison,
and the CCB, are referred to in
Chapter 21.

'American' as possible! The Committee was indeed directed to include any advantages found in using the American books but not to be unduly influenced by USN practice. O'Brien also quotes Admiral Cunningham, then First Sea Lord, who had initially resisted the use of American books in the Pacific, as directing the Committee to 'use the International Code flags, and don't use the damn word 'Task'!'

Nevertheless, the Task Force system, circular formations, the axis and rotating it, and reorienting the screen all made their appearance in the revised Conduct of the Fleet (COF), the bridge book that contained the instructions for organising and manœuvring the fleet.

The most obvious change in the Fleet Signal Book (FSB), which provided the means of signalling the instructions and manœuvres laid down in the COF, was the adoption of the International Code flags and pendants, and the USN numeral flags, in place of the old RN ones. Some special RN flags and pendants were retained, but at a stroke this reduced significantly the number of different flags which had to be carried in ships and memorised by signalmen. One or two favourites disappeared - the Blue pendant for turns together became, quite logically, the 'Turn' pendant, while the Red and White pendants for wheeling in succession were replaced by 'Corpen'. Fixed Light Manoeuvring Signals were abolished.

Some completely new books were produced, for example the Action Information Signal Book which provided instructions and brevity codes for use on the many voice circuits now needed by those manning what used to be called 'the Plot'.

By the time these publications were introduced in 1948, co-operation with Western Union countries, including combined exercises, had become a regular feature for European navies. Common procedures were needed, and the new British books were used; some of the navies concerned had anyway had their ships integrated into the British fleet during the war, so that they were familiar with British procedures, and in some cases did not even need the books translated.

"From: *Chequers*
To: *Glory*

Happy Christmas ... "

However the international scene was shifting rapidly, and hardly had the new British books been introduced when, in 1949, the NATO treaty was signed, thus extending the requirement for common procedures to include the US and Canada. By this time new US books had also just come into force, and it was found that these departed quite significantly from their wartime ones, so that much of the well meant effort to bring the British books more into line had been wasted.

Another Committee was set up, this time in Washington, under the auspices of the CCB, and in May 1950 Keith Campbell-Walter, by now thoroughly experienced at rewriting signal books, found himself at it again.

The aim was to produce a set of books which would be used not just for NATO purposes, but within each navy as well. The main work was carried out by an Anglo-US working group; other nations were consulted on matters of policy as the work progressed but the detail was left to the working group, and within eighteen months a whole series of new NATO books was beginning to flow off the production line. The RN was in a fairly strong position, with the other European navies opting to keep to the British system as nearly as possible, but there were severe obstacles to be overcome. The Americans did not have a single bridge book like the Conduct of the Fleet, but a number of separate books for each type of operation. In the end it was agreed to adopt the RN system in principle, and the result was that the new NATO equivalent of the COF, the Allied Naval Manœuvring Instructions (ANMI), bore a striking resemblance to it. It is more usually known by its other title, ATP1 (Allied Tactical Publication No. 1).

The 1948 British Fleet Signal Book had already adopted many of the best features from the American General Signal Book, and the new NATO publication, the Allied Naval Signal Book (ANSB), turned out to be not dissimilar to the FSB except for the language, for it was accepted that this would have to be 'American'. This at least had the advantage that the work of printing and publishing the books, and subsequent amendments, would be undertaken by the US - using their paper too, something which was still in short supply in Europe! It did result in some changes in spelling - pendant finally became pennant after a period of some uncertainty, for example, and a good deal of new phraseology had to be learnt - 'Despatch is necessary' became 'Expedite the action', the 'Admiral' became what was really meant, the 'Officer in Tactical Command' (OTC), while Flotillas became Squadrons, the term Flotilla reverting to its dictionary sense of 'a small fleet', i.e. two or more Squadrons.

All the familiar groups changed too: 'Freddy Duff' no longer meant 'Stop engines'; this was now 'Speed Sierra' (a new phonetic alphabet had also been adopted - see Appendix 10). 'Duff George' meaning 'Manœuvre Well Executed' (and Negative Duff George' when it wasn't!) became 'Bravo Zulu' with the rather more prosaic meaning 'Well Done.' 'TQ' - 'There will be time for the next meal now', changed to 'AD24' - 'Mealbreak: Flag and Commanding Officers will have time for the next meal'. Surprisingly, it was still possible to 'Splice the Mainbrace' ('AD28'). Other old favourites disappeared - thus the Equal Speed Manoeuvres were scrapped, although the same manœuvres could of course still be carried out by signalling each movement separately. The Gridiron ('EA') also went from the NATO book, but was included ('XTA 160') in the 'green pages' containing a few signals retained for RN use only.

A new series of all the 'procedural' books had to be drafted, and these were issued over the next two or three years as Allied Communications Publications (ACPs). Thus ACP 125 contained the instructions for Voice Procedures, ACP 129 for Visual Procedures, and so on. Although these were 'Allied' publications, control of them remained with the 'CANUKUS' organisation.

The introduction into the fleet of three different sets of signal books within four years was not a record - in 1779 the books changed twice in one year, and not content with that they were altered again by Admiral Rodney in 1782!

The Korean War

Belfast was at Hokadate, in Japan, on 25 June 1950, and the officers were in the wardroom enjoying their pre-dinner drinks, when a messenger pinned up a notice: 'The North Koreans have crossed the 38th parallel and are attacking South Korea.' Raymond Dreyer, Flag Lieutenant to Rear Admiral Andrewes, FO2 Far East Fleet, remembers the general feeling: 'Thank goodness we are not involved.'

> *'The Admiral thought otherwise, and having got libertymen recalled, signalled the American COMNAVFE (Admiral Joy, HQ in Tokyo): "Reporting for Duty." This seems to have impressed the USN - a foreign Admiral reporting to them for duty in a war that his government didn't even know was on! The Americans were ready to do whatever he suggested!'*

Fortuitously FO2 with part of the British fleet was spending the hot summer months in Japanese waters, and had joined the occupation forces of Japan under COMNAVFE, so was already in close touch with the Americans.

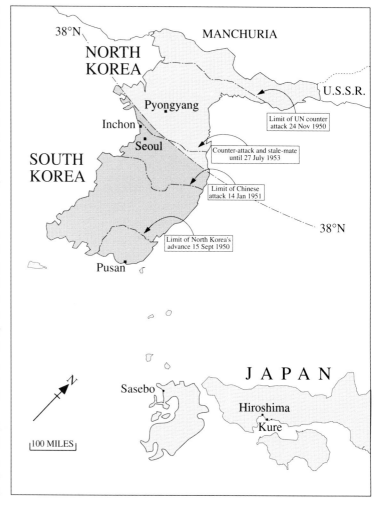

The Korean War 1950-53

A few months before this, the Far East Fleet had been exercising with the Americans, using US books, so they were already well briefed when the war started. Although NATO was in being, the new NATO books and procedures had not been developed, so there was no alternative but to 'go American' again, as the BPF had done a few years earlier. The principal difficulty in fact seemed to be that the British radio operators had problems understanding accents from the different parts of the British Isles rather than those of the Americans or any other Allied ships involved. The latter included Canadian, Australian, Dutch, Norwegian and Colombian ships at one time or another.

Formal orders arrived from the Admiralty on 28 June directing the C-in-C, Admiral Brind, to 'place the Royal Navy at present in

Japanese waters at the disposal of the US Naval Commander for Korean Operations' (Vice Admiral Joy).

Early in July a combined force including the US carrier Valley Forge, and the light fleet carrier *Triumph* attacked targets in North Korea. The US Admiral was in Tactical Command:

> *'It all seemed so familiar ... as it was just what we had done so often during the exercises in March with very similar forces. We didn't feel out of things and were already getting back into the easy use of American signal books ... in fact things did work well, thanks very largely to our previous practice and knowledge of American ways, signals and, frequently, language.'* [2]

Under the now familiar Task Force system, the British, primarily responsible for the West coast of Korea, became Task Group 96.8, and the Americans, in the East, TG 96.5. TG 96.8 was in turn divided initially into three Task Units, TU 96.8.1, 96.8.2 and 96.8.3, each with a cruiser in command, which carried out patrols in rotation. The aim was to enforce a blockade of the coast occupied by North Korea, prevent infiltration of the coast held by the South, and provide support with carrier-borne aircraft and naval gunfire as required. The British did also operate from time to time on the East coast, bombarding shore batteries and shooting up trains which were carrying supplies for the North Korean army.

South Korean Liaison teams were embarked, usually consisting of a naval officer, a civilian interpreter and a signalman. The civilian was soon dispensed with, since there had not been time to carry out adequate security screening of these people, and some seemed of rather dubious origin!

The main British and American base was at Sasebo where the facilities were quite unable to cope with so many ships. A Headquarters ship, with a large reserve of electric power, and space for communications facilities comparable to those in a cruiser, was a firm requirement. Eventually a Yangtse River steamer, the *Wusueh*, was converted in Hong Kong dockyard, renamed HMS *Ladybird*, and despatched to Sasebo. She served until April 1953 when she was relieved by the *Tyne*.

The build-up of UN forces inevitably took time, and the South Koreans were quite unable to hold back the North, until by early August only a beach-head around Pusan was in their hands. This was just sufficient to allow land forces, principally American, to build up and counter attack. Assisted by a large-scale amphibious landing at Inchon, the Allies advanced and by the end of November had occupied more than half of North Korea. Then the Chinese joined in to support the North Koreans, and by January 1951 the Allies had been forced back South of the 38th parallel. Gradually the situation stabilised and long drawn out truce talks dragged on for the next two years, with the forces facing each other more or less across the 38th Parallel.

[2] Vice Admiral Andrewes, Report of Proceedings

'Train shooting, very like rabbit shooting, as they popped in and out of their tunnels, was an enjoyable relief from what we called the 'Corpen Club', screening the carrier', commented John Henley, commanding Charity.

HMS *Ladybird* at Sasebo

With his promotion in December 1950, Vice Admiral Andrewes had become senior to his 'superior', Rear Admiral Smith, USN, but this made no difference to the smooth working of the forces. However he was surprised one day in February 1951 when Smith arrived to 'report for duty!' His appearance had preceded the receipt of a signal from COMNAVFE directing Admiral Andrewes 'to relieve Rear Admiral Allan Smith as CTF 95.' (The Blockade and Escort Force had been re-designated TF 95 after the Inchon landings in September 1950; the USN carrier force, TF 77, was part of the US 7th Fleet and operated quite independently.)

Admiral Andrewes' staff was not complemented for this, but by agreement Admiral Smith retained operational control of all except the west coast forces, leaving Admiral Andrewes to deal with matters of policy. Nevertheless the flagship's communications organisation came under great strain; during the first fourteen days over five thousand signals were handled, including 3,000 in cypher. Long and detailed secret operational summaries arrived daily; according to Dreyer:

> 'These seemed to include the position of almost every soldier anywhere near the front line! Fortunately they were easy to identify from their delivery groups and we could ignore them when necessary, without any apparent adverse effect. One report gave the lettered co-ordinates of the position where an aircraft had shot a man (a North Korean); "Maybe he was an important man!" said the Admiral.'

All RN ships read the Singapore Broadcast, but cruisers and carriers in addition read one of the USN broadcasts from Guam. Dreyer commented:

> *'The main Guam broadcast, read by all USN ships, was full of much useless and incredible garbage, resulting in serious delays to important traffic. The USN's communications generally suffered from their having no specialist communication officers, and therefore no one in a position to ensure that only messages which ships must receive reasonably quickly were sent by radio.'*

Another reason for the heavy signal traffic was that every Task Element and ships operating independently had to signal a Sitrep every evening. As John Henley put it:

> *'This gave the impression that our gunfire was deadly accurate and that the shore batteries were taking a tremendous battering. Perhaps the Press were impressed; no one else was!'*

Dreyer noticed that signals from USN operational authorities always ended 'Keep a good lookout for mines.' He asked about this, and was told it was to protect themselves from any Congressional enquiry into the loss or damage of a ship. The Congressmen would ask if the ship had been warned, and if not, would blame the operational authority!

The Command arrangements changed in April when Rear Admiral Scott-Moncrieff, junior to Smith, arrived to relieve Andrewes, and at about this time it was decided to place TF 95 under the direct command of the Commander, 7th Fleet. It was hoped that this would ensure closer co-ordination and allow a greater degree of flexibility in the use of ships. However as TF 77 operated out of Yokosuka and TF 95 from Sasebo, there was little personal contact and the exchange of information and intelligence actually got worse.

This was the first major war waged by the United Nations, although for all practical purposes the forces involved came under American command; there was already a US command structure based in Japan, and it was obvious that the Americans would make much the largest contribution to the war effort. The lack of a joint headquarters was a complication which hindered inter-service liaison and co-operation, and the US command system tended to be rather rigid. Although with the Task Force system the juggling of decimal places could cater for almost any situation, the manner in which it was operated was inflexible. Orders were voluminous and detailed (although well indexed, luckily) and direct communication at a junior level was frowned upon, all intercommunication being supposed to go up through the chain of command and down again. Nevertheless personal relations were good and misunderstandings were invariably sorted out by discussion.

It is often said that the main barrier to Anglo-US co-operation is the language, and the use of slang on voice circuits sometimes caused difficulty, as did the different meanings attached to words or phrases;

Rear Admiral Scott-Moncrieff
'transferring his flag' by jackstay

'presently' meant 'now' to them, 'later on' to us, for example. The word 'consensus', familiar now, was then new to the British who felt that discussions were often cut short and important decisions made simply by majority voting. Other allies were of course less well placed, and to operate successfully in a tactical force some needed a nucleus of English speakers or a liaison team; others found no difficulty, the Dutch in particular operating as if English was their first language.

Equipment compatibility was another problem. USN ships usually had more sets and operators, while the transmitters and receivers in other nations' ships often had different frequency coverage or modes of operation. FO2's signal staff had to be used to help out the hard-pressed communication complements in British ships, at the expense of his own communications. The sheer volume of situation reports, opsums etc. customarily required by the US Commanders, overloaded the system; this was partly the result of the rigid command structure already mentioned, but also to the desire to have everything on record for political reasons, much of it in 'journalese' for the benefit of the press, and all marked with an unduly high precedence. Admiral Scott-Moncrieff:

> '*Truly, the premium placed on public information was often higher than that placed on the security of cyphers, or even of current operations.*'

Thus were the requirements of the media in a war fought 'in public' first experienced.

*   *   *   *   *

The following exchange took place after a jackstay transfer off Korea:

> From: *Glory*
> To:　　*Crusader*
>
> > We sent a bag with teeth intact,
> > You sent it back still fully packed.
> > The next event we'll try by chopper
> > Flown by our most expert dropper.
>
> From: *Crusader*
> To:　　*Glory*
>
> > We're sorry that the bag unpacked
> > Returned to Glory all intact.
> > Our Coxswain, poised as seems most proper
> > To catch his teeth, will wait your chopper.
> > With many thanks your Dentist due,
> > Will try to stick them in with glue.

Loyal Toast

Rear Admiral Scott-Moncrieff, was dining in Ladybird in 1952. The Loyal Toast 'The King' had just been drunk when the Chief Yeoman entered with a signal. The Admiral read it, then tapped the table and said: 'Gentlemen, The Queen.'

Chapter Fifteen

Morse to Satcoms

'Fitting one ship with the latest gun might have
some virtue, fitting just one with a new
communications fit has none!'

Producing new Signal Books and procedures for NATO was a relatively simple exercise compared with the problems of working with the different varieties and standards of radio equipment fitted in the ships of NATO's navies. Overcoming this problem was exacerbated by the post-war decline in defence budgets, and the growing gulf between the USN on the one hand, with relatively vast R & D and production facilities, and the minimal resources available to the navies of some of the smaller European countries. It was many years before a reasonable degree of 'inter-operability' was achieved.

In the late 1940s, for example, the RN and most European navies were expanding their fit of VHF sets, while the USN was turning over to UHF, thus the ability to inter-communicate on tactical and manoeuvring nets was very limited. New techniques had been developed rapidly during the war, so that the equipment in most ships was becoming obsolescent, while the demands for additional channels continued unabated. It was only possible to make major changes to a ship's radio installation when it underwent a long refit, so that it could be many years before some ships had been modified. Thus, even within one navy, ships could have very different capabilities and full 'compatibility' was rarely achieved. This was a continuing headache for signal officers drawing up communication plans.

International Co-operation

The first major post-war international exercise was VERITY, which took place under Western Union auspices in the summer of 1949. British forces included the Home Fleet, the Training Squadron, ten submarines, minesweepers, MLs and MTBs, and various RFAs. The French contributed a light fleet carrier and five cruisers as well as several escorts, and other forces came from Belgium and Holland. So it was a large scale operation, designed to pave the way towards closer European naval co-operation. It was agreed that English should be the basic language, and RN communication procedures were used. Small liaison teams were provided in the foreign ships, but as advisers and 'interpreters' of signal publications only, not for manning any of the communication circuits.

RN Signal Publications and certain special flags were provided to the other navies to allow for pre-exercise training, together with crystals for some air and shipborne equipments. Liaison teams were briefed at the Signal School and Signal Training Centres, and in Home Fleet signal exercises Midshipmen were tasked with acting as foreign voice operators speaking broken English! Morse circuits were built into the signal plan to provide an alternative to voice, should this prove necessary.

The ships taking part assembled at Penzance for three days for an intensive communications work-up. Once at sea, the various phases were taken fairly slowly at first, but confidence in the accurate transmission and reception of manoeuvring signals was quickly gained, and the standard of communications steadily improved. All in all, the exercise seems to have been quite a success. One report summed it up: 'There was a general consensus of opinion that communications throughout were excellent. It had previously been feared that difficulties in language and technique would prejudice the whole efficiency of the operation but these fears turned out to be groundless.'

WEU exercises became a regular feature of the annual programme. The 1950 Summer exercise ACTIVITY was conducted by the Dutch, with the carrier *Karel Doorman* as flagship; the 'complan' was kept fairly simple, and again there were relatively few communication problems. This was a good augury for the future, and these exercises laid the groundwork for the eventual introduction of the NATO Signal Books and wireless procedures, based to a large extent on the principles of the RN publications, with which the Western Union navies had become very familiar.

Captain Jack Broome, of PQ17 fame, was not only a well known author but also a talented artist. In the 1950s he produced a set of drawings for the Signal School based on the new NATO phonetic alphabet, one example of which is shown above.

NATO

The advent of NATO opened up new requirements, opportunities and challenges. Communications inevitably played a vital part of the organisation, and the RN had to provide their share of the staffs to man the new headquarters; these included the Major NATO HQs for SACLANT at Norfolk, Virginia, CINCHAN (Portsmouth), and of course SACEUR (Paris) until the French pulled out of the integrated military side of NATO, then Brussels). There were also subordinate headquarters to be established, equipped and manned, such as CINCNORTH (Oslo), CINCSOUTH (Naples), CINCEASTLANT (Northwood) and CINCAFMED (Malta), as well as smaller headquarters such as COMNAVBALTAP (Denmark), COMGIBMED (Gibraltar) and many others, several in the UK, such as COMNORLANT (Rosyth) and COMCENTLANT (Plymouth). The Commanders and many of their staffs in some headquarters were often 'two-hatted', combining national and NATO jobs.

NATO headquarters were 'mixed-manned', sometimes by four or five nationalities and often by the three services of the nations concerned (and usually 'over-manned' to accommodate national requirements), so the variety of uniforms, male and female, plus civilians, produced a colourful and polyglot team, though in naval circles the use of English tended to predominate, particularly where the French were not involved. It was not long before national identities became submerged and all worked together without difficulty. The naval members had some advantage since inter-communication was fundamental to the operation of a mixed force of ships, and they were already used to working with common doctrines and procedures. On the planning staffs it soon became natural to think of someone as the 'frequency planner' or the 'comsec officer' rather than the Italian Army Colonel or Norwegian Air Force Major.

Inevitably NATO spawned many Agencies, Committees and Working Groups; a particularly effective one was the European Naval Communications Agency (ENCA), established in 1951 (despite its title, the US participated). It was subordinate to the European Military Communications Coordination Committee (EMCCC) in Paris, but the Secretariat was in London, and the Agency was chaired by DSD. In 1965, to emphasise its NATO-wide responsibility, ENCA was re-designated the Allied Naval Communications Agency (ANCA), and was joined by the Canadians. At the same time, most other NATO C-E agencies moved to Brussels to be near the Imternational Military Staff, but by general agreement ANCA continued to be based in London, and chaired by the RN.

ANCA's tasks, broadly, were to formulate NATO naval communications requirements, to achieve inter-operability between maritime forces, develop policies and plans, and agree procedures and operating standards.

The first twenty years or so of NATO also involved building up the 'infrastructure', such as the comcentres in each headquarters, and the NATO-wide communication links and radar systems, which involved the expenditure of vast sums of money, and much negotiation over competing national and NATO interests. In the Northern Command based at Oslo, for example, there was a particular need for efficient communications with the STRIKEFLEET; as described earlier, communications are notoriously difficult in high latitudes, and this led to the development of elaborate multi-frequency trans-mission and reception systems between the fleet and the Northern Command. Other requirements were for tropo-scatter radio-relay systems through the region and in Norway these, as well as the radar stations, were often sited on top of mountain ranges. It was early days in the development of micro-wave radio relay systems of this sort, but the Scandinavians were particularly adept at solving the difficulties, having a considerable interest in achieving effective communications throughout the region for their own national purposes. Because of the problems of access, many of the stations had to be designed to operate unmanned for long periods, and considering the state of the art at the time, remarkable success was achieved.

As a result of the predominance of naval affairs in the Northern Command (the first CINCNORTH had been Admiral Brind), and the limited resources of the region, AFNORTH headquarters was smaller than the other major NATO HQs, which meant less paper and quicker decisions. The British played an important role (after Brind the C-in-C was always a British General), the Chief Signal Officer an RN Captain (later Commodore 'to keep up with the NATO Jones''), and the Comcentre was run by a Royal Signals Major. The Command stretched from North Cape to Kiel (the same distance as London to Rome), and the headquarters were manned by various permutations of Norwegians, Danes, Americans, British and Germans.

The same principles applied throughout NATO, although the problems, and the nationalities involved, differed widely. For the RN, a considerable number of additional communicators had to be found to fill the established posts.

Other international organisations sprang up, such as CENTO (US, UK, Turkey, Pakistan and Iran - hard now to remember this alliance!), and SEATO, but these were on a very limited scale compared with NATO, and although there was an RN communications input this was relatively minor, and neither of these organisations survived for very long.

In parallel with the NATO organisation, the wartime Anglo-US and Commonwealth liaison continued, and this was especially close in the intelligence and communications fields. The mechanics of liaison on signal matters, now generally referred to as 'Communications-Electronics', or C-E, developed through various permutations into what became the AUS-CAN-NZ-UK-US Naval Communications Board, its functions being broadly similar to those described for ANCA in the NATO context. Highlighting the inter-dependence of Command and Communications, this Board was subordinate to what, in modern parlance, is known as the Command, Control and Communications (C3) Board, the successor to the earlier CCB.

Ship-Shore Communications

The wartime ship-shore and broadcast organisation was much too elaborate and expensive to justify its retention in peacetime just to meet the needs of the Navy. However the rapid increase in commercial traffic to and from merchant ships meant that a shared system could be viable. After discussion with the Departments concerned, it was decided that merchant ships should continue to use a broadcast system, despite their pre-war preference for direct working, and that naval fixed services would carry commercial traffic. The new joint system came into force on 1 January 1946.

One of the relay stations was sited on the top of Gausta Mountain, the highest peak of the Hardanger Vidda. To ensure all-weather access, a very steep tunnel was driven up inside the mountain, through which personnel and stores were carried in a miniature train. The great day came when they broke through and started to commission the station, but as the warm air came up from below the frozen rock near the top started to thaw and bits began falling down the tunnel. This meant adding a concrete lining, at considerable unplanned extra expense to NATO!

This had a number of advantages - the navy retained access to a world-wide ship-shore system, the merchant service had much improved facilities over those available pre-war, their radio operators remained familiar with the wartime organisation, and a regular liaison between the two services was established.

The hub of the system was Burnham W/T, manned by both naval and civilian operators. Annual traffic levels had grown from a few thousand words in 1923 when the station was opened, to some nine million words (458,000 messages) in 1950, of which about 16,000 were naval messages. A number of naval 'search' operators watched for ships calling, themselves read any naval messages with a precedence, and handed others over to 'working' operators, naval if practicable but not necessarily. The operators could select any one of a large number of omni and directional receiving aerials, and could control any of the transmitters at Portishead and Criggion, while the main control room could key the home station naval broadcasts when required.

This joint arrangement between the Post Office and the navy continued for some thirty years, but with the coming of Radio Teletype (RATT) and other technical developments, the naval telegraphists were finally withdrawn from Burnham at the end of 1971. The facilities however continued to be available to the navy.

Vice Admiral Rae McKaig, then Flag Officer, Plymouth, presents a *Mercury* ship's badge to Mr T N Carter, Officer-in-Charge, Burnham W/T, to mark the final withdrawal of RN Communicators in 1971. Captain Douglas Poynter, Director of Naval Signals, is behind Admiral McKaig.

New requirements, New Techniques

One stimulus to new developments in the Royal Navy was provided by the decision to use HMS *Vanguard* as the 'Royal Yacht' for the Royal Tour to South Africa in 1947. In addition to the ship's normal radio fit, there was a requirement for high quality voice, radio teletype and facsimile, none of which had previously been fitted afloat in the RN, all required to work over distances of up to 5,000 miles.

The transmission requirement was met by a prototype STC DS10, which would radiate 5kw on CW, and 3kw on voice. An extraordinary array of special aerials, designed to match the optimum ship-shore frequencies, was rigged on the mainmast, and from the mast to the after superstructure, but this had to be completely unrigged every time the ship was dressed or undressed! The fax was a prototype Muirhead set, needed primarily for high quality transmission of Press photos, taken by *The Times* photographer. A good deal of BBC recording equipment was set up in another office, and a special 'W/T Control Room' was equipped to act as the overall nerve centre.

The installation was designed by ASRE, and Bill Heaton, a scientist from the Communications Division, together with an STC engineer, went on the trip, and together with the ship's staff managed to keep everything working. Radio teletype reception proved difficult on the outward trip, and at Cape Town whip aerials were fitted on the foc'sle and quarterdeck to provide 'space diversity'; with the addition of 'visual' (oscilloscope) as well as aural tuning, much better results were achieved.

The radio telephone became a great feature, and was available to the ship's company when not otherwise in use, at ten shillings a minute! The DS10 went off the air once during a live broadcast by the BBC's Frank Gillard, but otherwise there were no major mishaps. The experience was a useful contribution to planning the way in which radio communications afloat might be developed.

Vanguard was asked not to fire saluting guns whilst alongside in Cape Town as the horses of the mounted police on the jetty were not trained to cope with gunfire!

HMS *Vanguard*

The Royal Navy's last battleship, at the time she was used for the Royal Tour to South Africa in 1947.

In 1953, with the new Royal Yacht, *Britannia*, still working up, the Royal Tour to Australia and New Zealand made use of a chartered liner, SS *Gothic*. An RN communications team was embarked, together with a Royal Cypher party which included three WRNS signal officers.

Again the ship was specially fitted out, this time with a 20 kw SWB11 transmitter which managed to energise practically everything metallic in the after part of the ship, as Godfrey Talbot of the BBC discovered on the day they left Tonga. Standing below the aerials, the steel headband of his earphones suddenly got quite 'hot'; he was informed that this was good for thinning hair!

In many ports of call *Gothic*, being the senior officer, had to conduct morning and evening colours - it was an unusual sight to see a merchant ship conducting affairs for the many warships often present.

The new radio equipment fitted in the post-war fleet, consisting of the Type 600 series MF/HF transmitters and the B40/B41 receivers, was a considerable improvement, giving a reasonable Voice capability, and the possibility of at least a limited radio teletype facility. But it was clear that new types of modulation were being developed for which the equipment was not suitable, nor were ship layouts efficient, with transmitters remote from the main office, connected to their own individual aerials, and with control arrangements that provided little flexibility.

In 1953 a study was initiated with the aim of advising DSD on future communications staff requirements for some sixteen years ahead. This was conducted by Bill Heaton and Commander Raymond Dreyer, and reported in March 1954. In the past the requirements for naval communications systems had generally been conceived 'intuitively' by signal officers, an approach justified by the fact that most of the operating and processing of signals was conducted by human operators; it was realised that in the future automation was going to play a much greater part, and the design parameters would have to be stated more precisely, considering the particular facility as a whole, or from 'end to end' of the circuit, rather than as individual pieces of equipment.

The Study group's report broadly presaged the introduction of equipment with much greater frequency stability and a single sideband capability, which would allow the introduction of reliable radio teletype (RATT), greatly improved quality on voice circuits, on-line crypto, multi-channelling, and eventually the possibility of high speed data circuits. The latter were going to be essential to cope with the increasing amount of information provided by the new radars and electronic warfare equipment, which needed to be exchanged at high speed between the major units of the fleet.

The direct result of the study was the development of the Integrated Communication System (ICS), work on which started in the late 1950s, and which would gradually be fitted throughout the fleet, the first ships being equipped with ICS in the middle 1960s. The basis of the ICS was an accurate and stable frequency source from which any required MF or HF transmitter and receiver frequency could be derived. The system also incorporated broad-band transmitting aerials using suitable parts of the ship's superstructure, common aerial working, a measure of space diversity, and central control and monitoring. It was many years before ICS could be fitted widely in the fleet, and so that some advance could be made more rapidly, as well as maintaining a degree of inter-operability during the long change-over, many ships had to be fitted with items of commercial SSB equipment, an 'interim fit' known as COMIST.

Automation first went to sea in 1955 with the fitting of limited RATT facilities in Home and Mediterranean Fleet ships. This equipment provided facilities for receiving a RATT broadcast, plus one UHF RATT tactical net. It featured 'visual' tuning, which had demonstrated its worth in *Vanguard*, but 'noise' proved a problem at first and it seemed that RATT would not be as reliable as morse, albeit much more efficient when it worked. At this stage, it was concluded that morse would continue to be a requirement for the foreseeable future. Reliability of RATT gradually improved, but it needed the frequency stability of the ICS system before it became really efficient and was accepted as the primary means for both strategic and tactical signal circuits.

Admiral Sir Rae McKaig was in DRE in the late 1950s:

'The RN had got so used to using USN ship equipment that the moves to UHF, and the COMIST programme, were the first that the RN and the Dockyards had had to cope with where compatibility was an issue. I remember having to wrangle with Bath to point out that whereas fitting one ship with the latest gun had some virtue, fitting just one with a new communications fit had none!'

While 'automation' was beginning to make its appearance afloat, a big advance ashore took place in 1957 when the first 'computer', known as STRAD (Signal Transmitting Receiving and Distributing), was installed at Whitehall W/T. In essence, this automated the Tape Relay procedure, recognising address, precedence and routeing instructions, and switching messages as appropriate between the fifty IN and OUT circuits. Messages for local addressees were fed by teleprinter to the Main Signal Office, others were stored and 'queued' in order of precedence and time of receipt, and then re-transmitted in turn over the appropriate circuits. It is difficult to appreciate now how big the first computers were - STRAD occupied some 900 square feet of floor space - but was expected to replace about 100 communicators, although it is unlikely that this was achieved.

The plan was for STRADs to be fitted at all major communications centres where justified by the volume of traffic. In the event, with the reductions East of Suez, and further technical developments, only one other of similar design was installed, at Mauritius W/T, which was planned to be the hub of defence communications east of Suez. There had been naval wireless facilities in Mauritius from time to time since 1915, but the modern station was only commissioned in 1960, to replace the transmitting and receiving stations in Ceylon and Singapore which were closed down when those countries gained their independence.

By the 1970s Mauritius W/T was running about a dozen fixed services or contact circuits, ship-shore, and both CW and RATT broadcasts. But its life was relatively short; the withdrawal from East of Suez and the advent of satellite communications completely altered the situation, and the station finally closed in 1976.

Receipt for Ceylon West W/T

As countries gained their independence RN facilities had to be abandoned or handed over to the local authorities.

Skynet

In 1965 the new post of Assistant Chief of the Defence Staff (Signals) was established, the first incumbent being Rear Admiral Edward Ashmore. He recalls visiting a US Communications station at Pleiku in Vietnam where he was able to see and operate a satellite terminal connected direct to the USA through one of the first two satellites placed at synchronous altitude:

'This demonstration was a great encouragement to me since a major project during my time as ACDS(S) was to be directly connected with this novel type of communication.

'Hermann Bondi, the distinguished physicist, had been directed to write a report for the Government on the military uses of space. He had recommended that Britain should invest in space communications, possibly in space reconnaissance, but ignore the rest. In my view, and that of the Defence Signal Board, it was high time we did, and this launched me on a fascinating exercise which took the best part of nine months to achieve a satisfactory outcome.

'We felt that the British defence system at that time required a communications satellite at synchronous altitude over the Indian Ocean at about 75 degrees East, to establish absolutely firm communications between Whitehall and our forces in the Near, Middle and Far East. There was no such military satellite extant at that time, the Americans relying on a system of drifting multiple satellites known as the Interim Defence Communications Satellite Programme (IDCSP). We took some interest in this but, through lack of power and continuity, it failed to meet the needs that we envisaged of communicating rapidly with small antennae such as could be used tactically ashore and afloat. The test satellite over the Pacific through which I had communicated from Vietnam had a very limited capability in comparison with what we had in mind as something that the Chiefs of Staff could reasonably be asked to approve.

'Armed with an agreed Joint Staff Target I went to the States to see which way we should go. We were entirely reliant on them for a booster to put our satellite in orbit and there was no way a suitable satellite could be manufactured in the UK in the timescale we had in mind.

'We found that the Ford-Philco factory at Palo Alto in California, where the IDCSP satellites were built, could meet our requirements and produce our 'bird' ... and we decided to have it launched by the Thor Delta B, a rocket dedicated to a single pay-load which had a very high record for reliability.

'Relying on the US to launch our satellite, we had to negotiate a Memorandum of Understanding with them - we could not allow the Americans to exercise command and control over our satellite at all times, as they expected, since this would allow them to move it ... or indeed to switch it off if they wished. Although we were ahead of the Americans, there was no doubt they would not be far behind and would soon overtake us and I felt, therefore, that an agreement on inter-operability between our satellite and anything they put up was important to both sides. The negotiations were *difficult, but with the help and advice of the Presidential Special Adviser on Communications, an Agreement was eventually achieved.*

'On return to the UK we got approval for 'Skynet' (the name coined by one of my staff, Captain Gerald Sampson), money available, orders placed and the project running in, I think, record time. Harry Pout, on the Chief Scientific Adviser's staff, described it as a 'tour de force'. The management of the system on the ground was quite properly given to the RAF and the money came off the Air Force budget, which gave me a little quiet satisfaction since I knew that in the long term this system would be of more value to ships at sea than to almost anybody else.'

The first fruits appeared in 1967 when HMS *Wakeful*, trials ship for ASWE (ASRE under its new name), was fitted with the first experimental shipborne satellite aerial system. This was a six-foot dish with stabilised auto-tracking, plus two transportable cabins containing the terminal equipment, which enabled the RN to take part in the US IDCSP trials programme - one of the benefits of the close liaison established between the RN and USN in the communications field.

The trials were designed to prove the practicability of using ship-borne terminals, and the successful outcome enabled ASWE to proceed with confidence in the development of a streamlined transportable system to be ready for service in the fleet by the end of the 1960s.

The advantages of 'Satcoms' were becoming clear: world-wide coverage could be achieved with only a few satellites, off-setting the loss of overseas bases with their ground-based radio stations, while reliability should be much greater than with conventional HF, particularly in high latitudes. Furthermore, ships' transmissions would be difficult, if not impossible, to DF, thus over-coming some of the problems imposed by having to keep radio silence on 'conventional' circuits. Looking further ahead, the very large bandwidth likely to be available in future systems meant that there was the possibility of perhaps hundreds of channels being accommodated on one satellite circuit.

Britain's first defence satellite system, Skynet 1A, was launched in November 1969, and placed in geo-stationary orbit some 23,000 miles over the Indian Ocean, giving coverage roughly from the Eastern Atlantic to Hong Kong. This was in fact the world's first operational military geo-stationary satellite. By this time 'earth' stations had been set up at Cyprus, Bahrein, Gan, Singapore and in the UK, plus two mobile stations. *Intrepid* was the first European warship to have an operational satellite system, being fitted with a six foot dish aerial; a similar system was fitted later in *Fearless*, both being obvious 'command' ships with space for the equipment which again was in two transportable cabins. Various combinations of

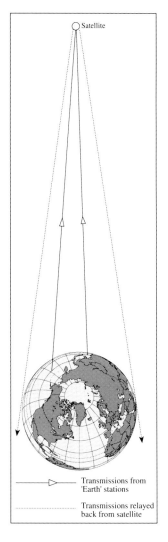

○ Satellite

▷———— Transmissions from
'Earth' stations

·········· Transmissions relayed
back from satellite

Skynet coverage

A satellite in geo-stationary orbit some 23,000 miles up can provide communications coverage over a very wide area, overcoming the problems with HF, particularly in the difficult high latitudes. Most military satellites operate in the UHF or SHF bands, the later allowing the use of a large number of voice, teletype or high speed data channels.

speech and telegraph channels could be used, a usual set-up being one duplex secure speech and two duplex secure 75-baud telegraph circuits, plus an engineering channel.

Skynet 1A in fact failed within a year, and the second (1B) was lost on launch, so the initial pioneering period was short, but sufficient to demonstrate a revolutionary improvement in the reliability and quality of long distance communications. However the system had been designed to be compatible with both US and NATO systems, and this enabled the UK to continue to have access to other satellites until a new and more powerful British defence satellite had been designed and built by Marconi Space Systems. The first of these, 2A, was unfortunately lost due to a fault in the launch rocket, but Skynet 2B was successfully put into orbit in November 1974.

Meanwhile the development of a smaller 3'6" dish system, known as SCOT, for general fitting in frigates and above, was progressing well. Again, this was designed to be transportable, so that with a limited number of sets, the equipment could be moved from ship to ship as they moved to and from operationally important areas.

Future Ship Radio Systems

A front-line destroyer or frigate in the 1990s requires a quite staggering Command, Control and Communications (C3) infrastructure compared with its forerunners. Although modern equipments are more reliable, and easier to operate than their predecessors, many of the various items of equipment are still scattered throughout the ship and lack full remote control facilities. At the same time, despite the efforts made to improve things, there has continued to be a severe shortage of radio operators, imposing an unacceptable workload both at sea and in harbour.

The aim in the future will be to provide a resilient and flexible system which really will reduce the manpower requirements, to be achieved by the introduction of a fully automated and integrated communications system, or 'FICS'.

A single operator 'Control' station will allow transmitter and receiver frequencies and bandwidths to be set up remotely, with the ability to tune them, select voice and telegraph equipment and appropriate aerials, in accordance with the relevant communications plan which will be stored in the database. The ultimate aim, as expressed by the Application Officer at Portsdown, Commander Bee [1], is:

> *'to provide a system which automatically responds to the operational user's requirements, and where the myriad of signal messages, voice and data streams from shore and other ships, strike the antennas and are then whizzed round the communications 'bus' to the users practically at the speed of light, untouched by human hands!'*

Needless to say, this will only be achieved gradually over many years, since existing equipment cannot just be discarded, and amongst

[1] RNE Vol 45 No.1

other things FICS will require extensive new cabling round the ship - this will be fibre-optic rather than the old-fashioned copper and thus much easier to install. Indeed fibre-optic cable has already demonstrated its value by making it much easier to fit and connect up additional equipment needed at short notice to meet some developing crisis.

Submarines

Submarines and wireless were invented at about the same time, and the introduction of wireless equipment into the already crowded hull posed a number of problems, not least space for the operator! The early boats were fitted with 'spark' transmitters, capable of about 1 kw output, most of which was dissipated in the rather crude aerial system, so that it achieved a range of only 30-50 miles. Towards the end of world war one those termed 'overseas' submarines (employed on operational patrols in enemy waters) were fitted with the Poulsen 'Arc' which, with improved aerial design, could achieve ranges of 350-400 miles. [2] The surviving 'H' boats were still fitted with Poulsen equipment when the second war broke out.

[2] More details of early submarine equipments and their operator's experiences will be found in Chapter 19

From 1917 messages to submarines were transmitted by the 'I' method between the depot ships at Harwich, Middlesborough and Blyth at routine times, but the submarine had to surface to receive these transmissions.

Thus operations were severely constrained by the fact that the boat was completely out of touch when submerged, so the role of the submarine was immeasurably enhanced when it was discovered, in the 1920s, that very low frequency radio transmissions penetrated the surface of the sea. VLF morse broadcasts, such as Rugby on 16 kHz, became the main method of passing messages from shore to submarines (those with acute hearing who stand under the aerials can sometimes hear the transmissions on these very low frequencies!).

In the 1950s a scientific analysis of the VLF system, carried out by Freddie Kingsley at the Admiralty Signal and Radar Establishment, unearthed some facts about the peculiar properties of underwater VLF reception which had not previously been appreciated. It was found that the rate of attenuation of the signal in sea water meant that for every six feet of depth the signal strength was halved; and, surprisingly, whatever the angle of incidence at the surface of the sea (ie whatever the range from the transmitter), the signal was always propagated vertically downwards. The latter fact, in particular, had a crucial bearing on the design and position of the 'fin' aerial - as luck would have it, a new aerial was being designed at that time and in the proposed position it would have received very little if anything at all!

In any case, the optimum operating depth for a submarine is not usually near the surface, and the search for some means of achieving reception of the broadcast at greater depths led to the idea of using a long buoyant wire aerial. This can be streamed from inside the submarine, and trails upwards with about 150 feet floating on the surface. It is virtually invisible, although it is said that maritime patrol aircraft have sometimes been surprised to see a row of seagulls travelling along at a steady four knots!

In the 1960s this idea was further developed into a towed buoy, designed on the paravane principle so that it would remain at a set depth just below the surface, and this carried a more sophisticated aerial system. The buoy, which is stowed in the casing, and can be streamed or retracted from inside the boat, is designed to be used when the submarine is deep. The obvious problems with towed aerials, particularly the buoy, is that they impose some restriction on the submarine's manœuvres.

One problem with very low frequencies is that the small bandwidth available means slow transmission speeds, while VLF stations with their huge aerials take up a lot of land and are costly, so that there are very few of them, and anyway there is a very limited number of available frequencies in this band. The British Telecom station at Criggion, near Shrewsbury, transmitting on about 20 kHz, is used as a back-up for Rugby, while in the 1960s a NATO VLF station was built at Anthorn, near Carlisle, and another on the west coast of Norway. Also in the 1960s, under the 1951 ANZUS treaty, a US VLF station was built at North West Cape, near Exmouth Gulf in Australia; this completed the US world-wide chain, and also gave the RAN use of the facilities at the station, which included HF ship-shore and a number of other services.

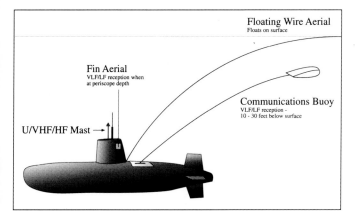

Typical aerial systems carried by a modern submarine

The advent of RATT with on-line encryption to replace morse on the submarine broadcasts did much to improve things, but the transmission of messages from submarines remained a serious problem. The normal HF ship-shore organisation had to be used, just as for surface ships, which meant that an aerial had to be above the surface throughout the time taken to establish contact and transmit the message. One development was to use an expendable radio buoy, which could transmit stored messages, if necessary with a built-in delay to allow the submarine to move away before transmission.

Submarine communications have once more been revolutionised with the advent of satellites. An omni-directional UHF aerial is used and while this still has to be put up for both reception and transmission, two-way communication at high speed data rates is now possible, so the exposure time can be relatively short. Furthermore, the submarine can choose the time at which it calls for its traffic, rather than having to wait for the regular routines, and the shore authority knows exactly when a message has been received by the submarine.

UHF satellite coverage (using USN or NATO facilities) is more or less world-wide, and this gives an important alternative to the VLF broadcasts. The latter are still the primary means of communicating with submarines, and the recent development of 'minimum shift keying' (MSK) allows several channels to be keyed on one VLF broadcast, thus increasing traffic capacity and allowing a small number of submarines to be allocated to each channel.

Thus communication developments have more or less kept pace with the nuclear powered submarine's main asset of being able to remain submerged almost indefinitely, the limiting factor generally being the welfare of the crew.

The Fleet Air Arm

The Navy only regained control of the Fleet Air Arm, from the 1918 merger with the Royal Flying Corps, just before the outbreak of war, the decision having been taken in July 1937 and implemented over the next couple of years. For many years thereafter the Navy relied on the Air Force both for material, including radio, and personnel; the latter could be found serving in aircraft carriers well into the 1950s.

DSD had no direct responsibility for staff requirements for airborne radio equipment, only for ship and ground radio (responsibility for the hardware passing to DRE when that Department was set up in 1943). The RAF MF/HF equipment, T.1082/R.1083, was generally fitted in aircraft and was fairly reliable - although this had a theoretical R/T capability, the range achieved was usually only a few miles, and virtually all communication was by CW morse at that time. An improved version, the T.1115/R.1116, arrived in 1940 with a better performance, but tuning was tricky and R/T quality very poor.

The RAF produced a crystal-controlled HF R/T set, the TR9, at the beginning of the war for use in single seat fighters, but this too was difficult to operate and could be unreliable. It wasn't until 1942/43 that 4-channel crystal-controlled VHF sets arrived, which much improved matters, although the rapidly increasing requirements for VHF channels in ships produced considerable problems in terms of mutual interference, the production and distribution of crystals, and in finding aerial sites (until it was found that a dipole at the yard arm would give adequate results).

There was no airborne radar at the beginning of the war, and few radar fitted ships, but the rudiments of a fighter direction system were set up in *Ark Royal* in 1940 during the Norwegian campaign by Lieutenant Commander Charles Coke, an Observer who also acted as the ship's Air Signal Officer. However her Skuas, the first monoplanes, designed to be both dive bombers and fighters, had to operate entirely visually and had little chance against enemy shore-based bombers. Signalling between aircraft was principally by wing-waggling.

After *Sheffield* and *Curlew* arrived on the scene with their Type 79 air warning radar, Coke was able to exercise control of the ship's aircraft with slightly greater effectiveness when one of them was in company. Reports from radar fitted ships, if present, or visual reports from others, were passed by flag signal until it was decided to break wireless silence, and Coke, sitting alongside the telegraphist on the reporting net, would plot the reports and then pass the necessary information himself by W/T to the aircraft, the observer then having to work out the course to steer to intercept. As experience was gained and more radars appeared (*Illustrious*, commissioned in April 1940, was the first carrier to be fitted with radar), own fighters were tracked as well as targets, and the more positive procedure of directing the fighter onto its target was adopted. The procedure was somewhat lengthy, but the adoption of a single-letter code helped to speed things up.

Rae McKaig, who served in 1941 for a short time in *Renown*, flagship of Force H based at Gibraltar, operated the 'command plot':

'My station was on the bridge where, with the aid of chalk and a circular blackboard, I displayed the 'air picture' to the Admiral, either by reading Sheffield's flag hoists myself, or listening to the Yeoman of Signals. Admiral Somerville took a keen interest and occasionally interjected command guidance or requests for information by Aldis light from Ark. The Italian's mode of attack by high-level bombing gave detection ranges of 70 to 80 miles and sometimes 100-plus, if my memory serves me right.'

The author performed much the same task in *Valiant* in the Eastern Mediterranean, but including reports from her own Type 279 and, an order of magnitude improvement, the use of a perspex mooring board and chinagraph pencil!

From *Ark Royal* Coke was sent to set up a Naval Fighter Direction Centre at Speckington, beside the air station at Yeovilton, where officers were trained with the famous ice-cream tricycles, fitted with miniature radar displays, metronomes to regulate pedalling and thus 'air-speed', with a compass rose painted on the tarmac, and controlled by operators, themselves under training, using low-powered R/T sets. Another development was the introduction of the Naval Aircraft Code, to provide some short-term security. This involved an encryption frame with a daily changing transposition card, and was much dreaded by the observers and TAGs who had to work it in an open cockpit.

In 1943 the Fighter Direction School moved to Dale in Pembrokeshire and live training with aircraft became routine. Coke meanwhile had been appointed to Arbroath to help set up the Naval Air Signal School which brought together the operational aspects of communications involving aircraft, air stations and ships. Observers who qualified became signal officers of aircraft carriers, including some escort carriers, Naval Air Stations and certain Air Staffs.

The early VHF sets worked in the band 100-124 MHz, but the demand for more channels resulted in sets being developed to cover the band 100-156 MHz. Some ship tactical circuits were able to be shifted out of this band, which was becoming severely congested, when the American TBS, operating in the 60-80 MHz band, became available under the Lend-Lease scheme in 1943.

There was no inter-aircraft radio in the early years of the war, and nothing very sophisticated between the front and back seats. Commander Stewart-Moore, CO of 820 Squadron in *Ark Royal* in 1941, described [3] the scene in his Swordfish:

> *'Between the Observer and Pilot there was about six feet of half inch rubber tubing which was supposed to act as a voicepipe. All messages between aircraft had to be passed either by naval semaphore or by the flag waving system of morse code used by the Army in the Boer War.'*

By the last two years of the war, four-channel push-button VHF sets were fitted in virtually all aircraft, with an HF W/T capability also in multi-seat aircraft. Post-war requirements to meet the needs of longer range aircraft led to the development of VHF air-to-air relay systems, and the general turnover to UHF to provide more channels and better quality voice; then came the requirement for gapless cover out to some 700 miles to cater for the Buccaneer with its low-level strike role, solved by the use of HF Single Sideband techniques - though frequency prediction for an aircraft opening at 600 knots could be a problem! The Phantom with its high performance ASV followed, but relied on UHF (the 'state of the art' PTR175), and height, which was generally acceptable as Phantoms normally operated in an air defence rather than a strike role. The Sea Harrier also does not have HF, but at least the modern UHF sets are synthesised which gives an almost limitless number of possible channels (and gets rid of crystals). HF is fitted in virtually all helicopters, which can help with those operating at low level at a distance from the fleet, such as A/S Sea Kings 'at the dip', although helicopters tend not to be very good HF 'platforms'.

In 1961 Captain George Baldwin was CO at Lossiemouth, a Master Diversion Airfield, when General Curtis Le May, C-in-C US Strategic Air Command, landed in his special command aircraft:

> *'The first person out was a USAF Sergeant Signaller with what looked like a normal walkie-talkie. He switched on and reported "Command One - on the ground - Lossiemouth, Scotland." "Who are you talking to?" I asked. "The General's office at Headquarters in the US"' came the reply. This was the first I had heard of SSB!'*

All aircraft now have VHF for civil work, although this did not apply to some of the earlier helicopters. The Wasp and Wessex at one time had 12-channel UHF sets only, lacking VHF apparently on the basis that they would not need to go to civilian airfields. Needless to say, they often did, and as Colin de Mowbray commented: [4]

> *'We all experienced the situation of hovering at an airfield boundary flashing a light or firing a green 'Very'. My worst experience was competing with a 747 at Puerto Rico!'*

[3] Memoirs, IWM 91/29/1.
An account of Swordfish in action against the Bismarck will be found in Chapter 21

[4] Letter to the author

Airborne electronic warfare assumed importance, with both passive and active devices being developed and evaluated in the 1950s by 744 (later 745) Squadron flights, and then in 1958 the first EW Squadron, 831, was formed at Culdrose with the Sea Venom and then the Gannet. In 1966 831 was reformed as the joint RN/RAF 360 Squadron at Watton.

Captain Baldwin remembers a pilot in 807 Squadron who fell deeply in love with a Wren R/T operator at Yeovilton in 1942. The Squadron later embarked in Furious, and for a time was disembarked at North Front, Gibraltar. One day, flying at 25,000 feet over Gib this pilot was astonished to hear his girl quite clearly on VHF (then quite a new toy). He wasn't able to reply, but after that it was difficult to keep him out of the air, and on several more occasions, because of the anomalous propagation conditions, he was able to hear her again. The story has a happy ending, as in due course they were married!

The fleet acquired its own Airborne Early Warning (AEW) capability, in the shape of the American AN/APS 20A equipment, fitted to the Skyraider, in about 1952, introducing an important new air defence 'weapon'. The Gannet took over in 1959, fitted with the AN/APS 20F, remaining in service for nearly twenty years until the task, and the equipment, were handed over to the RAF for the Shackleton AEW2 (with considerable support in the form of RN officers and ratings to help in the early stages).

This left the navy without its own AEW capability, the absence of which was to prove a serious embarrassment in the Falklands campaign in 1982; the situation was retrieved to some extent by the rapid fitting of the 'Searchwater' in the Sea King 2. This system, a derivative of a surface surveillance radar, was capable of detecting and tracking sea-skimming missiles and low flying aircraft, the advanced processing equipment able to pick out targets against sea clutter, although the picture then had to be 'told' by voice. The main advance for the future will no doubt be the introduction of air-ground-air data links, particularly important for the air defence of the fleet.

Electronic Warfare

Electronic Warfare has been a subject of interest to the Navy since wireless first went to sea, when the interception of the enemy's transmissions provided useful intelligence which could give one's own side a tactical advantage. In the first world war, this was achieved by the shore-based intercept and DF of German radio transmissions, which gave the Admiralty, and the Grand Fleet, valuable information on the movements of the High Seas Fleet.

Tactical EW at sea came into its own with the introduction of HF DF and its use in the Battle of the Atlantic and, since it involved the use of the 'ether', this new 'weapon' was clearly one to be looked after by the Signal Branch. Later, with the advent of radar, the Navy began to appreciate the significant part 'Radio Warfare', as it then came to be called, could play in a tactical situation. Thus, to minimise its advantage to the enemy, strict control over our own radar transmissions had to be exercised, in the same way as had always been the case for communications, and an 'Emission Control' (EMCON) Policy came to form a fundamental part of any 'signal' plan.

As well as 'passive' intercept, the possibility of jamming enemy transmissions had to be considered. Initially this was a matter of disrupting enemy tactical communications, but this proved extremely difficult to achieve effectively in practice, and it could be counter-productive since the advantage generally lay in listening to these transmissions.

As radar systems were developed for gun and, later, missile control, as well as surveillance, it was realised that the intercept and analysis of these signals could not only give early warning of the enemy's presence but also identify the type of ship, aircraft or missile. Thus things were rapidly getting rather complex, and there was a feeling that it was something of a 'black art', and a matter for the experts. This was not helped by the complicated terminology which also developed. The word Electronic replaced Radio, quite logically, and the subject was divided into its three components, defined broadly as:

❋ *Electronic Support Measures (ESM) or Passive EW*
The interception and analysis of enemy 'radio'
transmissions;

❋ *Electronic Countermeasures (ECM) or Active EW*
The disruption of enemy transmissions, to reduce the
effectiveness of his communications and surveillance,
and of those weapons which depend on electronics
for aiming, guidance or homing;

❋ *Electronic Counter Countermeasures (ECCM)*
Measures taken to reduce the vulnerability of one's
own 'radio' systems to the enemy's use of ESM or ECM.

Over the years a whole range of ECM devices were developed. Noise jammers were soon found to be dangerous since they identified the user as a warship and also provided a homing beacon for some types of missiles, so they gave way to more sophisticated decoys and deceptive measures. These included the generation of false targets, either electronically or by means of chaff or infra-red flare type decoys, and break-lock devices.

The evolution of ECM systems gave a spur to the development of ECCM, and each influenced the other as they grew in sophistication. This soon led to the need for specialists to operate the EW equipment on board ship, and a sub-branch of the Telegraphist Branch was formed with the title Telegraphist (S) (for Special). Included in the (S) specialisation were linguists (the successors to the original Coder (Educational) branch which had taken on the interception and transcription of tactical voice transmissions - the 'headache' operators). In 1963 the branch split, the 'tactical' EW operator becoming a Radio Operator (W) (for Electronic 'Warfare'), while a new section was formed to take on the signal intelligence task; the linguists were the initial nucleus of this new team, which resumed the title of Radio Operator (S). Language training took place at RAF Pucklechurch, until they moved in 1959 to RAF Tangmere where they set up as an independent unit with their own language school.

In due course, as the requirements grew more sophisticated, the RO(S) sub-branch was itself split into two streams, the linguists, whose language requirements changed depending on the main threats, and the analysts, who had to be able to intercept and if possible identify any electro-magnetic transmission.

In 1978, in order to attract suitable volunteers (from all branches of the navy), they became Communication Technicians (CT), a concept similar to that of the Artificer, so that after their initial training the CT would immediately achieve the rate of Petty Officer. At the same time, RAF Tangmere finally closed and the unit moved to Leydene.

Meanwhile the RO(W), originally trained to much the same standard as a 'straight' telegraphist, gradually became more specialised in the increasingly complex tactical EW field, and in 1970, as the need for morse had declined (new entry radio operators then only had to achieve 10 wpm), the RO(W) dropped morse altogether. Instead of operating the tactical EW equipment in some special 'office', situated wherever space could be found, he could now remotely control this from a console in the Ops Room, so that he became an integrated member of the Ops Room team.

HMS Edinburgh
Type 42 Destroyer

The large dome on the bridge roof houses the 909 Seadart control radar, with IFF Interrogator on top. The HF DF aerial is at the top of the foremast, above the UHF polemast. Navigation radar can be seen in front of the ensign, with various VHF/UHF aerials at the yardarms. The 992 medium range air surveillance radar is at the top of the mainmast, above the UAA-1 'cotton-reels'. The second 909 is aft of the mainmast. Of a number of HF whip aerials, one can be seen beside the forward 909 dome. The ship was not equipped with SCOT at the time; the aerials would be fitted either side on the sponsons in front of the funnel.

At the same time technical developments in the EW field became directed more towards improvements in software, to give the ability to adjust rapidly to changes in potential enemy systems and thus to the threat.

By the time the Operations Branch was formed in 1975, it had become clear that the RO(W) was no longer a true 'communicator' and, as he worked directly to the Warfare Officer, it seemed more appropriate for him to train alongside his Ops Room colleagues; it was therefore decided that he should in future be a member of the Seaman branch, in a new sub-specialisation, the Seaman(EW), and his training was transferred to Dryad. Transfer to Seaman(EW) was optional for existing ROs(W), and many were understandably reluctant to do so. Thus for several years there was a mix of RO(W) and Seamen(EW), but this gradually worked itself out as transfer to the new branch became essential if advancement was to be achieved.

Chapter Sixteen

The Post-War
Communications Branch

*'For centuries our sailors have been masters of terse
and vigorous English ...'*

I n 1941 a new, temporary, branch of Radio Mechanics had been
introduced to cope with the maintenance of the increasing
number of radar equipments being fitted in ships. With the war
over, the decision was taken to rationalise the position by forming
an Electrical Branch which, amongst other responsibilities, would take
over the maintenance of W/T equipment from the Communicators.

A number of Warrant Tels, Chief and P O Tels, and some
Leading Tels, transferred to the new Branch, with junior rates
being found mainly from new entries. The new scheme operated
from 1 January 1947, although training in W/T maintenance necessarily
continued at the Signal School for some time, until HMS *Collingwood*
had been equipped to take over. (An Air Electrical School had earlier
been established at HMS *Ariel*, Worthy Down, near Winchester).

The course routine at the Signal School and Signal Training
Centres began to settle down, Long Courses were extended to a year,
and Air Signal Officers were 'converted' for normal signal duties. A
new departure was the introduction of courses lasting about six months
for foreign officers. Early courses included officers from Argentina,
Belgium, China, Denmark, Eire, Egypt, Greece, Netherlands, Norway
and Sweden. Long Courses for NATO officers started in the early
1950s. Foreign ratings were trained too, usually prior to joining ex-RN
ships which had been transferred to them. China, for example, (then
under Chiang Kai-Chek) acquired the cruiser *Aurora* and the Hunt
class destroyer *Mendip* (renamed *Chungking* and *Lingsu* respectively)
and their communication teams spent eighteen months being trained
at *Mercury* (though their service in the ships didn't last beyond the
Communist take-over a couple of years later!).

Radio Operators and Mechanics for the newly established Ocean
Weather Service, many of them ex-RN, were trained at *Mercury* in

1947. In 1950 the Coder Educational reappeared for National Service training, both as educational assistants, and as linguists, while refresher courses for Reserve officers and ratings became a regular feature.

Music was heard emanating from classrooms as touch-typing and morse-typing were taught to both Sigs and Tels, and indeed to officers' courses. Apart from the need to read fast morse on a typewriter, teleprinters had been brought into use on most landline circuits, distribution copies of signals had to be typed, and it was evident that the trend towards 'keyboard' equipment would continue.

In 1948 Warrant Telegraphists and Signal Boatswains were combined and became known as Warrant Communication Officers; only a year or so later they became Commissioned Communication Officers, and in the mid-1950s Special Duties Officers (SD(C)). In the same year HMS *Scotia*, which had trained some 22,000 young Communicators, closed down, and new entry training concentrated at Ganges (for Boys), Fort Southwick, and Cookham Camp, Chatham.

An important change in the way communicators were drafted occurred in 1957 when, in line with most other branches, the three port divisions gave up this task and a centralised system was introduced under the new Commodore Naval Drafting, who took over Lythe Hill House, Haslemere, previously the home of the Admiralty Signal Establishment.

A year later a major change occurred with the introduction of new Branch titles, and revised standards of knowledge. The aim was to reflect the actual duties of the sub-specialisations more accurately (for example 'voice' radio was used more by signalmen than telegraphists), to take account of the introduction of RATT Broadcasts, less use of flags and semaphore, and the growing importance of electronic warfare. Thus the primary skills of the signalman became automatic telegraphy, flashing and voice, those of the telegraphists AT and morse, while the telegraphist (S) had to be adept at fast morse, the operation of EW equipment and the classification of EW intercepts.

A secondary aim was to give those leaving the service titles that would be understood outside and more nearly matched civilian 'job descriptions.' The result was that the traditional titles 'Signalman' and 'Telegraphist' were lost, to be replaced by 'Tactical Communication Operator' and

Signal traffic has always been subject to Parkinson's Law, filling all available circuits, to be followed by 'Minimise' which usually has little effect! See Chapter 2 page 18 (introduction of the electric telegraph, 1855), and Chapter 17 page 212 (the Falklands, 1982).

SIGNAL DIVISION
ADMIRALTY
Whitehall, LONDON S.W.I

No. 29/1/D   1st June, 1961.

The Commanding Officer,
H.M.S. HIGHFLYER,
c/o G.P.O., LONDON

We are tackling with great vigour the problem of the continual rise in naval signal traffic and I sincerely hope shall achieve results shortly. Otherwise we shall just have to impose Minimise or else the network will break down!

DIRECTOR OF SIGNAL DIVISION.

COMMANDING
OFFICER
-6 JUN1961
7/4368
H.M.S. "HIGHFLYER"

'Radio Communication Operator', which it must be said did not roll easily off the tongue. The Yeoman of Signals became a Communication Yeoman (and Chief Communication Yeoman), while the senior radio rates became (Chief) Radio Supervisor. Needless to say, these changes did not receive universal approbation, and it was hard to drop the old ones; the Communication Yeoman, inevitably, continued to be referred to as 'Yeoman', so this historic title survived.

The 'Sparkers' Badge

The changes were not overlooked by Parliament. Lord Conesford asked if a Leading Signalman was now to be referred to as a Leading Tactical Communication Operator, and if so, why? Confirming this, Lord Selkirk, First Lord, agreed that the new title was rather cumbersome, but said it would normally be abbreviated to LTO. 'Does that mean', asked Lord Conesford, 'that in future a naval officer will never make a signal but will operate a tactical communication? Is the First Lord aware that for centuries our sailors have been masters of terse and vigorous English? Will the Admiralty honour this tradition instead of wallowing in gutless verbosity?' The Earl of Dundee: 'Will an admiral now be called a leading personnel operator?' Earl Attlee: 'Have the sailors expressed themselves in terse English on this change?'

The Commons were not very impressed either. Mr Iremonger: 'Is my hon. Friend aware that this will appear ... as part of a deep-laid plot to 'drearyise' the Royal Navy ...?' Mr Allan (Parliamentary Secretary to the Admiralty): 'I think that the navy is as gay as it has ever been, if not more so. My hon. Friend probably remembers the title 'POOW', Petty Officer of the Watch ... in civilian communication centres his opposite number is called a Supervisor ... the new term more accurately describes his function.' [1]

The next change came on 1 January 1963, with a first step towards the tentative aim of producing a 'combined', more flexible, communicator, at least at the junior levels. The 'Tactical' title was dropped, except as a suffix, so that all ratings became 'Radio Operators', with the suffix (G), (T) or (W). The (G)s were in effect the old telegraphists, (T) the signalmen, and (W) the electronic warfare experts, but now they all had over-lapping skills.

At the same time all new entries were 'unspecialised', being classified simply as 'Junior Radio Operators' or 'Radio Operators 3rd class' (depending on age). They were trained in basic procedures in the four primary means of communication - automatic telegraphy, voice, flashing and W/T morse. They then went to sea, to be employed as required in each of the departments in turn in order to consolidate their skills. They only specialised as ROs (G), (T) or (W) when they reached the Able rate.

1963 also saw the demise of the 'buntings' crossed flags badge, replaced by the 'sparkers' wings, except for existing Yeomen and Chief Yeomen who were allowed to wear their old badge for the rest of their time in the service. Happily, this particular change was later reversed, and the Bunting's badge once more replaced the Sparker's wings for the RO(T).

The Demise of the 'Bunting's' Badge

In 1963 a 'farewell ceremony' was held in the Granada Bar, Gzira, Malta, attended by many signalmen from the fleet, together with Rear Admiral Viscount Kelburn, Flag Officer, Malta, Captain Robert Mackenzie, Captain D7, and Commander Brian Shattock, FCO. A signalman's gold badge was duly cremated in a chalice of flaming ormig juice, and 'buried' with a suitable headstone! The words of 'The Lay of the Last Signalman' were read.

Lay of the Last Signalman

On a thickly-wooded sponson, where the last projector stands,
The museum pair of hand-flags hanging idly in my hands,
With my jargon half-forgotten, of my stock-in-trade bereft,
I wonder what's ahead of me - the only Bunting left.

The relics of my ancient craft have vanished one by one.
The cruiser arc, the morse flag and manoeuv'ring lights
have gone
And I hear they'd be as useless in the final global war
As the helio, the fog-horn and the masthead semaphore.

The mast is sprouting gadgets like a nightmare Christmas tree.
There are whips and stubs and wave-guides where my halyards
used to be.
And I couldn't hoist a tackline through that lunatic array,
For at every height and angle there's a dipole in the way.

The alert and hawk-eyed signalman is rendered obsolete
By electrically-operated Optics of the Fleet,
and the leaping barracuda or the charging submarine
Can be sighted as a blob upon a fluorescent screen.

To delete the human error, to erase a noble breed,
We rely upon a relay, and we pin our faith to Creed,
So we press a button, make a switch and spin a little wheel,
And it's cent per cent efficient - when we're on an even keel.

But again I may be needed, for the time will surely come
When we have to talk in silence, and the modern stuff is dumb,
When the signal lantern's flashing or the flags are flying free -
It was good enough for Nelson, and it's good enough for me.

'Headstone' in memory of the Bunting's Badge

The badge changes evoked memories of his youth in Signal Commander Bill Paris, who wrote to the Signal School at that time: 'At 82 I suppose I am now the senior member of the Branch to have worn the 'crossed flags'.

I remember with pride the day I was entitled to sew them on. I joined Impregnable in 1896 as a Boy 2nd class, and after a short period of training became a Signal Boy, and believe me I thought I was the cat's whiskers! Before joining the navy I was employed in the counting house of Eyre & Spottiswoode, at that time the King's printers, who printed all the naval signal books, and I learnt the rudiments of signalling, colours of flags, morse and semaphore, and became Poop Signal Boy.'

The 'unspecialised' new entry was not a great success. As soon as he had acquired a reasonable grasp of his duties in one sphere and was becoming some use to that department, he had to be moved to another to continue his training, so the scheme became unpopular and the men concerned unsettled. Course was reversed from 1 January 1970 with new entries once again being trained as ROs (G), (T) or (W) before joining their first ship.

Semaphore was another casualty. The qualifying speed had been reduced to 8 wpm in 1962, after agreement within NATO that individual navies could go their own way. However experience showed that at this speed it was not really a worthwhile means of communication, and the training effort could not be justified, so from 1966 semaphore was no longer taught in the RN. This did not mean it was never used - most senior rates kept it up, and intra-RN it continued for many years to provide a rapid means of conversing between two ships, for example when replenishing at sea, since there was usually at least one senior rate in each ship with the skill. (Semaphore at night was not unknown, for example in carriers, using aircraft handler's flightdeck wands!)

By this time the use of morse telegraphy was diminishing fast, as most non-voice circuits, both long distance and tactical, converted to RATT or Data. It was difficult to keep up standards because of the lack of practice, and again the training effort was out of proportion to the need, so the speed required for new entry radio operators was reduced to 10 wpm, and it was abolished altogether for the RO(W) and WRNS. To cater for the occasional need, frigates and above had to have at least two morse trained LRO(G)s (to 18 wpm), and to meet these and other requirements, such as service in submarines or minor war vessels, the necessary morse standard had to be achieved in pre-joining training (PJT).

Minimum training standards had of course to be agreed throughout NATO which added further complications and sometimes delay in the revising of course syllabi. To encourage high practical standards, a NATO Communications Competition was introduced, hosted by each country in turn and held once a year. Teams comprised four operators, under the age of 24 or with less than six years in the communications branch, one each to compete in four practical skills. In 1966 for example, these were: flashing reception at 12 wpm, morse telegraph reception at 25 wpm (or more if desired up to 34 wpm), morse telegraph transmission (20 wpm), and teletype transmission (40 wpm).

The Warrant Officer was re-introduced into the Navy in 1970, but this time as the senior rating, rather than the junior officer as it had been until 1949, with the equivalent status to the WO1 in the Army. The naval title was 'Fleet Chief Petty Officer', thus Fleet Chief Communication Yeoman (FCCY), Fleet Chief Radio Supervisor (FCRS), and Fleet Chief Wren Radio Supervisor. Promotion was by selection, they were addressed as 'Mr' by superiors, and 'Sir' by

Above: Competitors in NATO Communications Competition held at HMS *Mercury* in 1973

Lieutenant Collins (left) with competitors from Canada, Germany, Itaaly, Netherlands, Norway, US and UK. The Netherlands won on this occasion. PO Wren Carol Gibbon was apparently the first communicator to enter.

Left: Lord Mountbatten meeting the winning competitors.

subordinates, but were not entitled to a salute. Their function was to take over some managerial duties, and with a shortage of signal officers and no reduction in tasks, they soon found themselves taking on many instructional and operational jobs previously done by officers.

In 1972 with the raising of the school leaving age, the 'Boy' entry from HMS *Ganges* disappeared. This marked the end of a long era in which the Communications Branch had benefited from a regular stream of keen and well trained youngsters, selected principally from the 'AC' Boys, those with higher education standards.

Royal Marines

The old style Royal Marine W/T Officer ceased to be trained soon after the first world war, the remaining dozen or so transferring to a 'Special Supplementary List' in 1922 and, like other specialisations, wearing a red armlet with a gilt anchor and the letters WT on it. This custom seems to have died out by 1945.

During the second war the RM Signal School moved to Saundersfoot, near Tenby, and then for a short time to Ringwould Camp near Deal, before settling at Eastney in 1947, where it remained until 1973. It then moved to the Commando Training Centre at Lympstone, where it became the Royal Marines Signals Wing. Training continues there, with specialised courses also at the Army Signals Wing.

As well as being deployed in ship's detachments, signallers became involved in the Mobile Naval Base Defence Organisation (MNBDO), and increasingly in amphibious and other combined operations. Nowadays their main tasks are with the Commando Brigade and landing craft units, ship detachments being limited generally to the amphibious ships, at the time of writing *Fearless* and *Intrepid*.

The Operations Branch

As the pace and complexity of modern warfare increased, with missiles controlled and guided by radio, increasingly sophisticated sensors, and data links to feed the information from ship to ship, a wholesale restructuring of the seaman and communications branches in the RN was seen to be needed. Most of the 'users' of radio circuits were no longer communicators; the latter provided the facilities, but in general only operated the long haul circuits and tactical manoeuvring nets. At the same time, things were moving towards a user/maintainer concept in the manning of weapon systems, which no longer matched the traditional seaman branch structure.

The trigger to the re-structuring came in 1974 when the seamen officer specialisations were abolished, and replaced with common training as Warfare Officers. The four schools (*Excellent*, *Vernon*, *Mercury* and *Dryad*) continued to play their part in the training of warfare officers, but together were formed into the School of Maritime Operations (SMOPS), overall co-ordination of training being under the direction of the Captain of HMS *Dryad* who assumed the title of Captain, SMOPS.

The Seaman and Communication Branches were combined to form a new Operations Branch, although the Communicators remained a separate and distinct group within the new branch and, for most of them, there was no significant change in their training or tasks. The exception was the tactical Electronic Warfare specialist, the RO(W), whose task, as noted earlier, was to be transferred to the Seaman sub-branch.

One further change occurred at this time - the formation of a new communication sub-specialisation for service in submarines, the RO(SM). The plan was for this new rating to combine his communications and EW tasks with those of the Seaman (RP). With the restricted complement in submarines, this was aimed at giving more flexibility, and the possibility of a full career in the submarine service. It envisaged existing Seaman (RP)s cross-training to become RO(SM)s, but unsurprisingly not many either wanted to do this or were able to complete the necessary conversion course. After a somewhat shaky few years, in 1979 the sub-branch was split, RO(SM) reverting to being the communicator, while the RO(TS) (for 'Tactical Systems') became responsible for the EW and RP functions.

The officer structure also went through a number of changes. The training of the Warfare Officer of course included some communications and EW, but he was not a deep specialist. Some of the tasks previously performed by Long Course Signal Officers were absorbed by SD(C) officers, and some of the latter's tasks were in turn taken on by the Fleet Chief (who, from 1986, was referred to as Warrant Officer rather than Fleet Chief). Specialist Long Courses had ceased after 1971 in order to get the new Warfare Officer

The Admiralty Board meet at Leydene, October 1969

Front L to R: Admiral Sir Horace Law, Controller; Admiral Sir Michael Le Fanu, First Sea Lord; Dr David Owen, Parliamentary Under-Secretary of State for the Royal Navy; Admiral Sir Frank Twiss, Second Sea Lord; Vice Admiral AF Turner, Chief of Fleet Support;

Back L to R: Captain Sir Peter Anson, CSS; RJ Penney, AU-S of S; S Redman, D U-S of S; Vice Admiral Edward Ashmore, VCNS; Basil Lythall, Chief Scientist, Royal Navy; Commander Nigel Fawcett, Executive Officer.

structure under way, but it was evident that specialists would still be needed to fill the more senior posts on flag officers' staffs, in the Admiralty, on inter-service and other planning staffs, and in NATO.

Thus from 1975 some Warfare Officers underwent specialist courses lasting about two months, those specialising in communications becoming known as Advanced Warfare Oficers (C) or AWO(C). Although the course was relatively short, they already had much more sea experience than was the case with the original Long Courses, and indeed by the time they specialised would be either senior lieutenants or junior lieutenant commanders. In 1983 the specialist element was incorporated into the Warfare course, and their title was changed to PWO(C).'

The Commonwealth

The close relationship with the Commonwealth continued after the war, with many officers and ratings coming to *Mercury* for training, but gradually their own facilities were built up and overseas training was reduced.

The RAN School of Signalling, established at Willamstown, Victoria, in 1913, was transferred in 1920 to the new Flinders Naval Depot at Western Port, Victoria, now HMAS *Cerberus*. In the late 1950s the name was changed to the RAN Communication School, which in 1992 occupied a new purpose-built facility, still within *Cerberus*.

In the early years most of the Instructors came from the RN, either on loan or permanent transfer, and training was confined to Signalmen and Telegraphist courses. These were gradually expanded to include Coders (1939) and female Telegraphists (1942), and then advancement courses and pre-commissioning training for all ratings, and some communication training for junior officers. In general, the functions could be equated to those of a large Signal Training Centre in the RN, particularly during the busy period of World War II. Courses closely resembled those of HMS *Mercury*, and the exchange or loan of instructors was quite common until the late 1960s.

The new RAN Signal School which opened in 1992

All RAN Signal Officers were trained at *Mercury* until the mid-1970s, though some RAN officers continued to do the RN AWO(C) and PWO(C) courses in the UK up to 1984. Since then virtually all officer training has taken place in Australia.

Some RNZN officers and ratings trained at *Mercury* after the war, but their relatively small requirement was largely met at home or by the RAN.

In the RCN, before the second world war, all communications training was carried out at the RN Signal School at Portsmouth. In late 1939 a naval communications school was set up in Halifax dockyard, moving in 1941 to HMCS *St Hyacinthe* near Montreal where many of the Instructors were ex-RN. Their own Long Courses were started in 1944.

After the war the school moved back to HMCS *Stadacona* at Halifax for a time, then in 1951 it moved again to HMCS *Cornwallis* at the western end of Nova Scotia. This remains the New Entry establishment, but in 1966 communications training was split between HMCS *Naden* on the west coast, which in general carries out initial operator training, and HMCS *Stadacona* in the east, for senior rates and officers.

The three Canadian services were 'merged' in 1968, although only 'naval' communicators serve in ships. But the communications branch has gone through several re-structuring exercises, of particular interest in view of experience in the RN. Soon after the war, with reductions in the size of the navy, the apparent decline in visual signalling, and the advent of an Electrical Branch, signalmen and telegraphists were combined as 'Communicators' or CMs. However this seems to have been premature - it was soon found that the 'buntings' were as busy as ever, and the 'sparkers' had no time to learn all about fleetwork, so in 1951 they were split again into

HRH Prince Charles being greeted by the author on arriving at Leydene for the Sub Lieutenants' Course, 1972

Communicator Radio (CR) and Communicator Visual (CV). Their titles were somewhat long-winded though self-evident, eg Chief Petty Officer First Class, Communicator (V), though in that case he was still generally referred to as 'Chief Yeoman.'

In 1959 the CR and CV trades were renamed Radioman (RM) and Signalman (SG), but in 1964 the RMs began to merge with Electrical Technicians as operator/maintainers. Further changes of title took place in 1968 to avoid confusion with the Army and Air Force; the RM became a Radioman Sea (RAD SEA), the RM Technician changed to Communication Technician (COMM TECH), and the SG was renamed Signalman Sea (SIG SEA).

After some twenty years, a measure of de-merging took place in 1985, with more title changes; the RAD SEA became the Naval Radio Operator (NRADOP), and the SIG SEA reverted to Naval Signalman (NSIG). At the time of writing consideration is being given to re-adopting the operator/maintainer concept, and merging the radio and visual branches again.

The Warfare Officer principle had been adopted by the RCN with their Operations Room Officer (ORO), but without specialists. However in 1991 it was decided to split the ORO, along similar lines to the PWO, with 'Above Water', 'Under Water' and 'Command Control and Information Systems' (CCIS) specialists, the latter equating to the PWO(C) in the RN.

Finally, *Mercury* introduced a regular series of Long Courses after the war for India and Pakistan. With independence, these two navies split in 1947, but as far as officers were concerned, joint courses at *Mercury* continued to be acceptable. The Indian Signal School moved from Bombay to Cochin, and a new Pakistani School was set up at Karachi. Initially, many of their senior rates came to *Mercury* for training, particularly when taking over British-built ships, but gradually all training was transferred to their own schools.

*　　　*　　　*　　　*　　　*

By 1990 manning difficulties in the RN, caused partly by the demographic downturn, resulted in the decision to employ the WRNS at sea, and to integrate them with the male branches. At the same time a review of requirements in the light of further developments in communications technology, and the need to improve flexibility, finally led to the historic decision to amalgamate the Radio Operators (General) - the old Telegraphist, and (Tactical) - the Signalman, sub-branches. It was also urgently necessary to improve job satisfaction and reduce 'stretch', which had become a severe problem, resulting in reduced manning standards (which only aggravated the difficulties). The increased flexibility which common skills should bring about would also, it was hoped, allow the introduction of one in four watchkeeping at sea in peacetime, something which had rarely been experienced by communicators.

The new scheme started with a common course for new entry Radio Operators (no suffixes to their titles now) lasting 24 weeks, with new combined courses gradually working their way up the branch structure.

This was by no means the end of the restructuring process, but first let us return to the early 1980s when the Navy found itself at war again.

Actually, I'm an ex-communicator!

Chapter Seventeen

War Again

*'From MOD UK. 7 April 1982. Operation CORPORATE.
The overall aim of HMG in the current situation is to bring
about the withdrawal of Argentine forces from the Falkland
Islands and Dependencies, and the re-establishment of
British Administration there, as quickly as possible.'*

A large part of the British Fleet was assembled at Gibraltar in early April taking part in the Spring exercises, and this enabled a sizeable force with communications already well worked up to be deployed to the south very quickly.

Communications to the South Atlantic, as we have already seen, have always been difficult, but this time the use of 'satcoms' was well established in the fleet and made a significant contribution to the success of the operation. Reliable and secure two-way communications were available between the UK and the Task Force Commander right from the start, particularly valuable at a time when the political and diplomatic situation was still evolving. Admiral Woodward, Flag Officer First Flotilla and Commander Task Group 317.8, has recorded how valuable he found the ability to hold regular, secure,

HMS *Broadsword*
Type 22 frigate

Broadsword, seen here off Gibraltar, took part in Operation CORPORATE. The sponsons on which SCOT satellite aerials would be fitted can be seen just forward of the funnel. The Exocet missile launcher is on the foc'sle, with Seawolf launchers in front of the bridge and on the after superstructure; their control radars are in front of the foremast and aft of the mainmast.

conversations with CINCFLEET (CTF 317) or the Chief of Staff at Northwood throughout the operation, and of course this facility was available to his staff, and other task group commanders.

Not all ships had SCOT terminals however, although most were fitted 'for but not with.' Only some twenty were available, and these were hastily transferred where necessary so that the majority of fleet units involved in the operation at any one time were so equipped. The *QE2* was also fitted with SCOT, from scratch, in the space of five days, a job that is normally only done during a refit (she also had a self-contained 'naval' wireless office built into the bridge structure). Only a few of the non-military ships had Satcoms, but with superhuman efforts some 30 commercial 'Inmarsat' terminals were obtained and fitted in all the RFAs and in a few of the 'ships taken up from trade' (STUFT).

Several satellite systems were involved - UK, US, NATO and commercial - which provided many voice, teletype and data links, both long haul and between units. These included several broadcasts, ship-shore circuits, a number of secure voice channels connected to the Defence Secure Speech System (DSSS), and three maritime rear links (MRL) between Northwood and *Hermes, Fearless* (Commodore Amphibious Warfare and CTG 318.0), and the South Georgia guardship. One satellite secure speech circuit was patched through continuously from *Hermes* to Northwood via the DSSS. In practice, the US DSCS satellite proved particularly useful, partly because Skynet, stationed above the Indian Ocean, was not well placed for operations in the South Atlantic, the Falklands being on the fringe of its coverage.

Falklands area, showing Exclusion Zones

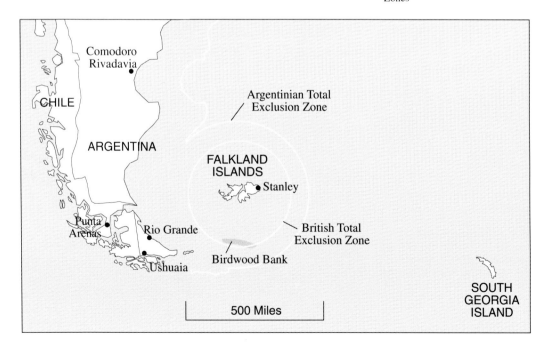

Despite the major contribution of satellite communications, many HF circuits were required too, both for long haul circuits, including back-up for satcoms, and as the primary means of linking the various task groups and units. Indeed the need for these circuits was such that it became necessary to exploit the whole MF and HF band, whether specifically allocated for maritime use or not - a practical solution in the South Atlantic though probably not elsewhere. A library of some 850 possible frequencies was built up, and their effective use was aided by an ionospheric sounder ('Chirpsounder') which luckily had been transferred to *Hermes* from *Coventry* before the latter was lost. Management of the signal plan, which had to be revised at frequent intervals to take account of the tactical situation, interference and changes in the task organisation, was a substantial and continuing task, largely carried out by the staff WO Radio Supervisor, Dave Eggar, aided by his desk-top computer.

The greatest threat to the force was assessed to be that of the Exocet-armed Etendards, and the main counter to this would be the ability of EW operators to detect a hostile approach; any detection had to be passed to those concerned with the utmost speed, which largely determined the EMCON policy adopted. As Woodward commented: [1]

[1] *'One Hundred Days'* by Admiral Sandy Woodward.

> *'To gain a critical, perhaps life-saving four minutes, we needed all the radars and inter-ship communications active, to provide us with the best possible picture of what was going on ... While the enemy did not have particularly good DF equipment, there was a serious gap in our air defence. We lacked Airborne Early Warning. I therefore assessed the balance of advantage lay with comprehensive communications between British ships and aircraft, despite the risk of the Argentinians charting our whereabouts from them.'*

Hugh Balfour, commanding HMS *Exeter* in the later stages of the operation, commented:

> *'The UAA1 operator had a whistle and if he blew, there was silence and an instant response. We rehearsed this every watch. Our EW equipment was good, the operators very well trained and motivated, and a match for the enemy. One sweep was enough ... We didn't have SCOT, but the use of secure speech equipment allowed a relaxed exchange of ideas before clarification of intentions and was invaluable. Close cooperation between RPs, ROs and TOs was essential and was achieved in Exeter.'*

Virtually all warships, though not RFAs or STUFT, were fitted for secure speech. Woodward wrote:

> *'... I had spoken to three or four of my captains on 'encrypted voice' UHF radio. This circuit was given the appropriate codename 'Cackle' (as in "Captain, sir, the Admiral wants to speak to you on Cackle").'* The use of secure speech nets

between senior officers was invaluable, but as with all 'telephone' conversations, with no printed record of what was said, it was found to be highly desirable to make a written record of the gist of important conversations; wisely, decisions taken were usually the subject of follow-up signals. [2]

The operation provided the first real test of the PWO system which had been introduced some ten years earlier. Woodward gives a good picture of life in an Ops Room:

'Each man has a communications headset on like a civilian airline pilot's with a slim space-age microphone ... Each is connected somewhere, the quiet murmur of his reports going perhaps to the navigation area, or to his fellows in the team on board, or via radio to other ships and their Ops Rooms. On the internal nets, the Captain can switch in to the PWO talking to the Sonar Controller, or the Link Operator briefing the Surface Picture Compiler, or the Missile/Gun Director talking to the Surface Detector; perhaps the Yeoman of Signals talking to his young signalman on the bridge ... The communications networks are a sort of 'underground' tower of Babel, a mass of words and headsets, microphones and strange jargon-language ... Near the centre of it all stands the Advanced (or Air) Warfare Officer, assisted by the PWO. It is their job to co-ordinate all the information and act appropriately on it.'

In the flagship Woodward decided to have two 'Group Warfare Officers' at Captain level who could act as his deputies, one of them always being on watch and ready to take real-time decisions. The PWO system seems to have proved itself well in this first 'missile age' conflict.

Despite the tremendous advantages of satcoms, there were snags too, one of which had serious consequences. When a ship was transmitting over the SCOT system, her ESM equipment could be degraded; although this problem had been indentified, a suitable technical solution had not, at that time, been evolved. Early on in the operation Exocet-equipped Argentine Etendards approached the picket line while *Sheffield* was transmitting on SCOT; she failed to detect either the aircraft's radar, or to pick up the missile on her own radar, despite being alerted by *Glasgow*, one of the other two picket ships. *Sheffield* was hit, caught fire and had to be abandoned. The problem was partly overcome by fitting SCOT with special filters, but the lesson had been learnt the hard way.

As ever, the volume of traffic seemed to increase to meet the capacity of the communication channels. Despite MINIMISE being enforced and re-enforced, the usual exhortations to be brief, and rebukes for unnecessarily lengthy or badly drafted messages, severe back-logs still occurred - as much as 1,000 messages at Whitehall Comcen at one time. But the capacity of modern communications

[2] In a letter to the author, Woodward commented: 'We learned, on the spot, always to have a staff officer listening in, if possible, or at least to have a full and immediate debrief, and to follow up with a hard copy (effectively 'minutes of the meeting').' He also mentioned the question of 'style' in signals: 'I became increasingly aware that the staff write signals in 'staff' style and I write them in very much my own. If you are trying to put over something important or difficult, your personality should be apparent in the words, so that the recipient can recognise 'his master's voice' ... and will know that his boss will have him very much in mind. Encrypted voice now allows simpler, harder-toned follow-up signals, because the 'master's voice' bit should already have been done.'

A Sea Harrier taking off from HMS *Invincible*

Invincible has two pairs of SCOT aerials to ensure all-round satellite access, even at low altitudes; one pair are in the domes on sponsons above the bridge, the others are on the after superstructure. The big dome in front of the bridge houses the forward Type 909 Seadart fire control system. The large horizontal aerial above the bridge is the Type 1022 air search radar, and that at the main masthead the Type 996 surface search radar; below this are the UAA-2 ESM aerials. At the forward edge of the bridge roof, looking rather like a perforated dustbin lid, is the UHF Satcom aerial. The polemast at the forward end of the flight deck carries the UHF DF aerial. The Goalkeeper gun system is in the eyes of the ship, another is situated on the island abaft the 'workboat'. The Seadart launcher is on the foc's'le with a curved blast deflector behind it.

'It is essential to understand that 'Command' is a matter for those involved in fighting the ship, and Communications in all its aspects is a fundamental element of Command. It is not an engineering function - the other services have suffered from this approach ...'

Rear Admiral Hugh Balfour, who was in command of Exeter

systems is outpacing the ability of the 'user' to absorb it all, and there is the danger of some vital piece of information being submerged and not recognised. Woodward's Staff Officer Operations (SOO) was Jeremy Sanders (a Communicator, as it happened). Woodward again:

'He looked after the bigger picture on a longer term basis. For example, I would receive more than 500 signals a day from the HQ at Northwood, MOD, Ascension Island, other ships, etc., and Jeremy saw every single one of them, filtering them by assigning action on each signal to appropriate staff officers and ensuring that I only saw those signals I absolutely had to. No commander in the field can operate without such a person ... No matter how great the harassment factor, Jeremy would somehow handle it. Every couple of minutes during the day he dealt with sudden needs, obscure commands, implicit suggestions, conversations on Cackle, translating my wishes into clear and precise written instructions ... he was also in charge of what the Americans describe as 'compliance', in other words, having issued the order, he was the man to check that this did indeed happen ... it would have been totally impossible to have run such an operation without a man such as this.'

This was the first naval war in which a substantial number of the 'media' were involved. They had come to expect that their despatches would be carried over 'military' circuits and given a high priority. However it was obvious that the available communications systems would be fully loaded, if not overloaded, and this indeed proved to be the case. The problem was largely solved as far as voice and telex was concerned by routeing media traffic over the commercial Inmarsat system, via 'media guardships' (which also solved an accounting problem!). This left film and TV material for which the only technically suitable means would have been the military satcom system, and this could in any case only cope with a black and white picture. Furthermore, while media traffic was being passed, operational traffic would have been delayed; clearly this was unacceptable, so this material had to be sent home by air, as and when practicable. The TV men were not happy.

Naval communications also had to cope with an interesting personnel problem, the result of delays in the receipt and despatch of mail. The normal rules were that if a ship had been unable to land mail for ten consecutive days and was unlikely to be able to do so for another seven, everyone on board could send one message of up to 30 words by radio each week. Obviously, once the task force had passed Ascension on the way south, this criteria was met by several thousand people! Again, the plan adopted was to pass these messages to Inmarsat guardships for transmission over the commercial satcom system to appropriate UK comcentres, which could then send the messages on via the Post Office. By the end of the operation some 50,000 of these messages had been handled. Mail to the fleet was less of a problem - on many occasions it was dropped from the air in watertight containers.

HMS *Coventry*
Type 42 Destroyer

Coventry was lost during Operation CORPORATE. The photo shows her Type 965 warning radar; this was replaced in later ships of the class with Type 1022. The two big domes house the Seadart control radars. The 'birdbath' on the side of the hangar is an HF receiving aerial, and the twin cones on the midships screen, directly below the 965, are TV receive aerials.

Finally, a look at the statistics in the flagship. Between 15 April and 1 July the ship handled 170,000 signals (one every two minutes), of which no less than 62,000 required 'flag action', and 4,500 'special handling'.

Overall, there is no doubt that Operation CORPORATE was a considerable communications success, not only because of the technical facilities, but because of the dedicated work of the communicators who were seldom in less than two watches, many of them for more than two months without a break. Richard Hulley, the SCO in *Invincible*, wrote:

> *'I was really proud of our incredibly young communicators, many of them straight out of Kelly Squadron (the new entry training section at HMS Mercury), who behaved so impeccably and performed so professionally.'*

The ARMILLA Patrol

In 1980 the Navy returned to the Gulf when war flared up between Iraq and Iran, and it was decided to maintain a presence in the area which would also give British merchant ships, and indeed those of other nations, confidence that assistance would be available if required. So began the ARMILLA patrol, which since then has maintained at least two destroyers or frigates plus afloat support east of Suez ready to respond to events in the Gulf.

Strategic communications were primarily by satellite, all RN ships deployed to the Gulf being fitted with SCOT if they did not already have it. Satcoms were backed up by a conventional LF/HF broadcast, but despite using directional aerials from the UK this was not usually readable 'round the clock'. The RFAs did not have SCOT and had to rely on LF/HF broadcasts supplemented by commercial satcom equipment, particularly valuable when they were not in company with the task group, and thus outside V/UHF range.

The Gulf area

Propagation conditions in the Gulf could be variable, anomalous propagation often producing surface radar detections at over 100 miles, although at the same time the close range picture could be degraded. UAA1 fitted ships produced useful EW results, again often at very long ranges. V/UHF communications could be similarly affected.

The USN had a much larger force, built round a carrier group; they operated independently of the British but a close liaison was established. Not surprisingly it was evident that, when units from the Pacific Fleet were involved, they were less *au-fait* with the NATO doctrine and procedures which were second nature to the Atlantic Fleet and to the British ARMILLA ships.

The Gulf War

Ten years experience of operating in the area proved invaluable when, in 1990, Iraq invaded Kuwait; the ships of the ARMILLA patrol were already on the scene and able to respond as necessary to the crisis. The operation was codenamed GRANBY and forces were built up to enforce the resolutions of the United Nations. This was a totally different situation from Operation CORPORATE in 1982, when only the RN were involved at sea. In the Gulf war, ships from many nations, not all belonging to NATO, arrived on the scene, in some cases more as a token political demonstration than to add to the allies' offensive capability, but this added numerous complications over communication links and operating procedures, signal books and security.

By January 1991 when offensive operations commenced RN forces consisted of four (later rising to eight) destroyers and frigates, an MCMV squadron, and a large number of support ships. Commodore Chris Craig, had become Senior Naval Officer Middle East (SNOME), and CTG 321.1, some weeks earlier, flying his broad pennant in HMS *London*, and had begun to assemble an ad- hoc staff; *London*, a Type 22 frigate, had neither adequate room nor technical facilities for supporting what amounted to a flag officer's command, and it was a tight squeeze - at one stage the number of SNOME's staff exceeded the number of ship's officers. There were some base facilities in the UAE, but command was exercised from the flagship. However ships operating in the northern Persian Gulf worked with the US Task Force and came under USN Tactical Control.

SNOME did not have any additional communications staff initially, but was lent Commodore Amphibious Warfare's signal officer, Lieutenant Commander Paul Daykin, who joined him as his Communications, Electronic Warfare and Amphibious Warfare adviser - all areas which needed detailed advance planning if multi-national maritime operations were to succeed. This fortuitous choice ensured that most of the knotty problems were resolved before the outbreak of hostilities.

Inevitably there were some problems over inter-operability, not only RN-USN but also amongst the USN, both in terms of actual equipment fits, interpretation of the Complans issued by different Commanders, and inadequate information on individual ship and aircraft capabilities. Even within the RN, although extra equipment was fitted where necessary, there were some differences in capabilities. Despite all the difficulties, the long 'work-up' and personal contact with the USN paid dividends, and co-operation and inter-communication was remarkably successful. Ships of other nations did not operate in the northern Gulf or work with the USN Task Force.

Strategic links to UK were provided by a number of satellite channels, using SCOT (SHF), and also USN (UHF) satcoms, for which RN destroyers and frigates were fitted; these satellite links were backed up by LF/HF Broadcasts.

Commodore Craig requested a suitable codeword for use in signalling the outbreak of war to his ships; he proposed the stirring and memorable word 'Agincourt'. He was allocated 'Walkman.'

'My 14-year old son would have been delighted' he said, 'Henry V must have turned in his grave.'

A number of strategic HF RATT Broadcasts were required for the RFAs and the MCMVs, as well as to back-up the satellite circuits. The Gulf is difficult to cover adequately with HF from the UK, so additional HF transmitters in other parts of the world were also keyed from the UK, some via satellite links. These measures reduced the period of difficult reception to the few hours of twilight, morning and evening.

For MCMVs, and for the RFAs when in company, it was usually possible for the appropriate HF broadcast to be read by an RN ship acting as guard, traffic for them being re-transmitted on a local UHF net, which provided some relief for their hard-pressed operators. Two Netherlands ships were SCOT fitted and were asked to help by receiving the UK Primary Fleet Broadcast via Satcom and re-radiating it at HF/UHF for the RFAs.

Inevitably there were some hiccups. 'Early one morning', recalls Daykin, 'I was woken up with a signal from an RFA saying that the normally reliable Dutch 're-rad' had faded; the RFAs, unable to read the UK backup HF broadcast, were desperate. I called up the Witte de With to ask what the problem was. After a pause, their operator said "They've just moved the crane next to our aerial." It only then dawned on me that she was not in the Gulf but on her stand-off in the Seychelles!'

Martin Butcher relieved Daykin in December:

> *'It was apparent that I would be employed predominantly on other duties, and the call went out for a CRS to join the staff to continue Paul's good work. CRS 'Mac' McKeever arrived pm 5 January, the evening prior to HMS London sailing for the last time before the outbreak of hostilities, and immediately assumed day-to-day responsibility for communications matters. Both McKeever and the flagship's Radio Supervisor, Mark Hoare, were awarded the BEM for their excellent work.'*

Kevin Robertson was *London's* PWO(C), and was pretty fully occupied as a defence watch PWO, another reason for requiring a CRS for day-to-day management of the complan. Robertson comments:

> *'The variety of allied units in the theatre required a large number of tactical circuits to maintain command and control links between them; RN ships had to give careful consideration as to which should be manned, and priorities were forever changing. A close relationship between the main communication office and the ops room was essential if we were to maintain an accurate tactical picture for SNOME. London's communications were therefore stretched to the limit, and some key tactical circuits were monitored by relatively junior and inexperienced ratings.'*

Robertson recalls being asked by a radar operator if he required a report on an aircraft attack on an Iraqi patrol boat. 'Having said yes, I was informed: "I think the attack has been successful sir! 50% of the boat is on fire and the other half has sunk!", an assessment that brightened up an otherwise routine morning watch.'

The naval EW battle was characterised by the reluctance of the Iraqis to transmit on radio or radar for fear of attracting attention, no doubt the result of experience gained during the war with Iran. Conversely, from a position of strength, and with a 'silent' enemy, the allies' emission policy was relatively relaxed. For those in the front line, the need for a rapid reaction when a threat developed, to control the complex and fast-moving battle, was largely met by the use of a real-time data circuit, Link 11.

The speed of modern communications, civil as well as military, was well demonstrated on one occasion when the Iraqis were firing Scud missiles into Saudi Arabia or Israel. Butcher recalls:

'Considerable intelligence effort was devoted to detecting their launch, determining the impact area, and warning operational units. We had a USN UHF satcom secure voice circuit on loudspeaker, over which we heard the warning of a Scud firing. Having reported this to the Commodore, we were discussing the likely target when an excited American voice from a recce aircraft announced: "The Scud has just hit Tel Aviv - I just saw it on CNN." Sure enough, about five minutes later confirmation arrived over official channels, but in the meantime CNN had sent TV pictures live via satellite to the USA and then back out again via satellite to be picked up by the crew of this aircraft over the northern Gulf, all in the space of a few seconds!'*

The mail service to British forces worked well. Ships initially received daily deliveries by Sea King from RFA Argus, the sorting point for the Task Group. Later, with the increasing number of ships, this service could only be provided every two or three days. In comparison, the Americans seemed to have problems of a different magnitude. In February, London picked up a signal on an inter-ship circuit from an American oiler complaining that she had received no mail since October, and offering to pay a share of the cost of chartering an aircraft to bring it out!

Communications personnel were at full stretch, as always, throughout the operation. Traffic levels were high, but by judicious use of the plethora of satellite and conventional channels, back-logs could usually be avoided. Despite 'Minimise' instructions, Parkinson's Law made itself felt as usual and signals tended to fill the available capacity. To take one example, USN ships signalled daily 'opsums', listing their activities in great detail, not only to their CTG but also to the whole Task Group, which added a significant 'clogging' factor. Another 'hazard' was posed by computer-generated messages, which were difficult to control, and often extremely long due to the number of ships and authorities who needed to be addressed individually.

CTG 321.1, Commodore Craig, reported that the traffic handled in his flagship between 17 January and 27 February totalled 42,729 in and out signals, or rather more than 1,000 a day!

"Did you - or did you not - Pass That Signal?"

Epilogue

The year 1993 marked the end of an era. Just over half a century earlier the Signal School had been bombed out of its home in Portsmouth and moved to Leydene, while a few years later, in 1946, the Electrical Branch had been formed. This incorporated the Radio Mechanic Branch which had been introduced in the war primarily to cope with the new radar systems, but was also to take over all radio maintenance. Many of the founder members were signal officers and telegraphists who had a bent for the technical as well as the operational aspects of radio.

By 1992 things had come full circle. With the reliability of modern equipments and their 'repair by replacement', it was decided that the time had come to adopt or, as far as Communicators were concerned, to revert to, the User/Maintainer concept. This would be done by merging the Operations and Weapon Engineering Branches into a new Warfare Branch, thus complementing the change in the officer structure that had already taken place with the introduction of the Warfare Officer in 1974.

The new Warfare Branch is to be introduced in 1993 mainly from the new entry stage, although there will be some cross-training of existing junior rates, and it will take some eight years for the change over to be complete. Ratings will be known as 'Operator Mechanics', the various groups having distinguishing letters; thus OM(C) for Communications, OM(UW) for Underwater (the old TAS rating), and so on. The submarine radio operator becomes an OM(CSM), and the electronic warfare specialist, who had already been in the seaman branch for some years, now becomes an OM(EW). The only communicators unaffected by all this will be the Communication Technicians who will continue their important role in the Sigint and 'Y' field. As the new system works its way up the Yeoman and the Radio Superviser will eventually merge as a Petty Officer (Communications) or PO(C).

The new Warfare Branch is to adopt the existing WEM badge, which becomes common to all specialisations, but with the appropriate distinguishing letters below. There may be some theoretical logic in using the same badge for the whole branch, but it does seem a pity that the various specialisations will have nothing more than a letter or two to give them a visible identity.

So what does the future hold? The communications facilities provided by the Branch are now mostly operated by others, an enormous amount of information can be passed over high speed data links, and much else is transmitted by secure voice 'person-to-person' or indeed 'command-to-command'. The days when information and instructions all came by clearly defined, concise and identifiable messages reproduced on 'hard copy', have long since gone. But all this has to be planned, organised and managed, and the challenge for the Communicator seems likely to be greater than ever.

The badge to be worn by Warfare Branch Communicators

The last word comes from Captain Mike Caswell, Chief Naval Signal Officer:

'This book is emerging in 1993 at a critical moment in the evolution of Naval Communications: HMS Mercury finally closes and moves into HMS Collingwood just as the inception of the Warfare Branch melds maintainer and operator together.

'For a period yet, ships will have two Petty Officers (C), and no doubt one will be referred to as 'Yeoman'; but the evolution of technology has already changed the Communicator's role from an equipment operator to a systems manager. For the foreseeable future, it will be vitally important that a warfare trained Communications Officer acts as the 'C3' system manager, with a staff capable of fully understanding and operating the complex computerised Communications and Command Support Systems, together with the data, message and voice information exchanged through these systems.

'This is a far cry from the gentler days of the flag-hoist and the morse key. But the ability of the Royal Navy to continue to conduct its warfare tasks effectively through the year 2000 and beyond will depend even more than in the past on the Communicator's management of the new high-tech means of information exchange.

'The aim will continue to be: CELER ET FIDELIS.'

Chapter Eighteen

Sail to Steam

'We want signal books to give us what we want, we do not want to be dragooned by signal books ...'

Vice Admiral Sir George Tryon, 1891

The Fleet at Sea in 1666

'On July 19 (at the Nore) about 5 of the clock in the morning, the Fleet weighed anchor and about 11 of the clock the same day we discovered 11 sail of the Dutch upon our larboard quarter, riding in the Gunfleet. About 12 we came to anchor in the rear of the White Squadron. At five in the afternoon the Generals called a Council of War of the Flag officers, which is done by hanging the Royal Standard in the mizzen shrouds.'

'...the 23rd (August) a pendant was set on the mizzen peak to call the Captains of the Admiral's division aboard ...'

'(On 31st August) ... the Roe ketch informs (the Admiral) that he left the whole Dutch fleet that morning ... whereupon the Generals presently ordered the flag of white and yellow to be hung upon the main yard, the signal for the fireships to come up, and at the same (time) hung up the black flag in his mizzen shrouds, the signal for his own division to follow.' [1]

[1] Navy Records Society, *'Naval Miscellany'*, Vol. III

Signal Problems 1779

Benjamin Thompson, an American scientist who came to England in 1776, was also known as Count von Rumford. He became friendly with Lord George Germain, Secretary of State for the Colonies, to whom he wrote on 20 July 1779 when he was at sea in HMS *Victory* conducting experiments in ballistics and gunpowder:

'My dear Lord, I can stand it no longer. Those interested in the disgrace of our Commander may laugh at our blunders

but I ... am hurt beyond measure to find how little dependence is to be put in our skill in manœuvring this great and respectable Fleet. You must know we never as yet had attempted but one simple manœuvre, and that is to draw the ships into a line of battle, one directly ahead of the other, and upon a signal to tack about all together. In this we have never succeeded. It has always been more than two hours before the ships ahead have got into their stations - the line has always been very crooked, and the ships at very unequal distances, and when we have come to put about confusion has commonly ensued, and we have been obliged to end our manœuvring abruptly by making the signal for the ships to return to their stations in the order of sailing. This has arisen sometimes from one cause, and sometimes from another, but I don't remember a single instance in which we have attempted to manœuvre when we did not make at least one evidently wrong and contradictory signal.

I thought we might possibly succeed better in divisions, and accordingly this morning after breakfast I contrived to hint this idea in the gentlest manner possible to the Admiral, Captain Kempenfelt being present. I received no answer, but about half an hour after, the Captain came down and proposed the measure to the Admiral. It was very well, but how to give the necessary order was the difficulty. The signals for the three divisions could not be made together - if the centre division was formed first that signal might then be hauled down and the signal for the Vice Admiral's Division to form might be made, and afterwards that of the Rear in the same manner. I saw in this way of proceeding the day would be much too short for the manœuvre. Captain Kempenfelt was silent. The Admiral looked at him for some time without saying a word. I saw no kind of difficulty in the thing. The printed book of signals lay upon the table. I took it up,

Page from Sir Charles Knowles' *'Fighting and Sailing Instructions'*, 1780

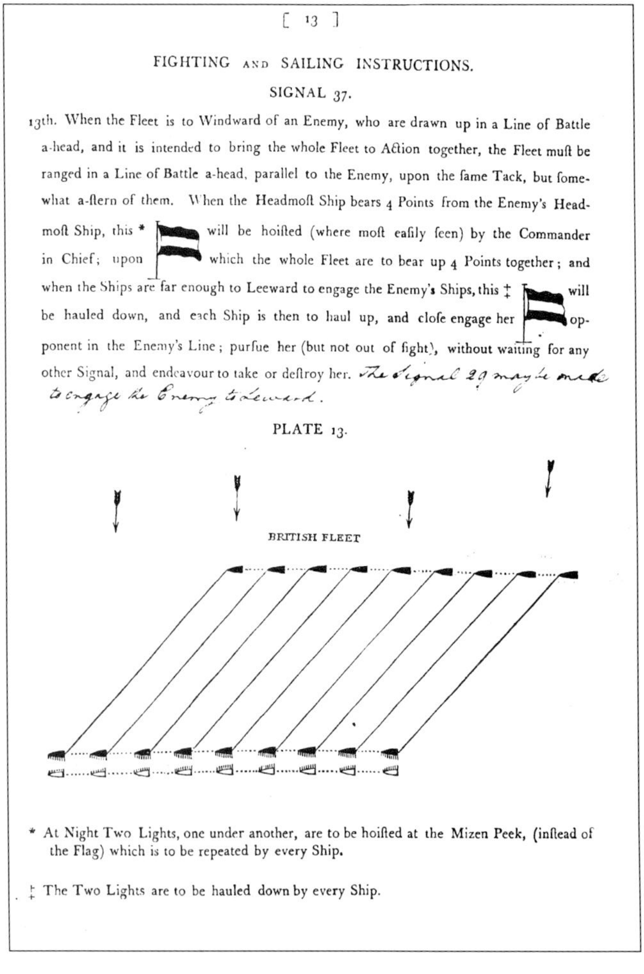

[13]

FIGHTING AND SAILING INSTRUCTIONS.

SIGNAL 37.

13th. When the Fleet is to Windward of an Enemy, who are drawn up in a Line of Battle a-head, and it is intended to bring the whole Fleet to Action together, the Fleet muft be ranged in a Line of Battle a-head, parallel to the Enemy, upon the fame Tack, but fome-what a-ftern of them. When the Headmoft Ship bears 4 Points from the Enemy's Head-moft Ship, this * ▮ will be hoifted (where moft eafily feen) by the Commander in Chief; upon ▮ which the whole Fleet are to bear up 4 Points together; and when the Ships are far enough to Leeward to engage the Enemy's Ships, this ‡ ▮ will be hauled down, and each Ship is then to haul up, and clofe engage her op-ponent in the Enemy's Line; purfue her (but not out of fight), without waiting for any other Signal, and endeavour to take or deftroy her. *The Signal 29 may be made to engage the Enemy to Leeward.*

PLATE 13.

BRITISH FLEET

* At Night Two Lights, one under another, are to be hoifted at the Mizen Peek, (inftead of the Flag) which is to be repeated by every Ship.

‡ The Two Lights are to be hauled down by every Ship.

and turning over a few leaves pointed with my finger to the following passage:

"If at any time I would point out that the signals made, relate to a particular division of the fleet, I will signify the same as follows: if to the division of the Admiral, a Dutch flag with a Red flag under it; if to the (second) division, a Dutch flag with a white flag under it; and if to the (third) division, a Dutch flag with a Blue flag under it."

'And why not (said I modestly) make the signal for the line of battle, and at the same time hoist the three signals for the three divisions in different parts of the ship? They made me no answer. Capt. Kempenfelt went upon deck. The Admiral took his hat and followed him. I was neither surprised nor angry ... why should I expect that my advice should be taken?

'In a few minutes I heard a gun, and going upon deck, saw a flag half blue, half white flying at the mizzen peak, and a Dutch flag with a red flag under it at the mizzen-top-mast head. This signal was soon repeated by all the flagships in the Fleet and their repeating frigates (as are all signals made by the Commander-in-Chief). The Royal George was just upon our weather quarter. As she is always to lead our division in a line of battle ahead upon the starboard tack, it was expected she would make more sail in order to go ahead into her station. Instead she laid her sails aback and was preparing to hoist out a boat. The Admiral had the fidgets to a most violent degree. Captain Kempenfelt, in a great passion, called out to the Lieutenant who had the watch to hail the Peggy cutter, and order her to go alongside the Royal George and desire Sir John Ross to make sail and go ahead into his station ... Happily the Peggy was not within hail, and the signal was obliged to be made to bring her to the Victory. This took up time and before she could come up with us we found out! - that instead of a signal for a line of battle ahead we had made a signal for the weekly returns of the ships of the Admiral's division. The Admiral was in Capt. Kempenfelt's cabin when the discovery was made or rather when the laugh became general upon the quarter-deck. At that moment I would have given all I was worth to have been anywhere else but onboard Victory.

'The first thing to be done was to inform the Admiral of the mistake. This nobody would undertake ... I accordingly plucked up courage and went into Capt. Kempenfelt's cabin, but I found the Admiral and the Captain so busy looking over the signal book together that I dare not interrupt them, and prevailed upon Captain Collins to do the business. The best thing to have done would have been to have stood by the signal as it was and received the weekly returns.

Instead the signals for the other divisions to form were afterwards made and obeyed, and by the time night came on we had the Fleet in three tolerable lines ready for manœuvring.

'There was not an officer in the fleet who did not see the blunder we made, yet there was not a ship of our division which did not send in her weekly account. It was curious to see the stifled grin of the Lieutenant as he gave these to Capt. Kempenfelt, and the spiteful manner in which the latter snatched them out of his hand.

'... be assured there never was a braver set of men existing than our present Sea Commanders. If we can fairly get alongside our enemies I shall not fear for the consequences, but I know if we attempt to manœuvre in sight of our foes we are ruined. Mais heureusement, en cela, notre Amiral n'est pas pedant.

Benjamin Thompson'

*   *   *   *   *

The idea of adopting Numeral flags had occurred to others besides Howe and Kempenfelt, but had not been taken up; Benjamin Thompson had no doubt discussed this with Kempenfelt, as is evident from a letter to Lord George Germain dated 4th September, 1779:

'I had intended to have sent you a proposal for carrying on a speedy communication of intelligence from one end of the sea coasts of the Channel to the other, and to London, with a velocity that shall surprise you. I shall undertake by means of flags properly disposed upon the heights along the coast, and from Portsmouth to London, to convey to you in the space of five minutes the most accurate account of every ship that is seen upon the coast, the place where she is seen, and the course she is steering; and the same of a fleet of ships, their numbers and whether they are friends or foes - and all this with not much expense. Ten signal flags at each stand will be quite sufficient to make as many signals as will be found necessary (as with this number of flags may be made more than 200 separate and distinct signals) and the stands need not be nearer together than 15 or 20 miles. As we are now going to beat the French, I suppose nothing of this sort will be necessary, but if an invasion was expected ...

'... if you like the idea I will send you my plan at large properly digested, and so plain that any person of the most moderate capacity shall be able perfectly to comprehend it and put it into practice ...

'... I made a mistake, more than a thousand signals may be made with ten flags, instead of 200.

Benjamin Thompson'

The two letters from Benjamin Thompson, and the following two from Kempenfelt, are taken from the Barham papers, Navy Records Society, Vol LXIII. (Admiral Sir Charles Middleton was created Baron Barham in 1805.)

Kempenfelt wrote to Sir Charles Middleton, Comptroller of the Navy, from HMS *Victory* 17 October 1779:

> *'... Signals pointed out by numbers ... I have long been acquainted with. They don't require many flags, however there must be three of each sort, or you can't express a number which consists of three figures of the same rank, as 222 or 333 etc. This numeral way of pointing out the signal is very convenient ...*

> *'I could in a very few days (less than a week) arrange our signals according to the above method, could I have those days to myself without interruption.'*

He wrote to Middleton again, from HMS *Britannia*, 2 March 1781:

> *'It has been a common saying that it is an advantage to go by signals that we have been used to, and when a new set comes out, to say we have our trade to learn again. This style was very proper with respect to the different signals used by different admirals formerly, when the signals were jumbled together without form or order, and when a long acquaintance with them was necessary to find out the meaning of any signal that was made in the chaotic state in which they were. But when signals are formed upon a proper plan they require no study to comprehend them, and when a signal is made you can immediately turn to the article or order attended to. If the greatest novice can't do this, the plan is faulty; when in any project for signals they appear intricate and difficult to comprehend you may be sure they are faulty; what is good must be clear and simple.'*

PLACE.	SIGNIFICATION.
Union Jack. Mizen topmast head.	For the Captain of a particular ship to come on board.
Mizen topmast shrouds.	For a Lieutenant of a particular ship to come on board.
Ensign Staff.	For a Midshipman of a particular ship to come on board.
Fore-topmast head.	For a Pilot to come on board.
Mizen peak.	To be kept flying on board a ship where a Court Martial is assembled.
Where best seen.	When this Jack is hoisted with one or two of the Signal Flags, whether above them, below, or between them, it denotes that the signal applies to a ship's number.
Mizen top-gallant-mast head.	To be hoisted by the ships, to which the Admiral has signified by signal that the Boats, Officers, &c. previously summoned are to be sent.
	To shew by their national Jack the country to which strange ships belong. N. B. If the strange ships be of a nation in amity, the same may be shewn by an English Jack, if the chasing ship has no colours of that nation on board. If the chase be suspected to be an enemy, it may, under similar circumstances, be shewn by a flag, or a jack, of any country at war with Great Britain.

D 2   PENDANTS

The meaning of a flag was often determined by the position in which it was flown

How to Baffle the Enemy

The 1799 Signal Book contained an intriguing instruction on how to change the meanings of the numeral flags while the fleet was at sea, if it was thought that they had been compromised.

> *'If the Admiral should have reason to believe that the enemy has got possession of these signals, he will make the signal for changing the figures of the flags, and when that has been answered by every ship, he will hoist the numeral flags, two or three at a time, the uppermost flag of those first hoisted is to represent 1; the next below it 2; and so on till all the flags have been hoisted, the tenth flag to represent the cypher, and the last being the substitute flag. To prevent mistakes, every ship is to hoist the same flags as the Admiral, and in the same order; the flag officers are to be particularly attentive to see that this is done, and to shew the distinguishing signal of any ship in which they observe a mistake. The figure which, by the new arrangement, each flag is to represent, is to be immediately entered in every ship's signal book.'*

The signal books of the day were hand coloured, and they also had space for an Admiral to add signals for use by his own squadron or fleet. Not surprisingly, there are often discrepancies between different copies. One wonders if the evolution described above, if it was ever carried out just before a battle, might not have caused as much confusion in the British fleet as amongst the enemy! Nevertheless, it may well have been used after the compromise of the 1799 signal book when the *Redbridge* was captured by the French in 1803, and it was decided to re-arrange the meanings of the numeral flags (i.e. flag 1 became 5, 2 became 1, and so on).

Popham's Code

Letter [2] to Sir Home Popham from (name illegible), 19 February 1805:

> *'Captain Patrick Campbell late of the Doris meant to call upon you to say how much the late Captain Jervis lamented he had not your telegraph signals to communicate to Sir Charles Cotton the sailing of the French Fleet from Rochfort. He was three days in company with the British Fleet, and the weather was so bad, he could not communicate the information he wished, that at last judging it important to do so at all risques, he got into his boat tho' the weather still continued so bad and was drowned. Thus had these Telegraph Signals been in use, a knowledge of the sailing of the Rochfort Fleet would have been communicated three days sooner, and the life of this officer and some of the boat's crew saved. Captain Campbell says to the Southward, they are in use amongst all ships, but off Brest etc. not known.'*

[2] Quoted in *'A Damned Cunning Fellow'*, by Hugh Popham

Example of Night Signals,
from the Signal Book, 1816

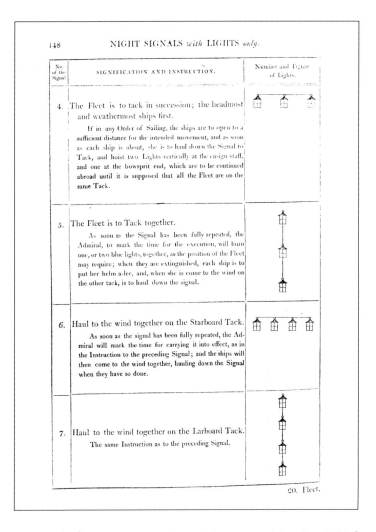

³ Nelson papers, Navy Records Society

To Captain Duff, in the Mars from HMS *Victory*, 4 October 1805. ³

Sir, As the enemy's fleet may be hourly expected to put to sea from Cadiz, I have to desire that you will keep with the Mars, Defence and Colossus, from three to four leagues between the fleet and Cadiz, in order that I may get the information from the frigates stationed off that port as expeditiously as possible. Distant signals to be used when flags, from the state of the weather, may not readily be distinguished in their colours.

'If the enemy are out or coming out, fire guns by day or night, in order to draw my attention. In thick weather, the ships to close within signal of the Victory ... and I have desired Captain Blackwood to throw a frigate to the Westward of Cadiz for the purpose of easy and early communication.

'I am, sir, with great respect, your most obedient servant.

Nelson and Bronte'

Every Man a Signal Tower

James Spratt, Master's Mate, was wounded at the battle of Trafalgar when commanding a boarding party from the *Defiance*. Swimming to the stern of the French ship *Aigle*, he entered her gunroom port, made his way to the poop, and attempted to haul down her colours. After a fight with French grenadiers, the boarding party captured the ship. For his wounds Spratt received a pension of £91.15s per annum, and £50.1s from the Patriotic Society. [4]

[4] Quoted in *'A Naval Biographical Dictionary'*, by William O'Byrne, 1849

From October 1806 to March 1813 he was in charge of the Signal Station at Teignmouth, and he was promoted Commander on the retired list in 1838.

On 30 May 1809 the Duke of Norfolk presented him with the silver medal of the Royal Society of Arts for his invention of a 'Homograph', a means of communicating at a distance by the positions of a white handkerchief. Spratt persisted in trying to promote his system, which he wrote up in a paper entitled 'The Homograph, or Every Man a Signal Tower', which formed the basis for an article in the *Nautical Magazine* of March 1840.

Figure 1 shows the ten positions which formed the basis of a numeral code, copies of which had to be held by each participant. Examples of a code quoted by Spratt included:

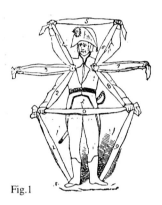

Fig.1

> 3   *Guard well the prisoners, as they are ten times our number.*
>
> 6   *As you are going to England to refit, I shall be obliged to you for your livestock.*
>
> 9   *We are in a very leaky state, relieve us or we perish.*
>
> 21   *Will you breakfast with me tomorrow?*
>
> 1000 *I intend to bag a noble fox tomorrow.*
>   *Meet me at day-break on the downs.*

Figure 2 shows the 'attention' sign, and Figure 3 the request for a repetition.

Spratt 'frequently conversed with his messmates at Spithead, from the green ramparts at Portsmouth, and from Plymouth Sound to the Hoe.' He suggested that 'The Homograph may be found useful to captains lodging on shore, by which they may communicate any orders, with ease and accuracy, to ships at anchor,' while 'Passengers in the East and West India and other fleets, may keep up a constant and friendly intercourse, to console themselves for the tediousness of a long voyage.'

Fig.2

Spratt's proposals prompted a whimsical report from 'The Semaphore on the Top of the Admiralty':

> '... I recommend that in your next number you mention the use of a stick, a sword, a spy-glass or, best of all, a short batten painted white .. for from all I can learn, a 'white handkerchief' is now a rarity in the service ...'

In the same year a Mr Knight Spencer was also presented with an award by the Society for his 'Anthropo-Telegraph', using round discs. Spencer wrote:

Fig.3

The Naval code of signals in 1940 (Top Right). The Navy had developed its own set of signal flags over the years and this bore no relation to any other flag code; indeed in the 19th century the naval and merchant flags were deliberately designed to be different. After the 1939-45 war, with the advent of the new Fleet Signal Book, the international code alphabetical flags and numeral pendants were introduced, together with USN numeral flags, but many special RN flags and pendants were retained. Nevertheless this made a big reduction in the number of flags and pendants which a ship had to carry.

Hardly had this code been assimilated than the work had to start all over again to produce a set of signal books and flags for NATO use (Bottom Right). This time the decision was taken to do away with 'national' systems, and to use the NATO books and procedures for all purposes. With the RN and USN taking the lead, and the RN having already adopted the International Code and USN numerals, the main changes this time were to design a common set of special flags.

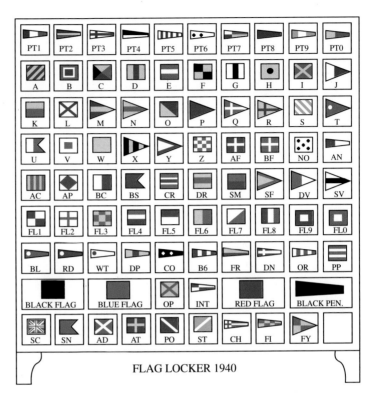

FLAG LOCKER 1940

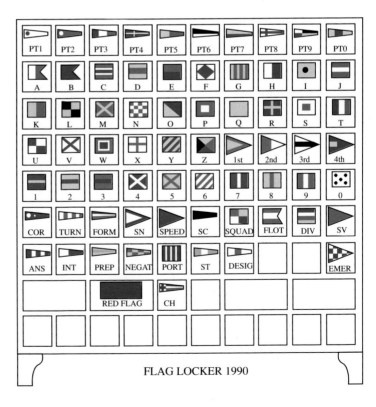

FLAG LOCKER 1990

Plate V

The Royal Yacht with her Majesty embarked (Above Left). The Royal Standard is worn at the main, the flag of the Lord High Admiral at the fore and the Union at the mizzen. If a foreign Monarch is embarked with the Sovereign, his standard will usually be worn alongside the Royal Standard at the main.

When a member of the Royal Family, other than the Queen, is embarked, his or her personal standard is worn at the main, the Flag Officer Royal Yacht's flag at the fore, and the white ensign at the mizzen. In the photograph (Above Right), Britannia is flying the Duke of Kent's personal standard. There are some exceptions to this; for example the Duke of Edinburgh, as an Admiral of the Fleet, flies the Union flag at the fore, and has the choice of several flags for the mizzen, such as the flag of an Elder Brother of Trinity House, or Grand Master of the Honourable Company of Master Mariners.

Right: HMS Boxer (Type 22 Frigate) at Hong Kong.

Her SCOT aerials can be seen in the white domes on sponsons just forward of the funnel; two aerials should allow access to a satellite whatever the ship's course. The Exocet missile launcher is on the foc'sle, and the Seawolf launcher in front of the bridge. An MF DF loop is at the for'ard edge of the bridge roof. HF whips are fitted to various parts of the superstructure. The ship is flying her signal letters, GBBK, and Code H, indicating that she has a pilot on board.

Plate VI

Communicators in action on board HMS Ark Royal.

1. The Tactical voice operator's position on the bridge which is manned whenever the ship is at sea.

2. ROs operating VDUs for the latest message handling system in the Flag Planning Room. The ship's main frame computer is linked via the satellite system into the Naval Shore Telegraphic Network (NSTN).

3. An LRO checking the SCOT satellite system.

4. Using a 15 inch signalling projector on the bridge roof. The 15 inch SP is superseding both the 10 inch and 20 inch projectors with which ships have been fitted for many years.

5. An RO1(T) working on the ICS 3 message handling system in the main communication office. This system is partly replaced by that shown in 2 above.

6. An RO1(G) tuning an HF receiver.

7. A WRO at the Supervisor Control Position, remotely changing a frequency for the Ops Room. This panel is used to connect the various radio equipments to the many operator positions around the ship.

1

2

3

4

5

6

7

Plate VII

Above: The pall bearers at the funeral services for Admiral of the Fleet Earl Mountbatten of Burma in 1979 were provided by the Signal School. At Westminster Abbey (Top Left) they were: FCRS G Dykes, CRS D Timmington and E Davies, LRO(G) I Murphy, R Milne, T Foster, M Watson, C Williams and RO1(G) S Witham. At Romsey Abbey (Top Right): Lieut G Perry, FCCY L Murrell MBE, RS C Morgan, LRO(G) G Burch, S Gardiner, W Fereday, LRO(T) D Eaton, RO1(T) M McKenna, JRO(G) R McKie. Many other Communicators were on duty, and some formed part of the Gun Carriage crew.

Right: Patricia Swallow CBE, Director WRNS 1982-86, qualified (Ce) in 1955.

Below Right: Dame Jean Davies DBE, Director WRNS 1961-64. She qualified on the first combined RNVR and WRNS signal course in 1942.

Below Left: Admiral of the Fleet Sir Edward Ashmore, GCB, DSC at the unveiling of his portrait in the main hall at Leydene, July 1985. The artist was Edward Hall, RPS.

Plate VIII

> *'My signals like those used in the Royal Navy, are numerical,
> and of course without limit as to the extent to which they may
> be carried, and with the assistance of Sir Home Popham's
> numbered dictionary, now generally adopted, every kind of
> communication may be made ... with the utmost certainty
> and celerity.'*

Commander (later Vice Admiral) Eardley-Wilmot seems to have
taken heed of the Admiralty Semaphore's suggestions. In his
Dictionary of Signals issued in 1850, he included homographic
signals to be made with a sword, tiller, stick, stretcher and handkerchief or flag, as well as others using hats, caps, balls, oars, boathooks
and even boat's thwarts, though some of his systems were rather
complex and needed several people to hold up the various devices!

Henry Eason - the First 'Professional' Signal Officer

The honour of being the first professional signal officer, in the sense
of being trained as a 'specialist', appears to belong to Henry Eason,
who became a Signal Boatswain in 1890 and was in the first batch of
Warrant Officers commissioned as Lieutenants in 1903. In the Signal
School records he is listed as No.1. (Specialist signal courses for
seaman officers did not start until about 1904).

Born in 1850 at Weymouth, he joined the Navy as a Boy at
Portland in 1864 and was among the first Able Seamen to be selected
for the embryo Signal Branch in 1870. He had a colourful career,
well documented in a series of manuscript diaries [5] kept while
serving at sea.

In 1872, when Henry Eason was serving in the frigate *Endymion*,
he was awarded the Royal Humane Society's Silver Medal for diving
into the sea to save the life of a shipmate who fell from aloft on a dark
night in the English Channel. Curiously Goff, the man he saved, and
Eason, were both involved a couple of years later in saving the life
of another sailor in the *Endymion* who fell from the fore-topmast
rigging, hitting the lower yards and netting on the way down and
ending up in the sea with no bones broken!

Eason joined the *Shah* as a Yeoman of Signals in 1876. The ship
was powered by sail and steam, and became the flagship of Rear
Admiral Algernon de Horsey, C-in-C Pacific, which entitled Eason
to be advanced to Chief Yeoman. He was very well reported on
throughout his career, though he had the usual ups and downs, as for
instance when leaving Montevideo:

> *'I was into a regular breeze this morning with the Captain
> ... it was a very trifling thing, only because the flags were not
> ready forward to indicate the cable coming in. He promised
> me he would take both my good conduct badges the next
> time. He was in a dreadful temper at the time with the
> Commander and the Officer of the Watch and no doubt he*

[5] Now in the possession of his grandson,
Commander Christopher Eason.

> *thought he would revenge himself on me. All day he has been
> firing away at everyone and everything.'*

A couple of months later:

> *'I and Butler, the Yeoman of Signals, were taken before the
> Commander today for neglect of duty because an officer
> ordered a certain signal to be hoisted and it turned out he
> wanted something else. I was told I should have made it my
> business to have looked at the book to see if it was right. So
> this just shows what a lot of use some of the officers are in
> the signals. This particular one don't know one signal in the
> book and I am sure he knows nothing of flashing.'*

Shortly after this, the *Shah* was engaged with the Peruvian rebel
turret ship *Huascar*; Eason was one of a volunteer boat's crew which
attempted to blow up the enemy with a 'fish torpedo' towed by the cutter,
but they were recalled at the last minute as the *Huascar* surrendered.

Later Eason records another incident:

> *'Yesterday I received a word of praise from the Admiral - the
> Flag Lieutenant said he was very much pleased with the
> smart manner in which I made out the signal ... whereby a
> deal of time was saved and prevented the ship going within
> range of the guns ..."*

In January 1877 Eason wrote that he had decided to re-engage for
another ten years,

> *'and I hope I shall live to serve it and years after so that I may
> enjoy the pension that I am now working for, depriving
> myself of the comforts of home. I managed to save up a little
> rum so that my messmates could drink my health.'*

Sailing from San Francisco to Pitcairn Island he wrote:

> *'To relieve the monotony of this passage I have started to
> read Froude's 'History of England' in 12 volumes. I have
> already got into the sixth.'*

After a party for the Pitcairn Islanders, the Admiral called the
Magistrate to the quarterdeck to present him with a Union flag.

> *'As I brought the flag forward the Admiral said: "This is
> our emblem of unity and loyalty. I hope you will take great
> care of it and do as much honour to that as you have to your
> island." I had the honour of giving it to him.'*

At Valparaiso the *Shah* met up with the *Triumph*. A novelty was a
display by the *Triumph* of her electric lights.

> *'The light was thrown upon this ship and lit up everything
> very plainly. We also made signals by it. In the first place we
> made a semaphore to them which they saw very clearly. The
> light was then thrown upon their semaphore and we read
> their answer. They next made a signal by the flashing system
> which could be seen at a very great distance.'*

On her way home the following year, the *Shah* was diverted to South Africa and Eason served ashore with the Naval Brigade in the Zulu war. On 16th March 1878 he wrote:

> *'Ordered to try and get some signals to and from Eshowe. We used a bedroom looking glass to make the signals with and I am glad to say we were more than successful.'*

And a few days later:

> *'This morning I made a little experiment with a small looking glass and was able to make signals to Fort Pearson very plainly.'*

But use of the helio was somewhat chancy; on 4th April:

> *'We cannot signal as there is no sun.'*

On May 2nd Eason's diary records:

> *'Mr Smith Dorrien and I started on an expedition to the coast. We had two of the mounted infantry horses and an escort. I took a small set of flags and a staff and halyards for signalling to the Forester if we could see her. We went about seven miles on a hill so that we could see the camp and the sea at the same time, but we could not see her.'*

Eason eventually arrived home after several eventful years, and as related earlier, made a considerable contribution to the development of a professional signal branch. Promoted to Warrant rank as Signal Boatswain in 1890, he took charge of the first Signal School which had been set up in HMS *Victory*. He was also employed to compile the Navy's 'Signal Handbook'; until then the only instructions were in QR & AI, a bulky and voluminous work not readily available to signal ratings. He was somewhat aggrieved both that the recommended award of £50 for his work was cut to £25, and that his name did not appear in the book when published in 1892 as he thought the Admiralty had originally promised. Their Lordships decided that:

Lieut Commander Henry Eason in 1916 with his sons Victor (left), Flag Secretary to Admiral Thursby, C-in-C Med., and Herbert, Assistant Paymaster, RNR

As can be seen, Eason looked a bit like King Edward VII. The King visited Portsmouth and Eason, now retired, took his grand-daughter to the Semaphore Tower to see the fun. As they drove through the town to the dockyard, the crowds cheered. 'They think I'm the King' he explained!

'...it would be informal for Mr Eason's name to appear ... but his contribution to the work will be duly noted in his favour.'

In 1900 Eason was promoted to Chief Signal Boatswain, and in 1903 he was commissioned as a Lieutenant. He retired in 1904 but was recalled in 1914 at the age of 64, promoted to Lieutenant Commander, and served throughout the war at the Signal Station, Portsmouth.

Eason was quite active politically, being at one time chairman of the local Conservative Association, and indeed he was inclined to blame political malevolence for the reduced award he was paid for the Signal Handbook, a Liberal government having been elected between the time the book was accepted and payment made! At the time of his death in 1924 he was the People's Warden at St Mark's Church, North End; an obituary in the local paper described him as 'the father of Signalling in the Navy.'

In one election campaign Lord Charles Beresford was the Conservative candidate for Portsmouth. Eason reported to him that he was bound to win because at a meeting his opponent had been asked by a young seaman:

'Will you give us hammock ladders if you are elected?.'

Unfamiliar with this old chestnut, the rival candidate promised that he would. As Eason told Beresford, such a man would never be elected in Portsmouth!

*   *   *   *   *

The following letter from Henry Eason is undated, but was probably written in the late 1880s, certainly earlier than 1890 when he was promoted to Signal Boatswain. Much of what he recommends was adopted.

To: The Editor, The United Service Gazette

'I quite agree with every word your correspondent has said relative to the pay of the Signalman in Her Majesty's Navy ...

'After the late cruize of the Reserve Squadron, there appeared in several papers a statement to the effect that 'the only thing found deficient during the cruize was the signal department.'

'This is a very serious matter, when we consider the extent to which the Squadron, especially when manœuvring, are depending upon the Signal department ... the reason is in the first place due to the continual drain from the Signal Staff of the most able, most experienced and most intelligent men. The men cannot be blamed as they are desirous of bettering their pay and position, which they cannot do if they remain in the Signals. Consequently they change their rating to Ship's Corporal, whereby they at once get an increase in pay, and other increase at three and six years, without taking into account their prospects of promotion to Master at Arms.

'Now I think Sir the first of these could be remedied by giving the signalmen a slight increase of pay ... the second could be remedied by establishing a school or training ship for signalmen where they could be instructed in all their duties, something similar to the Excellent for Seamen Gunners.

'I think that Boys should be selected as at present from the upper school in the training ships and sent to sea until

they had passed for 2nd class signalman ... no man should be promoted to first class signalmen unless he had first passed through the school ...

'In addition to their instruction in signals, they should also be taught to repair and make signal flags, it would be far better employment for them than setting up rigging, shifting boats, and holystoning decks ...

'I think a ship like the old Victory and placed as she is at present, is the very ship for what I have suggested ...

'I remain your humble servant,

H W Eason, Chief Yeo of Signals'

Signalling with Kites

Experiments with the use of kites for signalling purposes were made on a number of occasions from about 1901, when a Mr Stokes proposed the use of flags held aloft by a kite, plus the firing of a maroon rocket to draw attention to the signal. The Captain of the Signal School commented:

[6] Royal Naval Museum, ref. 87/30 and 1371/82

'...(my) opinion is that there is no call for this even if it is practicable which I doubt.' [6]

In 1903 Pensioner Writer Merrifield suggested hoisting a collapsible ball by day and a flashing lantern by night. This didn't get very far either, CSS commenting:

'...directional light impossible, all round light inadmissable in war. If distance is the object, then high power would be needed but would be quite impracticable at the end of a string.'

*   *   *   *   *

S F Cody, 'Inventor of the Cody Wire Kites as supplied to the British Navy', wrote to Captain Reginald Tupper, then in command of the cruiser *Venus*:

Alexandra Palace
Wood Green
Jan 12th 1904

'Dear Captain Tupper,

'Pleased to hear you are afloat once more as in my opinion it beats office life altogether. Many thanks for kind invitation to join you on board ... you may rest assured I shall always be pleased to assist you in any sort of kite experiments. I am sorry the Admiralty have such strong belief in Marconi's opinion of kites. Last summer when I was dealing with Admiralty I tried hard to get them to allow me to assist at the official experiments of wireless by kites, and if I am not

mistaken I promised that the aerial wire should not rise and fall if that were a detriment. I am of opinion that Marconi has never had kites properly handled.

'I assure you the result of last summer's kite experiments by H.M.V. does not surprise me in the least because they have attempted to work a new thing without first being properly taught. If you can get them to supply you with an outfit of my latest improvements I am sure we can prove their value for wireless.

'As you are not able to witness my man-lifting experiments to take place shortly I am sending an instruction to the Secretary of Admiralty asking them to send representatives.

I am, Dear Captain Tupper, Yours Very Sincerely,

S F Cody'

Samuel Franklin Cody was born in Texas in 1862, a relation of William 'Buffalo Bill' Cody, and was involved in ranching buffaloes and in 'Wild West' shows. He came to England to deliver some horses, and married an English girl. He invented a man-lifting kite in 1901, and demonstrated this to the Navy in 1903. He was one of the first people to fly an aeroplane in England, and was killed in a flying accident in 1913 while testing a new seaplane.

Further trials were undertaken in Mediterranean Fleet destroyers, HMS *Exe* subsequently reported that kites could be flown satisfactorily at 5 knots relative wind speed and could be used to hoist flags; four kites had been flown simultaneously. An aerial wire was also lifted and short distance communication established, but not long distance. (*Exe* was commanded by Allan Everett at this time, which perhaps contributed to the success of these trials.)

John Wells records in *Whaley* that:

'an intrepid young officer, later to become Vice-Admiral Astley-Rushton, was attached to a man-lifting kite and soared into the air to see if he could better observe the effect of gunfire from his swaying perch. His report was a master-piece of understatement.'

By this time adequate ship-borne aerials for transmitting and receiving wireless signals had been designed, and interest in kite aerials for this purpose lapsed. Experiments with kites and 'kite-balloons' for observational purposes continued, with varying degrees of success, until overtaken by the advent of the 'blimp' and eventually the aeroplane.

*　　　*　　　*　　　*　　　*

Another reference to kites appears in a letter written by Jack Diamond, a signalman who served in HMS *Dreadnought* during her first commission in 1908. He was awarded a prize by the flag lieutenant for being the best signalman on board and the first to pass the written exam for Yeoman. At the same time he passed his education test, although for some reason he didn't receive the certificate until 1929!

In a letter to Captain Christopher Wake-Walker in 1966 he wrote:

'I well remember the old Channel Fleet with names like Duncan (my ship), Cornwallis, Albemarle, Swiftsure and Triumph, the merchant cruiser Dido, together with Juno, Caesar and Albion.

'On the occasion of her joining, the Albion anchored in my Captain's cabin owing to an engine room mistake of Ahead and Astern. We had signals flying indicating ship's head, amount of cable out, and requesting her to anchor two cables astern.

'The collision necessitated us being 'copper domed' and sent back to 'Pompey'. This enforced departure was the prelude to an epic in communications for on arrival at Portsmouth we found Marconi waiting to try out his wireless. A kite aerial was rigged on Portsmouth Barracks parade ground and Duncan proceeded to the Isle of Wight. Lo and behold we received signals, rather faint, but as the height of the kite was increased so the signal strength increased. Marconi was so pleased that all the staff (twenty seven) received one golden sovereign each. Thus was born another form of long distance signalling to eclipse our 'Helio' and 'Searchlight'.'

HMS *Queen Elizabeth* and her Blimp, used primarily for observation, but also to experiment with wireless aerials. In the second world war balloons were used by convoys as protection against low flying aircraft.

The RN Pigeon Service

The RN Pigeon Service existed for over twenty years, the first recorded trials taking place in 1893 at Whale Island, where the pigeon lofts were fitted with electric catching traps which rang a bell in the Guardroom when a pigeon arrived. Another loft was set up at the Barracks in 1894 and trials were conducted with ships in the Channel. One ship with a pigeon on board had an engine breakdown when beyond signalling distance from Portland; a pigeon released in the dog watches duly arrived at Whale Island at daylight next morning when tugs were despatched to assist!

In the Mediterranean, Lieutenant Evan-Thomas, then flag lieutenant to the C-in-C, offered a prize for the first bird to fly from Sicily to Malta, but there is no record of the result. In 1896 a Committee was formed to investigate the establishment of a homing pigeon service for the Navy; the outcome was Admiralty Letter of 23 November 1896 which said:

> *'I am commanded ... to transmit for your guidance a scheme which has been drawn up for establishing lofts for training carrier pigeons at Sheerness, Portsmouth and Devonport:*
>
> *1. The Commander of the Signal School at Portsmouth to undertake general direction of all Home lofts;*
>
> *2. A Warrant Officer attached to the Signal School to superintend the training of the birds ...*
>
> *6. Treasury sanction has been obtained for the following expenditure:*
>
> > *£50 annually for each depot for food etc.*
> > *£15 for training purposes,*
> > *£80 for travelling and subsistence ...'*

Mr Barrett, Warrant Gunner, who was the original pigeon enthusiast, was appointed to this new post. Commander Tufnell and Mr Barrett selected sites for lofts - one at Gosport, completed in 1897, was said to be 66 feet long and could house 300 old birds and 300 young. Barrett is shown in the Navy List attached to the Signal School 'For training of homing pigeons' for many years, being joined by Boatswain Bailey 'For Portland Signal loft.'

The aptly named Mr Coop, whose permit issued under the Defence of the Realm act allowed him to keep up to 100 pigeons at home, remembers being called up, entered as a Petty Officer and sent to the Plymouth loft situated at the local Seaplane station. The pads of small, thin paper message forms, were headed 'Government Pigeon Service - To be taken to nearest Postal Telegraph office'.

Annual reports were rendered by the Captain of the Signal School.[7] In l903 the service 'has not come up to expectation, due to want of ships proceeding to sea. This will be minimised in future with the establishment of sea-going training ships such as the *Mercury, Iris,* etc ... All Higher Standard Signal ratings have been instructed

[7] Copies of some annual reports and other papers on the RN Pigeon Service are in the National Maritime Museum, reference MER/82A

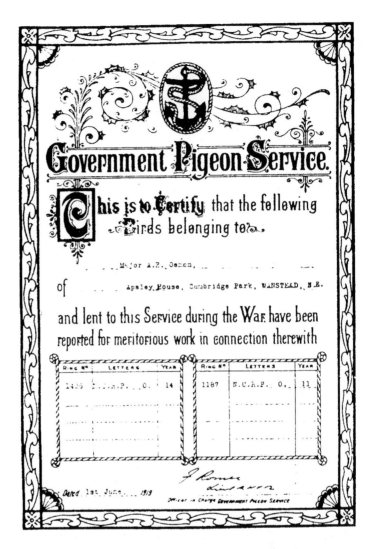

in the manipulation of Pigeons for Messages.' The statistics for the year included:

Number of birds 'liberated': 6,307
Number failed to home: 381
Average max flight per bird: 70 miles
Average speed of flight: 22 mph

In 1904:

'Salvage operations in connection with submarine A1 gave a great deal of exercise for Gosport pigeons. No message failed to reach its destination ... a bird with a strong breeze behind it delivered a message at the rate of over 90 mph.'

In 1905 a serious illness broke out at Sheerness and Devonport and the Captain comments:

'We must watch out for the slightest sign of disease - the loss

of the whole of the Military Pigeon Service was due to the neglect of this precaution.'

It went on to recommend a full twelve months training for officers before they took charge of lofts, and reported that three Warrant Officers had been given a six months course but this only qualified them to take charge of 'portable' lofts!

Pigeons were carried by seaplanes operating from Brindisi in 1916. On patrols across the Strait of Otranto they were used when outside wireless range, and in case of forced landing; the bird was thrown up or down sufficiently hard to clear the tailplane. As patrols were extended the pigeons became progressively less useful; if released nearer the Albanian mountains than the Italian coast the pigeons would escape in the wrong direction which they obviously found more attractive. The end came for the Brindisi pigeons when the loft was accidently burnt down and the service was disbanded.

By the end of World War One the pigeon had finally been superseded by wireless.

Signalmen in the Channel Fleet, c. 1905

Chapter Nineteen

1900 - 1918

*'A cruiser look-out is mainly a question of visibility ...
this may appear a simple remark, but is given for the
benefit of those who appear to imagine that Wireless
Telegraphy makes us see better ...'*

Allan Everett

Allan Everett was a prolific correspondent on Signal matters. Some of his letters survived in the Signal School archives, and are now in the National Maritime Museum. [1]

In 1891 he was discussing with Admiral of the Fleet Sir Geoffrey Phipps Hornby the relative merits of Equal and Unequal Speed manœuvres. Everett suggested that it was often quicker, and in certain circumstances safer, for ships to proceed independently to their new stations, and that the courses and speeds to steer could easily be plotted. Phipps Hornby did not agree, saying that while it was easy to draw lines and angles on a chart, these often bore little relation to the courses and speeds actually needed to reach the right positions. On 31st October 1891 he wrote to Everett:

'Signals for working at unequal speeds of single ships should be tabooed, because they cannot be definite. I hear the Torpedo men want to pass from Line-ahead to Line-abreast and vice-versa without altering course 8 points, because they think they may run into one another in turning these points. There is a sovereign remedy for such a state of things. If anyone thinks so let him be taken out of the boat, and put the right man in.

'To my certain knowledge, the Minotaur and Northumberland were, for six years (three under me), always next to one another and constantly doing that manœuvre, and yet they never succeeded in running into one another; so there is no reason why torpedo boats should do so, but the grave objection to that class of manœuvre is that it is indefinite. If an Admiral were to order such a thing, how can he tell how

[1] NMM *'Mercury* Collection'

Admiral Phipps Hornby was an early signal enthusiast who had taken a keen interest in the work of the Committee re-writing the signal books in 1886 ('The very size of the new book has already struck terror into the minds of some officers, but to whom the key was not known,' he wrote to the Chairman, 'you will make its acceptance far easier if you will give your reasons for the changes ...').

His son, a torpedoman, and W/T specialist, was a contemporary of Everett's, who no doubt knew the family, which would explain this correspondence between a young Lieutenant and an Admiral of the Fleet.

long his Captains may be in executing it, or how far his Fleet
may advance in doing so?'

Everett, who had served in a torpedo boat, didn't agree, at least as far
as these ships were concerned. Replying from the 'Telegraph School,
HMS *Victory*', on 14th November 1891, he wrote:

'*... a few words about unequal speed movements for torpedo*
boats. When steaming at high rates of speed in vessels where
the propelling power is so great in proportion to their
displacement, the slightest turn of the stop-valve makes a
very big increase or decrease in the number of revolutions
of the screw. This the boat feels in a very abrupt fashion,
gathering and losing way almost simultaneously with the
engines. Communication with the engine driver, for these
fine adjustments of speed, can only be attained by passing
the word along, and thus our station-keeping was generally
a series of dots and dashes, so to speak ...'

In an undated memorandum Everett again discusses Equal Speed
Manœuvres, this time arguing for a revision of the signal books to
reduce the number of flags required to signal each movement.

'The Commander-in-Chief of the Channel Squadron and Staff'

Vice Admiral Sir Henry Stephenson, KCB, with his Flag Captain, HSH Prince Louis of Battenberg on his left, his Secretary, Staff Paymaster Gillies on his right, and his Flag Lieutenant Allan Everett, on the quarterdeck of HMS *Majestic*. The caption in the Army & Navy Illustrated of 26 March 1898, reads:

'Vice Admiral Stephenson is not yet 56; his Flag Captain is known as one of the most Scientific officers in the Navy. He is the inventor of a 'course indicator' which has been adopted for use in the Navy, of an instrument for calculating the speed of ships and - in conjunction with Captain Sir Percy Scott - of a cone signalling apparatus which, tested under various weather conditions, has given very satisfactory results.'

In 1893 Everett was discussing new signalling methods with Rear Admiral Philip Colomb. Colomb had complained that there had been no significant developments since he had carried out experiments with electric lamps in 1858. Everett, now in HMS *Amphion*, wrote on 5th September 1893:

> '...a few days ago I met Evan-Thomas our new Flag Lieutenant who I'm happy to say is very keen about extending the distance limit of our day signalling. Now that cruiser people are beginning to think how the intelligence they acquire is to be imparted expeditiously to the main body ... this is recognised as of due importance.

> '...partly to obtain greater range and partly for other reasons we have, within the last two years, adopted an electric lamp of 64cp. The flashes are produced by means of a make-and-break key which closes and opens the circuit. Owing to its higher CP its range is much greater than the ordinary flashing lamp. Its speed unfortunately is slow as the current takes an appreciable time to heat the filaments from cold blackness to full incandescence and vice-versa ... As (this) takes 25 seconds its quickest rate of flashing is theoretically 2.6 wpm.

> 'I think it rather hard on us when you imply that we have "not been able to improve on the methods of 34 years ago". With all due humility to our forefathers I respectfully submit that in this case we have succeeded where they failed ... for it is to them that we owe the foundations of our knowledge but the things that baffled them and the difficulties they experienced are their legacies to us.

> 'Some years ago the needle telegraph instrument was supplanted by the Sounder, now the Sounder is beaten by electric typewriters and other self-recording instruments ... the Sounder is still generally used because its mechanism is simple and speed of sending as fast as one can write. This necessarily involves the use of trained telegraphists in the same manner as the flashing lamp requires trained signalmen.

> 'You say it is just as easy to flash from a high position as it is to exhibit (coloured) lights from the same position. I cannot agree because you seem to say it is as easy to pull a shade up and down from a height as it is to manipulate a simple switchboard (or key) from on deck. Now the higher you put your flashing lamp the longer the lanyard required for your obscuring shade, the greater the friction there is ... and the more chance of failure in action. On the other hand, with fixed electric lights the height is immaterial as that system is free from the mechanical disadvantages of the other.

> 'Now that ships are fitted with electric incandescent lamps for internal lighting ... it is all the more necessary that

Admiral Hoskins wrote to Evan-Thomas on 24 November 1893, after the latter had been appointed (on Hoskins' recommendation) as Flag Lieut to Admiral Sir Michael Culme-Seymour, C-in-C Mediterranean:

'... We have been trying as you know Prince Louis' distant signalling apparatus which is on the umbrella principle but the reports of it were not very favourable. It is as you say a most important matter and well worth attention of our inventors ... What do the French and Italians do? The latter are very ingenious at such inventions.

'As for Pigeons they will no doubt be very useful under certain circumstances but I cannot believe that they will be adaptable to the communications of a Fleet generally. Vessels on the outlook from a fortress might no doubt use them with advantage.'

Evan-Thomas papers, BL.52504-06

Vice Admiral Hugh Evan-Thomas, with his dog, known as 'Jack Jutland'

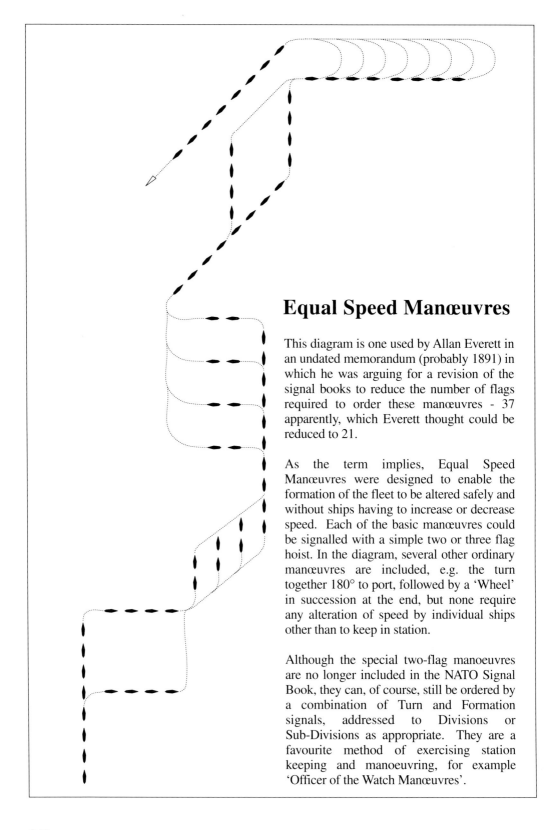

Equal Speed Manœuvres

This diagram is one used by Allan Everett in an undated memorandum (probably 1891) in which he was arguing for a revision of the signal books to reduce the number of flags required to order these manœuvres - 37 apparently, which Everett thought could be reduced to 21.

As the term implies, Equal Speed Manœuvres were designed to enable the formation of the fleet to be altered safely and without ships having to increase or decrease speed. Each of the basic manœuvres could be signalled with a simple two or three flag hoist. In the diagram, several other ordinary manœuvres are included, e.g. the turn together 180° to port, followed by a 'Wheel' in succession at the end, but none require any alteration of speed by individual ships other than to keep in station.

Although the special two-flag manoeuvres are no longer included in the NATO Signal Book, they can, of course, still be ordered by a combination of Turn and Formation signals, addressed to Divisions or Sub-Divisions as appropriate. They are a favourite method of exercising station keeping and manoeuvring, for example 'Officer of the Watch Manœuvres'.

flashing lamps ... should be placed clear of them ... they must be raised sufficiently high above the upper deck. If you can fix the lamp (or coloured light system) as high as you can along the topmast backstay, or jackstay, there is nothing to obstruct an all-round view.'

Writing from Malta on 27 October 1893, Everett mentions trials in the fleet of a red and white flashing light - red for dots and white for dashes, or vice-versa, saying that a difference in colour seems easier to read than the difference in time of (the flash) of a single coloured light. But he admits that this was mechanically complicated, and a stronger lamp is needed for the red to balance it with the white. He goes on:

'I am giving my attention now to distant signalling by day ... we have absolutely no established means of communicating intelligence at distances by day ... this problem is of paramount importance in war ... If we had an efficient means of communication every single merchant steamer might become as valuable as a cruiser in imparting intelligence! As far as the Navy is concerned the solution will, I think, be found in a truck semaphore, if our authorities will try it.'

Once formal Signal Books and Instructions had been issued, the problem arose of keeping them up to date to match new ideas, inventions and changing tactics. By the beginning of the twentieth century the Signal School had become the obvious authority to coordinate this work and Allan Everett, who became Superintendent (as a Commander) in 1900, was very involved and for a time seemed almost indispensable.

In 1898 we find the Admiralty thanking Lieutenant Everett 'now serving in HMS *Majestic*, for his valuable services while acting as Secretary to the Committee on the revision of the Signal Books', and in 1903 Commanders Miller and Everett were thanked for the care and ability evinced in the preparation of a pamphlet on the Mooring Board and Battenberg Course Indicator.

Shortly before he left the Signal School, Everett was again turning his attention to the problem of long distance signalling, this time in the light of developments with wireless. In a letter dated 26 January 1903 he comments on the Cruiser Instructions contained in the Signal Books:

'A cruiser look-out is mainly a question of visibility ... this may appear a simple remark, but is given for the benefit of those who appear to imagine that Wireless Telegraphy makes us see better ...

'If Cruisers can use W/T effectively the links in a look-out chain need not be so close together as to be in V/S touch, but still must not be so far apart that an enemy ship can slip between them without being observed ... but as W/T is by no means a reliable means of communication - and there is small prospect of its becoming so at present - V/S must still be considered the best means to employ'.

Everett was Flag Lieutenant to three famous admirals, Sir Compton Domvile, Sir Henry Stephenson and Sir Harry Rawson. In his book 'A Yellow Admiral Remembers', Humphrey Hugh Smith refers to the year 1897 when Vice Admiral Stephenson took command of the Channel Squadron: 'He brought with him as Flag Lieutenant the celebrated Allan Everett, the finest signal officer that the Navy had hitherto produced.'

(The term 'Yellow Admiral' was used to describe one who was placed on the retired list without ever hoisting his flag, as was the custom at the time when captains who were retired on reaching the top of the list were then promoted to Rear Admiral on the Retired List.)

In the same letter he says that he is often asked what is the reliable signal range for a Truck Semaphore:

> *'This is governed by the state of the atmosphere ... in the Mediterranean under most favourable conditions, signals have been read at 18 miles but generally speaking on an ordinary fine day 8 to 10 miles is all that can be relied on. In the Channel ... considerably less.'*

Everett goes on to highlight a problem that has been with us ever since - competition for the top of the mast:

> *'If it is true that some cruisers in the Mediterranean have had their Truck Semaphores removed so that a higher Wireless gaff could be erected, it means that a fairly practicable means of long distance signalling has been taken away so as to give place to what is, at present, unreliable. Surely both systems are not impossible in a cruiser?'*

Drum and Venetian Blind systems 1889

He also favoured the Truck Semaphore over other combinations of flags, balls and other shapes which had been tried, though without much success since the different devices were often not easy to distinguish, particularly when there was no wind, and the number of meanings which could be allocated was severely limited.

> *'In 1895 experiments carried out in the Mediterranean with the Sybille fitted with both Truck Semaphore and a large collapsing drum, the Truck Semaphore proved itself far superior. The drum would take eleven seconds to make the letter P in morse (at the rate of one second per dot) and the signalman has to keep his eyes rivetted on the performance for the whole eleven seconds, but by semaphore the whole symbol is shown in its entirety and only a glance is required to read it. The new pattern Truck Semaphore costs £350 which is amply justified by its value to the Service'.*

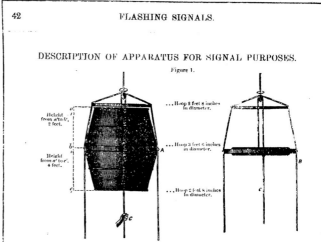

42   FLASHING SIGNALS.

DESCRIPTION OF APPARATUS FOR SIGNAL PURPOSES.

Figure 1.

Figure 1 represents the Collapsing Drum, which may be used for Distant and other Signals in the day time; A shows the Drum extended by the line *c*, representing an exposure of the Light, and B the Drum collapsed, representing a concealment of the Light.

The Drum is to be hoisted where most convenient, not less than 20 feet above the deck, which is a sufficient height for the most Distant Signals; it is self-collapsing, and is worked by hand.

Figure 2.

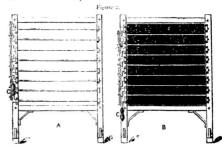

Figure 2 represents an apparatus which may be used for permanent stations on shore.

On Everett's death, The Times published a tribute from an old friend, Admiral Sir Sydney Fremantle:

"Ev', as he was known to his friends, was not only an accomplished professional sailor, but a man of high culture and of independent and original outlook ... he was an excellent raconteur, interlarding his talk with anecdotes of the distinguished flag officers under whom he had served. He had a way of infusing with humour the driest official communications ... 'Ev' showed no interest in sport or games, and took no exercise. On one occasion (when he was Captain of the Fleet, Home Fleet) a report went round that he was about to take up golf, and his debut was attended by a party of twenty or thirty of his friends. Unfortunately his persistence failed, and the nineteenth was the only hole played after the first two.'

Everett left the Signal School on 31 December 1903, but was expected to continue the work of revision he had started; in Admiralty letter of 16 January 1904 the C-in-C Mediterranean was informed that:

'Commander A F Everett, recently appointed to HMS Myrmidon, has not yet completed revision of the Cruiser Instructions in Volume I of the General Signal Book, upon which he has been engaged while Superintendent of Signal Schools. Their Lordships desire that he should continue this work under your directions ... the experience gained in the working of Cruisers under your Command will materially assist him ...'

In August of the same year Everett, and Flag Lieutenant Andrew Kerr of HMS Bacchante, were thanked for the proposed Cruiser Instructions 'together with the Signal Code for use therewith'.

By January 1905 Everett was in command of HMS *Exe*, and the Admiralty were asking how he was getting on with the revision of the Signalman's Handbook (presumably the one written by Eason in 1890) and whether 'owing to his many other important duties he has been able to find time to rewrite any portion of it.' Everett replied that he had deferred this work until he had finished dealing with the Cruiser Instructions, which took longer than anticipated, but:

'I now regret to find that my original notes and papers connected with the revision of the Signalman's Handbook (which I had brought out from England) must have been inadvertently destroyed. To recommence would entail more than my duties permit.'

Everett was promoted Captain and again served as Superintendent of Signal Schools from 1906 to 1908. Thus he was still involved in drafting and amending books, and in 1908 Their Lordships thanked him once more, this time for the final proof of the Boat's Signal Book, expressing their 'appreciation of the care and labour he has bestowed in connection with its compilation'. In 1914 he was Jellicoe's Captain of the Fleet, as a Commodore. He retired in 1925, after being C-in-C China Station.

*　　　*　　　*　　　*　　　*

Signalling Arrangements in Flagships

Allan Everett made another contribution to the development of signalling in the fleet when he was captain of the *Neptune*, and took up the question of the inadequate arrangements in flagships. The subsequent instruction from the Controller pointed the way towards the eventual formation of the User Requirements and Trials Section, or 'X' Section, of the Signal School. His letter of 16 January 1912 from *Neptune* to C-in-C Home Fleet reads:

'The following remarks concern signalling arrangements of ships destined as Flagships.

'I have served in six Flagships in which it has invariably been necessary to make considerable alterations in order to suit them for the extra special work ...

'In every Flagship I have served in, it has been deemed necessary to extend or alter the bridge accommodation in order that it may be possible to conduct movements of the Fleet without being hampered by Signalmen or the officers working the ship ...

'Application for a Flagship to be fitted with a third Semaphore (on the fore and aft line against a skyline) has invariably to be made.

'The provision of ensign and signal flag accommodation has been found inadequate ...

'The position of electric flashing lanterns, places to work them from, have been found unsuitable, mechanical semaphores in the wrong place. In the Hercules the place marked 'Signal House' was so small that it could not be properly used.

'I would therefore urge that the Superintendent of Signal Schools be consulted on these points when a ship is building ...'

In response, the Controller of the Navy wrote to the Admiral Superintendent, Portsmouth on 17 April 1912:

The Admiral Superintendent is informed that when drawings of Signal arrangements are being prepared for new ships the Superintendent of Signal Schools should be consulted through the Superintendent of the Yard at which the drawings are being prepared.

Percy Scott's Inventions

As mentioned in Chapter One, Sir Percy Scott, a gunnery officer, invented a number of signalling devices, though he usually had great difficulty in getting the Admiralty to adopt them. In 1886 he was promoted Commander and joined HMS *Edinburgh*; he tried to put more emphasis on training, but to keep up with the rest of the fleet had to give this up and spend more time and money on painting and titivating the ship: 'The nuts and bolts on the after-deck were gilded, magazine keys electro-plated, and statues of Mercury surmounted the revolver racks', he wrote. [2]

One of Scott's 'inventions' appears to have been based on an earlier proposal by Philip Colomb (referred to by Everett above):

'When the admiral wished to make a signal at night to all the ships, about half a dozen operators had to be employed making the signal in different directions ... even then it was

[2] *'Fifty Years in the Royal Navy',* by Admiral Sir Percy Scott

difficult, as the signalling lamp got mixed up with the other lights.

'*It occurred to me that if we could put a light on top of the mast the ships all round would see it, and the difficulty of its being confused with other lamps would be removed. Accordingly I had a lamp made with a screen which we could pull up and down by means of a wire ... many other ships copied it.*

'*This lamp had an interesting career, extending over many years. The authorities saw the wisdom of it but did not wish to adopt it ... So they turned it upside down, christened it the 'gravity lamp', and introduced it for use as their own invention. (But) this lamp proved a failure as the shade, by its own weight, would not cut off the light quickly enough, and frequently would not fall at all ... Finally, after years of trial and waste of money, they were compelled to adopt my original suggestion.*'

Scott took command of the cruiser *Scylla* in 1886:

'*I expected to find great improvements in gunnery and signalling. To my surprise everything was just as it had been ... I found that all the signalmen in Scylla, except the Yeoman, G H Glover, were quite unreliable in the work of taking in signals at night; and in October I put all the signalmen under instruction. By day they were exercised with a small venetian-blind shutter, which made the shorts and longs of the Morse code, and by night with the truck flashing lamp. The venetian-blind idea was new, so the Admiralty 'turned it down'. During the War twenty-six years afterwards, in 1917, it was resurrected and found to be very useful; it was also used horizontally for communicating with aeroplanes.*'

Scott's inventions were favourably reported on by the C-in-C's flag lieutenant, H G G Sandeman, who was scathing about the existing searchlight flashing system:

'*The obscuring disc is a most clumsy and unreliable contrivance. The disc itself shuts off very little light, it frequently carries away owing to excessive heat; the method of working it is irksome, the lever being too high up, on the wrong side of the projector, moving in the wrong direction, with too long a beat. In fact everything that can be wrong is wrong.*

'*Captain Scott has invented a shutter which is placed in front of the lens; it is worked by a handle on the right, moving at a short beat and in a suitable direction. It is a pleasure to make Morse with it.*'

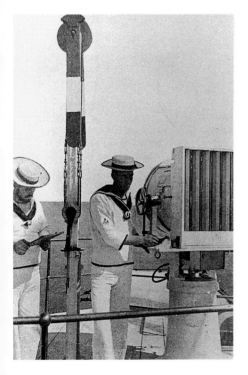
Scott's searchlight flasher in *Scylla*

Needless to say, Scott complained that,

> '*Important as the suggestions were it was many years before they were acted on ...*'

In 1908 Scott produced an idea for a cypher machine based on the typewriter principle, with two sets of concentric but independently revolving discs, plain and encyphered text being printed side by side. A committee set up under Sir John Fisher, and with Commanders Payne and Edwards as members, recommended against adopting any form of mechanical device. (A somewhat similar machine, devised by a Mr Alex Liwenthaal, had been tried in the Navy a few years earlier but not taken up). Scott tried again with a Mark II machine in 1909, but again this was not favoured. The Mark I was then tried in four ships of the fleet - *Dreadnought* thought the liability of capture was a disadvantage, *King Edward VII* reported that it was no quicker or more accurate than manual coding, *Indomitable* said it was slow and insecure, and *Shannon* said that Assistant Paymaster Youle could produce a machine which was simpler and speedier. Scott was informed that his machine was of no practical value!

Steam Signalling

The term 'Steam Radio' may be familiar, but 'Steam Signalling' was suggested as a useful idea in 1909, when the Admiralty asked the Signal School to comment on the following letter which had been received (author unknown):

> '*Improvements in or relating to Signalling Devices (Provisional Specification lodged at Patent Office, London)*
>
> '*This idea, for use primarily at sea, is intended to utilise the extraordinary visible character of steam. To carry this into effect I propose that there be a small cylinder or exhaust at the top of the mast, which would be connected by steam pipe to the main steam supply, the discharge of steam from this cylinder or exhaust at the top of mast being controlled by electrical contact mechanism from the bridge.*
>
> '*The message or signal would first be written on a tape in Morse characters, which tape would be operated by clockwork mechanism, so as to move at a definite and known speed.*
>
> '*The transmitting official in chart room watches the moving tape, and as each period (ie the space between the Morse characters) passes a certain marked point he would press an electrical contact, and thereby cause sudden discharge of steam from the mast head.*
>
> '*This discharge would be observed by the distant receiving official through telescope, and at each visible*

discharge of steam he, the receiving official, would press an electrical contact, and thereby imprint the periods between the steam discharges on a tape moving at exactly the same speed as the transmitting tape, thus the two 'Morse' records would coincide, and the message could be interpreted. The electrical contact for the use of receiving official could be fixed on side of telescope, and be operated by one of the fingers of either hand.

'From telescopic experiments I have made, I find that at a distance of 10 miles there is no difficulty in detecting a sudden discharge of steam, it is instantly visible; while in hazy weather when nearly everything is obscured a sudden discharge of expanding steam is readily seen. This latter point may be exemplified by watching a train in hazy weather some distance from point of observation, although it is impossible even with powerful telescope to see either locomotive or carriages, the steam exhaust, or discharge from funnel can be easily detected.

'I respectfully submit that signalling at sea by this means could be carried on at greater distances than by flags or semaphores.

'The liability of the 'wireless' system to occasional interruption by reason of the wilful activity of the enemy's transmitters, prompts me to respectfully lay this idea before you.

'The property which steam possesses of instantly expanding when liberated, thereby presenting a surface of great area and size, coupled with its power of reflection and refraction of light make it visible at very great distances.'

The Signal School was not impressed, commenting that the author of this 'ingenious invention' appeared to have ignored the fact that the searchlight was capable of being read at horizon distance.

*   *   *   *   *

Signalling by steam may not have found favour, but the steam siren could prove useful.

In 1917 Angus Cunninghame Graham was Flag Lieutenant to Rear Admiral D R L Nicholson, second-in-command of the 4th Battle Squadron, in HMS *Colossus*:

'A hazard befell us off Norway when all eight ships of the 4th Battle Squadron were approaching to support a convoy in what, in signal language, is called 'Divisions in line abreast, disposed astern'. Our division was leading with four ships abeam of each other and Admiral Sturdee (BS4) was with the other division in the same formation just over a mile astern of us. Suddenly we ran into dense fog. We had

to stand on towards the coast for as long as we thought safe, because we had heard nothing from the Admiral to tell us that he had turned and we could not turn back without risk of collision.

'A destroyer leading our anti-submarine screen reported rocks ahead. Luckily I had drilled the division to manœuvre by siren signals with which my admiral was able to turn the four ships together two points more than 90 degrees in order to make away from the land and at the same time clear the front of the other division if they were still close astern of us. In fact they were not.

'During the turn the rocks looked unpleasantly close. Our only casualty was one propellor knocked off a screening destroyer, commanded by Commander Alban Curteis, afterwards an admiral. This pleased him greatly, because it was not his fault and his week or so in a dockyard for the repair enabled him to get married, which the war had so far prevented. [3]

[3] From Admiral Cunninghame Graham's memoirs, *'Random Naval Recollections'*

How to Destroy Confidential Books

A Minute [4] by the Signal Section in the Admiralty, dated 12th August 1914, referred to the possibility of shore W/T stations being attacked:

[4] ADM1-8409/16

'Some means are required to encompass the immediate destruction of secret signal and code books at shore W/T stations ... it has been suggested that some acid could be used to effect this ...'

The Professor of Chemistry at Greenwich expressed the view that hot sulphuric acid, which acts almost instantaneously, would be most likely to achieve the aim:

'A suitable earthenware tank is needed. It should stand in a lead tray as the acid is liable to froth over after a few minutes ... there is no danger provided the acid is added to water already in the tank.'

A number of trials took place, but it proved difficult to get the acid between the leaves, the books emerged nearly intact, and the trials were eventually abandoned.

The final recommendation from the Admiralty was to tear off the covers, throw the books into a tray or bowl or fireplace, and saturate in paraffin:

'The opportunity should be taken of practising when obsolete books or documents have to be destroyed.'

From: C-in-C Mediterranean
To: Cardiff

Your Confidential Book Officer is to report to my office for destruction.

'Make Another Signal',
by Jack Broome

Early W/T Experiments

The first formal reference to naval W/T appears in the Torpedo School's annual report for 1896.

'*A series of interesting experiments have been carried out by Defiance to ascertain if it were feasible to transmit electric radiations to a distance without any conducting wires, the object being to provide a means by which torpedo boats might indicate their approach or proximity to friendly ships. The Defiance had constructed apparatus by which Morse signals could be slowly transmitted and recorded at short distances; and subsequently trials of apparatus by Signor Marconi, an Italian gentleman, were attended, and a brief summary of the results is given below.*

'*The principles on which Signor Marconi's apparatus were constructed were similar to those employed by Defiance, but more fully developed, and the instruments themselves were much more sensitive. The transmission of messages without conducting wires depends on the fact that, when a conductor is electrically charged or discharged with sufficient suddenness, it emits electrical waves into the surrounding ether, similar to sound or light waves. If a wire is handy, these waves will run along it and be felt a long way off, or they may be transmitted through the ether itself, and if they impinge on a particular form of microphonic contact they generally effect an immediate and marked alteration in its resistance, and thus will affect a current flowing through the circuit in which the microphone is inserted. A smart tap or mechanical vibration will restore the microphonic contact to its original state, thus preparing it for the next wave that comes along.*'

The Marconi Company offered to lend the Admiralty eight sets pending settlement of the royalty question, but:

'*Their Lords of the Treasury being unable to sanction the payment of royalty proposed by you (£100* per annum *per set), My Lords are of the opinion that it would not be right for them to accept the loan of the instruments, and that their only course is to proceed to set up installations on their own account and to manufacture the articles in question under the powers reserved to the Crown ...*'

The first twelve sets for fitting in ships were therefore made to Jackson's design. Marconi's royalty demand was finally agreed in April 1900 and the Admiralty entered into a contract for the supply of 32 sets at a price of £186-£196 each, subject to them passing a series of tests:

'*A ship at Portland (Minotaur) shall be fitted with the Marconi apparatus and another ship in like manner at*

> *Portsmouth (Hector); the height of the masts on both of*
> *these ships shall be 162 feet above the netting; communica-*
> *tion shall be made on these ships from Portsmouth to*
> *Portland and from Portland to Portsmouth and also to an*
> *intermediate ship, with a height of 100 feet, up to a distance*
> *of 30 miles ...'*

By this time Marconi had devised an arrangement for tuning transmitters and receivers 'by means of a coil of wire containing an exactly equal number of turns being inserted in both the sending and receiving wire.' This was demonstrated between Niton in the Isle of Wight and the Haven Hotel, Poole. Phipps Hornby was present:

> *'Niton and Poole communicated using the tuned system*
> *without interference from Hector at Portsmouth or Minotaur*
> *at Portland, although these ships were working all the time.*
> *The reverse of this was not so well shown, as both Hector*
> *and Minotaur experienced interference when Poole or*
> *Niton were working.'*

But the tuning system showed its worth when two differently tuned messages were sent at the same time from Niton and were separately recorded at Poole on two receivers, as were an 'untuned' message from *Hector* and a tuned one from Niton.

It was discovered at this time that 'doubling the aerial wire considerably improves the range of the apparatus ... where land intervenes the use of the double wire becomes absolutely necessary.' This led to the use of that familiar sight in early rigs, the wooden spreader used to separate the wires and form the large 'sausage' type aerials slung between the masts.

After a short sea appointment for the fleet manœuvres in 1899 in *Juno*, Jackson was appointed temporarily to *Vernon* 'to impart the results of the experience gained by him ...', when he effectively laid down the policy for the development of radio for the Navy. He stressed that the design must be to meet an operational requirement, equipment should be standardised so that operators would not be faced with unfamiliar apparatus and, as a result, the variety of spare parts which a ship would need to carry would be minimised.

Lieutenant (T) R S Phipps Hornby reported on 26 May 1898 from Marconi's experimental station in the Isle of Wight that:

> *'the experiments carried out on the 7th inst at the Needles with a signalling apparatus without wires on a system proposed by Signor Marconi ... was entirely successful, the signals sent from Bournemouth being received with remarkable clearness at Alum Bay at a distance of 14½ miles, and vice-versa, the speed of signalling being about 10 words a minute ...'*

The C-in-C Portsmouth, Lord Charles Beresford, and Commander Hugh Evan-Thomas, Secretary to the Signal Committee, were also present at the demonstration on 7 May.

*   *   *   *   *

The development of W/T was carried out entirely by the naval staff during the early years, the first 'Civilian Wireless Expert', Henry Madge, joining *Vernon* in 1904, followed by C L Glen-Bott in 1908, and W S Peake in 1911.

Peake's brother was a tutor at St John's College, Cambridge, who had in fact taught both Madge and Glen-Bott. Peake was working for the Cambridge Scientific Instrument Co. when he was sent to demonstrate a new instrument of theirs, the Duddell Thermo-Ammeter, at HMS *Vernon*.

'This was designed to measure currents of high frequency. Quite simple really - just a short high resistance wire with a thermo-couple in the middle connected to an ordinary milliameter.

'Partly as a result of that visit I applied for the advertised post of 'Assistant to the Wireless Expert.' A little later Mr Duddell made some experiments with an arc lamp and showed how responsive it was to vibration. He called it the Singing Arc, and at the time it was a bit of a joke.

'A little later, about 1913, I happened to sit at the mess table alongside Lieutenant James Somerville who had just come in from sea ... He had seen the Duddell notice and made some experiments with a singing arc and had transmitted speech over a short distance. About this time (1910 or 1911) Poulsen discovered that if you enclosed the arc and filled the enclosure with methylated spirit vapour the arc was capable of setting up HF oscillations in a suitable oscillatory circuit. It gave steady continuous waves as opposed to the shock trailing waves of the Marconi spark.

'Morris-Airey was in touch with Poulsen and used to receive his experimental transmissions from Denmark. Then a young man, CF Elwell, turned up with a (Poulsen arc) transmitter ... a heavy clumsy affair but it worked and we bought one or two for use in shore stations. When they began to talk about using it in ships I offered to design a more suitable model ... It proved a great success and was used very largely during the 1914-18 war. Its advantages were smaller, lighter, cheaper and much more steady, and enclosed by steel covers to reduce the leakage of magnetic field which would otherwise affect the ships' magnetic compasses.'

Experiments with Poulsen transmitters were carried out on a large scale in 1912-13 at *Vernon*, and Commander Payne visited radio stations at San Francisco where they had overcome difficulties with large arcs - improvements he noted included:

'automatic arc striking mechanism, better cooling arrangements, stronger magnetic field ... the transmitting switch which controls valves for starting and stopping the flow of gas or alcohol to the arc chamber, and rotation of the carbon electrode.'

One interesting thing which Payne noticed was that 'the operators habitually type the signals as they receive them in the telephones'. This did not have any impact at the time; it was not until it was found essential by the British Pacific Fleet in 1945 that 'morse-typing' was eventually adopted by the RN.

Experimental Poulsen transmissions were also carried out between Arlington (Washington, DC) and North Front, Gibraltar. At about the same time Captain Willis, RM, the W/T Instructor at

Vernon, described 'the new Heterodyne receiving apparatus fitted in the US cruiser *Salem*. This method of receiving signals is being tested for the first time in the US Navy'. Willis also mentioned that the wavelength used with the Poulsen equipment in the *Salem* was 4,100 meters, shortened by the operating key to 3,900 meters - probably the first reference to a form of 'frequency-shift keying'.

Wireless in the Early Submarines

After experiments in the Devonport Flotilla it was decided in 1911 that submarines should be fitted with wireless, and HMS *Defiance* was tasked to design a set, the required range being stated as 30 miles. The result was the Type 10 fixed spark gap transmitter, a very simple, robust device with an output of about half a kilowatt, the basic components being a large condenser for storing an electric charge, a coil of wire (the inductance) and two copper spark plugs with an air gap between them, enclosed in a chamber with a red glass window. A motor alternator produced a high voltage, and when the condenser was fully charged this caused a spark across the gap. The condenser discharged and a new charge was built up to repeat the process.

This oscillating circuit produced a magnetic field in the inductance coil which was transferred to an aerial circuit by a second coil. A powerful blower forced air across the spark gap to act as a cooler to prevent a continuous arc being formed. Getting the correct degree of coupling between the primary circuit producing the spark and the aerial was important. If the voltage in the aerial circuit was too high, the result was a violet-blue discharge around the aerial, which was not popular if the boat was on the surface at night!

The Type 14 Poulsen Arc transmitter, with an output of about 5kw, was fitted from about 1916 in those submarines operating further afield. This produced a continuous wave, instead of the modulated wave of the spark set, by passing a steady current between a copper anode and a carbon cathode, each mounted in heavy porcelain insulators. A magnetic field was produced across the gap by two pole pieces with field coils wound on them, and the aim was to produce an electric arc between the two electrodes and keep it burning.

The arc was burnt in a hydrogenous vapour produced by allowing methylated spirit to drip onto the copper anode and become vapourised. The vapour helped to lengthen the arc, so that when struck it bowed upwards. 'Old salts' were sometimes tempted to drink the meths, so 'ingredient X' had to be added to give it a less desirable taste. Escaping gas from the chamber could render the operator unconscious; Telegraphist George Cureton recalled that he always operated the Poulsen Arc with one foot holding the door of the cabinet ajar.

To keep it burning two circuits were needed, so that during a 'space' the arc burned on what was called the 'back shunt' circuit, being automatically transferred to the aerial circuit when the key was pressed.

An example of how wireless technology was progressed by telegraphists in the front line was related by Archie Symington.

In 1916 E41 was on a mine-laying operation in the Heligoland Bight. As the mines were dropped, it was clear that premature explosions were taking place. The CO surfaced in order to transmit a warning to the next boat due to leave Harwich. At a distance of 350 miles and with only a Type 10 transmitter, there was no answer to her signals. Finally, Symington tried putting more windings on the aerial coil, after which he got through, though back at base they couldn't believe it and queried the submarine's position. The coils in the other boats in the flotilla were immediately modified, though none achieved such a long range again.

The W/T 'cabinet' was about 5' high by 3' by 3', fixed to the side of the hull and suspended above the deck to allow access to the battery tank beneath. The cabinet was lead-lined to form an electrical screen, and to reduce the noise of the diesel engines thundering away next door. The operator had to hoist himself in by a rope or bar.

The early boats had two telescopic masts with about 100' of aerial slung between them. They were raised and lowered by hand, using a chain purchase from inside the boat, the evolution taking five or six minutes. They were normally only used at night, and in an emergency could be lowered rapidly by knocking off the brake. The 'E' boats had non-telescopic masts which stowed alongside the casing on top of the hull. The efficiency of these aerials was affected by spray, and in bad weather conditions the achievable range was much reduced. By the end of the war the jumping wire had been

Poulsen Arc Transmitter at
HMS *Dolphin*, 1918

This is similar to the transmitters
fitted in early submarines - indeed
the old 'H' boats in service in 1939
were still fitted with Poulsen.

modified to act as transmitting and receiving aerials and this produced a significant improvement.

Box and wing kites were also carried, beautifully made of cane and a fabric known as Jaconite Twill. They could lift a long wire aerial but handling this could be very difficult in the confined space of the bridge, and for obvious reasons they were not used in enemy waters.

The telegraphists also operated the hydrophones, as well as the Fessenden underwater sound signalling equipment. [5] The latter's transducer was an electro-dynamic oscillator, consisting of a vanadium steel plate about half an inch thick and 20 inches across, located on the outside of the hull, which was made to vibrate by passing an electric current through coils attached to it. Its resonant frequency in water produced a note of about 550 cycles and the effect was said to be like the equivalent of three tons hitting the plate; when transmitting, the steel deck would vibrate and produce a tickling sensation in the feet. The note was modulated by using an ordinary morse key. The normal range for passing signals between submerged submarines was about 3 miles, although this was sometimes exceeded (93 miles was once recorded off the North China coast).

The distance between two submerged submarines could be measured by stop watch, the originator transmitting F and starting the watch on the last dot, the receiving boat then transmitting when it heard the last dot, and the originator making a final F on the last dot of the other boat's transmission. Each could then work out the distance apart from a ready reckoner equating time with distance. The result either pleased the officer of the watch, or frightened him to death!

Telegraphist Geoffrey Clough recalls that there were usually two telegraphists per boat, working watch and watch.

'When not on watch there were always other jobs to be done, equipment to be maintained, CBs to be corrected, hydrophone listening watch when submerged, acting as officers' cook, bridge look-out, and engine telegraph operator on the bridge!'

[5] Professor Fessenden's apparatus, built by the American Submarine Signal Company, was brought to the notice of the Admiralty by the Consul in Boston in 1914, as a result of trials off Boston which achieved a range of 31 miles, and arrangements were made for a set to be sent over for trials in Portsmouth harbour. These too were successful, and it was approved to fit ten 'H' class submarines, and 24 others under construction, with sets on shore at Dover and Horse Sands Fort, Portsmouth, to control submarines in the vicinity.

The W/T Department's annual report for 1915 records that:

'there appears to be so much promise of development in the use of underwater sound waves (that) the Admiralty has decided to endeavour to develop its use in the same way as W/T is now being developed, and since the problems are closely allied to those already solved for W/T, by the same departments ...'

Zeppelins and Room 40

In his book *The Sky Was Always Blue*, Admiral Sir William James recalled his time as a Commander in Room 40 during the later stages of the first world war:

'A periodical excitement in Room 40 was a 'Zeppelin' night. The Zeppelins on their passage over the North Sea made their callsign at regular intervals so that the German directional stations could fix their position and inform them where they were. It was a crude form of navigation but the best available. Our stations did the same, so we were able to plot the Zeppelins, and warn the threatened areas to be on the alert.

'A night neither I nor anyone in Room 40 will ever forget was the night when the German wireless broke down. To our amazement the Zeppelins heading for the Northumbrian coast began to drift south and at the same time filled the air with wireless signals. They had got into a northerly current of air and, aware that they were drifting south, were urgently requesting their positions, but their shore stations failed them and five drifted over to France where they were shot down; several more never reached Germany.

'One of them dropped a bomb on Piccadilly Circus - next day we heard that one of the casualties, a woman, had been taken to a hospital and on being undressed was found to be a figure from Swan & Edgar's window!'

Wireless in the Air, 1912

Vice Admiral Sir Raymond Fitzmaurice, a (T) wireless specialist, served as a wireless officer in the Atlantic and Mediterranean Fleets and then, when the RFC was formed in 1912, he was appointed for wireless duties with aircraft. He was Director of the Signal Division from 1923-25, and in the second war became a Convoy Commodore. In 1914 he wrote an account [6] of his early airborne experiences:

[6] Reproduced in *The Communicator*, Vol. 16 No. 3, 1962

'I was appointed for W/T duties with airships with orders to obtain a transmitting range of 20 miles. My first experiment was with the airship Gamma; we had to fit up an assortment of odds and ends consisting of a magneto driven by belt from one of the balloon blowers and some Moschickie jars. I had to use what is called the balanced aerial system. This consisted of a double trailer let down from the bottom of the car on a drum, while the earth was made by wires triced to the bow and stern of the gasbag. Tuning was achieved by letting out or taking in the aerial until the ammeter gave a maximum swing; depending upon the wavelength used, you let out from 100 to 400 feet of aerial wire with a one-pound weight on the end to keep it clear of everything. My chief concern was to prevent sparking in the vicinity of the gasbag, as though hydrogen is only explosive with the proper mixture of air, one could never be sure where or when this most undesirable mixture would take place.

'The first experiment took place using a naval airship shore receiving station at Wittlesford. We experimented at short ranges and everything seemed to do well, though I thought that there was a loss of strength in signals whenever the airship entered cloud banks. Our first experiment at night proved to be most interesting. We planned to fly over Cambridge some twenty miles away and starting at 9 pm we

'expected to be back by midnight. We encountered a strong headwind and then on the way back we missed our camp and lost our way. At 1 am the mechanic informed the CO, Major Maitland, that only three-quarters of an hour's lubricating oil remained. It was evident that we could not land that night, so we switched off both engines to save our oil for landing by daylight, and free ballooned.

'I do not think that I shall ever forget the feeling of perfect peace and quiet one experiences when ballooning at night. The Gamma gradually sank as the hours went by and we had to throw out all our ballast. As the atmosphere became damper, it became imperative to lighten the ship. Major Matland declared that the wireless equipment must go, but I protested strongly and declared that one of the crew would be of less consequence, preferably the engineer who had failed to take enough lubricating oil. Just then one of the mechanics found another sandbag, but in his zeal, instead of opening it and emptying the sand, he threw the whole bag over. There was a sickening crash 2,000 feet below, very much like slate roofs falling in, and as the bag was marked HMA Gamma, we expected to come in for a coroners' inquest in the near future, but we never heard of it again, and never even knew in which county it happened.'

They landed safely at daylight in a field, but Fitzmaurice decided 'in order to lighten the load' to return to camp, with the transmitter, by train!

Semaphoring from an airship escorting a convoy in the first world war

'The great difficulty in advancing radio in aircraft at this time was due to the entire lack of knowledge of communications on the part of aeroplane makers. Another was the lack of flying time, and a series of smashes which reduced the number of aircraft. The life of the first machine allocated for W/T trials was very short; on her last flight both engines suddenly stopped; we were 2,000 feet up, above ground that looked suitable for landing, but an unseen dyke appeared and the pilot had to put the helm hard over and we got there all right but the plane broke up. Fortunately the W/T apparatus was undamaged.

'My next step was to go to Paris to see a new radio set designed by M. Rouzet. It was light (70 lbs), compact and beautifully made, consisting of a self-excited alternator of $^1/_4$ kw power with a safety cutter and clutch for clutching in and out from the main engines, an air-cooled transformer, a tuning coil primary and secondary for altering the wavelength, and a spark gap of special design which emitted a clear musical note.

'A new Short seaplane was ready in time to escort the Royal Yacht for the last 50 miles of her journey back from Flushing after the German Royal Wedding. Flying out to meet her, we sighted a battleship off the North Foreland. The pilot did not notice that she was carrying out gunnery practice and flew at 1,000 feet between the ship and the target. I did see it, but could not make him hear me. I saw a puff of smoke and a moment later we shivered all over and fell some distance. Evidently we had got into the vacuum of the shell!

'We then picked up the Royal Yacht and gave them a W/T salute, the first message the King had ever received from an aircraft. The apparatus worked excellently and our base at Grain held us in good touch all the time, the distance being about 50 miles.

'The next machine to be fitted was another Short seaplane; her life was briefer than most as she broke her back the day after acceptance trials through being stalled. After being repaired, she was burnt to a cinder by a spark from the magneto setting some petrol on fire!

'Things began to move and seaplane stations were built at Yarmouth, Cromarty, Firth of Forth and Calshot. The Hermes was commissioned as a parent ship for aircraft and was fitted with a special platform on the foc'sle to enable machines to fly off, while the quarterdeck was fitted with derricks to hoist the aircraft in and out. Seaplane No. 81 was a great advance, carrying M. Rouzet's latest W/T equipment and wings that could be folded. The main difficulty was starting the engines. *On one occasion flying at 500 feet we began to shake all over; I looked over the side and saw that some struts to the floats had smashed and the floats were swinging back and forth. Sampson, the pilot, put the nose down, but suddenly the back fabric of the upper plane tore where the wings fold. I spent a most uncomfortable ten minutes holding on to the fabric to prevent the tear spreading. Fortunately Sampson made a magnificent landing without doing further damage.*

'One day flying from Hermes I had been sending signals by W/T and had just reported a tramp on our starboard bow when the engine suddenly stopped. We made a bad landing and smashed the undercarriage; luckily the tramp came to our rescue and hoisted us on to her poop. She was a German timber boat bound for Tilbury. A few hours later Hermes came in sight, having realised that something was wrong. We were hoisted out and rehoisted onto Hermes, having had a very interesting day!

'Up to the present it has not been possible to receive signals in an aircraft due to the noise of the engines, but I have no doubt this will be overcome. There are few days when seaplanes cannot fly and they have a great advantage in speed and can mount higher than their natural enemy, the airship. They can carry bombs and guns and use wireless for spotting purposes; in fact I can see no limit to the 'heavier than air' machine. In a few years time everyone will fly and think nothing more of it than they do of present day motoring.'

When a number of US battle-ships joined the Grand Fleet in 1917, a Yeoman was sent to each ship to help them with British signal books and procedures, and a signal officer, Commander Money, joined Admiral Rodman in his flagship.

Returning to Scapa on one occasion the Admiral told his flag lieutenant to make the signal to revert to the usual notice for steam, The flag lieutenant looked up the two groups concerned - GDU and JCU - and, as it was not usual to make use of a formal phonetic alphabet, he shouted to the flagdeck:

'Stand-by boys, man the halyards - God Damn You, Jesus Christ You, shoot!'

Up went the correct hoists!

'Over the Mast in Bare Feet ...'

V B Ash joined HMS *Ganges* in June 1914, and after initial training decided to go in for W/T and was drafted to the *Impregnable* at Devonport. There he found the training pretty tough:

'We were called at 0600, scrubbed down five decks, at 0700 PT and over the masthead in bare feet with ice on the rigging, and the rope's end for the last one down!'

His first ship was HMS *Attentive*, Capt D 6th Flotilla at Dover. Then he joined HMS *Caledon*, light cruiser, fitting out at Birkenhead, before proceeding to Scapa as flagship of the 1st Light Cruiser Squadron. On 17 November 1917 they were in action with German battlecruisers and were hit by 9" and 6" shells, one near the wireless room:

'I was in a silent cabinet with the phones on, so what with the fearful noise of No.4 gun just above, I did not know we had been hit! The Paymaster Commander, in the coding room next door, heard it all right and dashed up on deck to see what had happened. Back down, he saw me still at my post

sending and receiving messages, as a result of which I was recommended for a medal or for higher rate 'for remaining on duty under great provocation!''

In 1925 Ash was in HMS *Somme*, 8th DF, bound for China.

'On passage we were press guard, reading Rugby. On receipt we would hoist 'Press ready for distribution'. We would then take station between the Divisions, and send the press by mechanical semaphore, on top of the 'monkey's island'. Thanks to my training in the Boy Scouts (by an ex-Yeoman of Signals in the Coastguard) I was almost as good as the Leading Signalman and we would take turns, one reading out and the other transmitting.'

Ash left the Navy in 1929 and after a spell as radio operator in a private steam yacht, he joined the Marconi Company as a radio operator. Some ten years later he was in the liner *Islami*, being used to take pilgrims to Mecca.

'We had brass arrows fitted to various deckheads, and every time the ship altered course the second officer had to go round and point the arrows towards Mecca!'

With the outbreak of war, Ash reported to the senior signal officer at Singapore; he was commissioned as a Sub Lieutenant RNVR and appointed as Port Wireless Officer, Penang.

A Quick Kill

E R Baker enrolled as a Signalman in the RNVR in March 1916. He recorded his war experiences in a very readable diary, now in the Imperial War Museum.

'Having passed the Doctor, we were asked if we agreed to be vaccinated. Before being given a chance to reply our papers were stamped 'This man agreed to be vaccinated'. Then a portion of Naval Regulations was read, so quick that it was not possible to understand its purport. Finishing, the Petty Officer said: "To cut it short, you are signing on for the duration of the war".'

After six weeks training at Crystal Palace, Baker was drafted in September 1916 to the old destroyer *Thrasher*, where a few months later he was involved in what seems to have been a very swift action:

'Thrasher from Capt (D). Trawler reports being fired on by sub 7 miles SE from Flamborough Head. Proceed with all despatch = 1310 7 Feb.'

'Capt (D) from Thrasher. Have forced enemy submarine to surrender and taken crew prisoner = 1345 7 Feb.'

'Thrasher from Capt (D). Well Done. Bring submarine in harbour if possible = 1353 7 Feb.'

> *'Capt (D) from Thrasher. Prisoners lst Lieut., Engineer, 14 men also 2 Britishers belong to collier Hanna Larsen = 1455 7 Feb.'*

The submarine, *UC39*, was taken in tow by HMS *Itchen* but sank before reaching harbour.

Baker spent his entire war service in the *Thrasher*. On 11 April 1918 he records:

> *'When going out through the boom I managed to lose a pair of binoculars over the side - these are valued at £6.11s.0d. What will happen I don't know'.* He consulted one Harry Humphreys who *'with 18 years service knows every hole and corner in KR. His advice was simple - say the strap broke - nothing will happen. I took his advice, and after a while another pair was issued and I heard no more of it!'*

Surrender of the German Fleet - 1918

From: C-in-C Grand Fleet
To: Admiral Von Reuter, Friedrich der Grosse

The German flag is to be hauled down at 1557 today Thursday and is not to be hoisted again without permission. = 21.11.18

From: Admiral Von Reuter
To: C-in-C High Seas Fleet

C-in-C GF on the 21st November gave orders that the German Ensign should be hauled down with ceremony and not rehoisted without special permission. I have lodged the attached protest. The question is whether under armistice conditions the internment should be similar in neutral and enemy ports because in neutral ports the hauling down of the flag does not take place. Ought not this also to happen in enemy ports? C-in-C GF says this cannot be allowed and further that while a state of war exists no enemy ship can be allowed to fly their ensigns in British ports while they are under a guard. I cannot acknowledge this decision.

Signed: Von Reuter 2200 25.11.18

This argument was dismissed by the British, and no German ensigns were hoisted again.

Chapter Twenty

Between the Wars

*'As a rule signalmen get into more trouble for boats and
officers coming alongside without being reported than
any other part of their duty.'*

Signal Handbook, 1890

David Joel

Before doing the Long Course, Joel had had some experience of
signalling in the light cruiser *Bellona*:

> *'The function of our four ships - Bellona, Blonde, Blanche and
> Boadicea - was to act as repeating ships stationed one mile on
> the lee side of each of the four battle squadrons in the Grand
> Fleet. Spending a lot of its time at sea, signalling by flags,
> short-distance W/T and searchlight seemed to be near perfect.*
>
> *'In 1915 I was selected to join the first wartime signal
> course in the Signal School at Portsmouth. I well remember
> Commander Collins, an ex-Signal Boatswain, who was a
> most excellent Commander of the School.*
>
> *'At that time W/T was the province of the Torpedo
> Branch in HMS Vernon, then an old three-decker in the
> stream, where we joined up with the Torpedo Long Course.
> The theoretical part was taken by Professor Cecil Fortescue,
> a brilliant scientist who, I believe, had no small part in the
> development of the thermionic valve. Frankly his lectures
> were well above my head, but if I had known that some
> years later as the first 'W One' I should step into his shoes,
> and have to teach the theory of radio to three Long
> Courses, I might well have paid more attention.'*

Joel became flag lieutenant to Admiral Gaunt in the Grand Fleet, and
stayed with him when Gaunt became C-in-C East Indies.

> *'Our headquarters were at Ismailia, and I lived in the
> flagship, Euryalus. We were mainly concerned with the
> Lawrence of Arabia war. I met Lawrence but he made no
> impression on me. Later Egypt was removed from our*

command and we departed for Bombay with the Indian Marine Ship Northbrook as flagship.

'We decided that the Indian Marine should have a proper signal branch of its own, acquired a suitable building in the dockyard, and set up a naval Signal School under my excellent Signal Boatswain, Mr W R Paris. Our pupils were Lascars from the Ratnagiri area on the southern part of the west coast. They were incredibly keen, and learned in record time. There was no guessing, as they knew no English!

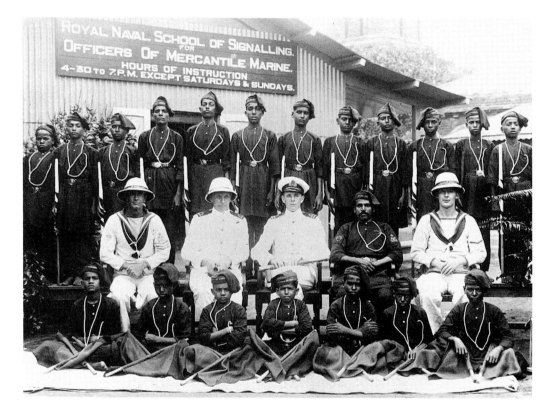

'After the war ended Lord Jellicoe, visiting the Empire in the battlecruiser New Zealand, decided that as a gesture to India he would take a dozen or so of my pupils with him. On the first flashing exercise on board they all got 100%!

'In 1921 I became 'W-One' at the Signal School in charge of all W/T training. The theory of W/T was a worry to me, but my predecessor, Major Miles RMLI, had written the excellent first edition of the 'Handbook of Wireless Telegraphy', which was a great help. I was lucky also for I used to travel by train every morning with Mr Brundrett, [1] one of the Signal School 'boffins', a brilliantly clever scientist and a 'senior wrangler.' He used to coach me on whatever was the subject of the day.

Joel, Paris and pupils at the Bombay Signal School

[1] Later Sir Frederick Brundrett, Chief of the Royal Naval Scientific Service

'I was once trying to explain something called 'grid detection' to the long course when someone asked if I could explain it by differential or integral calculus. I promised that at the next lecture I would provide the full mathematical explanation. That evening I asked Brundrett to give me the most abstruse formula he could on any subject, and got my PO Tel to write it up on the blackboard. I was not troubled again! Luckily there were some clever chaps on the course, and when asked to elucidate a difficult point, I would say 'Tell him, Wylie', or 'Tell him, Willett.'

'Tufty'

Captain Dicky Courage, known to some as 'Tufty', was one of the Royal Navy's most successful riders. As a Dartmouth cadet, his first ride in public was at the Hambledon Hunt on the first day of the General Strike in 1926, and as a Midshipman he rode on the flat in Malta, Greece and even against bare-legged natives with spurs in Samoa.

Filling in an application to train in 1931, the form asked 'Is your head lad permanent?'. 'I hope so' he wrote, 'It's my wife Philippa!'

He joined the Signal Branch as he thought this would be likely to allow him to attend as many race meetings as possible; he did manage to ride sufficient winners to lose his allowance.

It was on his best horse, Young Cuthbert, that in 1935 Courage realised his great ambition of winning the Grand Military Gold Cup at Sandown. This is sometimes referred to as the Soldier's Grand National, and he was determined that one day it should be won by a Sailor.

Courage, family and friends

His last ride was in the 1951 Liverpool Foxhunters in which he finished third on Prudence Glen. 'Of course they were real Becher's fences in those days' he says. 'The winner picked up £600 and we got £41.2s.6d. That works out at five bob a fence and 7/6 for Bechers.'

Clean Duck Suit

Commissioned Signal Boatswain Bill Trotter joined the Navy in 1928. After signal training at *Ganges*, he joined the *Emperor of India*:

'The Boys spent most of their time scrubbing, polishing brasswork, flag hoisting and reading flashers. In the Bay of Biscay the sea came down into the cable locker and flooded the messdeck, and if someone was late for meals it was put down to seasickness and the 'heavy gang' ate the lot.'

Later, Trotter took passage to the Mediterranean in the *Queen Elizabeth*.

'The Boys were again half-starved, being watch and watch and often late for meals which in any case were inadequate as the Petty Officer in charge of the Boys messdeck was mainly interested in mess savings. 'General' Gordon, the Signal Boatswain, selected me as 'boat man', and fitted me out in a clean duck suit, some three sizes too large to allow for shrinkage. With a pair of binoculars round my neck, it seemed to be me who shrunk.

'The Officer of the Watch told me to patrol the quarter-deck, report the approach of all boats with flags, affirmative or negative discs, with the number of fingers shown by the coxswain to denote the rank of the officer on board. Boats came from everywhere, and I was running about like a scared rabbit.

'After a while the C-in-C, Admiral Chatfield, appeared and commenced pacing the quarterdeck, so that I had to keep hopping out of the way. Other officers appeared, amongst them the Fleet Signal Officer, Commander Haines, Fleet Wireless Officer, Lieutenant Commander Mountbatten, the Signal Boatswain, and the Surgeon Commander, not to mention the Master at Arms, and two buglers. A finger beckoned. "Who are you? What's your name? Where did you get that suit?" Everyone fired questions, while the whole watch on the flagdeck, which was aft, were hanging over the rail trying to catch this one-sided conversation.

'The Admiral then entered the conversation, asking much the same questions but in a quiet manner. He told the Fleet Paymaster to see that all quarterdeck staff were dressed in drill suits, made to measure. He asked if the Boys got enough to eat, and when I told him we ate alternate meals he gave the Surgeon Commander a roasting, and said that all Boys were to be inspected for malnutrition!

'The outcome was that I got a new suit of clothes, much to the envy of my contemporaries, the messdeck Petty Officer disappeared and life for the Boys entered a period of tranquility.'

'Sandy' Saunders

Leslie 'Sandy' Saunders decided to specialise in Signals in 1919.

'A new branch was just coming into its own - Signals. With the development of wireless telegraphy, plus the manœuvring of fast moving ships, signalling had become too complex to be left to the untrained flag lieutenant. Further, these were the days of perks, and 'Haul Down' promotions were one of them. When an admiral hauled down his flag on completion

Leslie Saunders

One of the instructors at the
Signal School when Saunders
did his Long Course was
Charles Daniel, who had a
ready wit. He was instructing
them in the details of a new
silica wireless valve when one
of the class enquired:

"Don't these things give off
X-rays?" "Yes," said Daniel,
"But you can't rely on them."

of his term of appointment, his secretary and flag lieutenant
were automatically promoted. It had now become the rule
that the flag lieutenant had to be a trained signal officer and
to act as the Squadron Signal Officer as well.

'So Signals was clearly indicated, and I applied for this,
a decision I have never regretted, although 'Haul Down'
promotions regrettably became a thing of the past. But first
I had to have experience as a watch-keeping officer in a big
ship, and I was appointed to Revenge, flagship of Vice
Admiral Sir Sydney Fremantle, known as 'My Boy, Sid'.
This stemmed from the way his father, also an admiral,
constantly referred to him.

'My Boy Sid was an impressive figure with a well-
trimmed, pointed beard. One Sunday the wives and children
came onboard to morning service on the quarterdeck. When
all was ready, the admiral came on deck and took the chair
reserved for him. A small piercing voice piped up: "Mummy,
is that Jesus Christ?" My Boy Sid turned round, "Not quite,
dear child, but (addressing all and sundry) a perfectly
understandable misapprehension."

'The Cattistock Hunt organised a race exclusively for
the Navy at their annual Point-to-Point ... Geoffrey Congreve
and I thought we would have a go and arranged for hirelings
from the livery stables. The spectators seemed to think it was
a great joke to see the Navy on horseback. There were of
course a number of falls, as happened in other races too; but
in their case a hush would fall on the crowd and an ambulance
would rush to the scene, whereas in our case there were hoots
of laughter and shouts of "Man overboard!"'

In 1923 Saunders relieved Henry Cecil as Flag Lieutenant to Vice
Admiral Sir Michael Culme-Seymour, C-in-C, America and West Indies.

'Henry was a delightfully vague creature and passionately
musical. Often when the C-in-C wanted his Flag Lieutenant,
Henry had disappeared to play the organ in Hamilton.
Matters came to a head when, having arranged with the
C-in-C the seating plan for an important dinner party that
evening, Henry returned to his office, opened a drawer in his
desk to discover that it still contained the invitations!'

In 1926 Saunders was the Squadron Signal and W/T Officer, and
Flag Lieutenant, in HMS Cardiff.

'A new port, Port Fuad, had been built at the entrance to the
Suez Canal, and was about to be opened by King Fuad. Our
High Commissioner, Lord Lloyd, asked the C-in-C for a
cruiser to support him and Cardiff was detailed. H.E. and
his staff boarded us at Alexandria and we proceeded to Port
Said. Amongst the gaily decorated ships there, lay the
King's Royal Yacht, Mahroussa, and smart Egyptian motor

launches sped to and fro across the harbour. We learned that we should have to provide transport across the harbour for H.E. to the opening ceremony next day. This shook us thoroughly. Being an old ship, with an ancient and quite unreliable motor cutter, we had nothing to compare with the Gyppy launches. The possibility of a breakdown with H.E. drifting across the waters, or being taken in tow by a Gyppy launch, was a dreadful prospect. The Navy's resourcefulness came to the fore. We would row him across. We tackled our 12-oar pulling cutter; scrubbed and canvassed it inside and scraped and enamelled it outside, until it looked like a new-born baby. We selected twelve of our brawniest seamen - the tragedy was that they had no time to grow beards - and drilled them in boat drill , rowing together in perfect time, laying on oars with every oar beautifully horizontal and parallel to its neighbour, tossing oars with every oar perfectly vertical, and boating oars with smoothness and precision.

'And thus, the sailors in their No.1's with gold badges, the Union Flag in the bows and a large White Ensign at the stern, the Representative of Britain and my Admiral were solemnly rowed across the harbour. This stately proceeding, with its old-worldly tradition of sea-power, made an enormous impression on our hosts. They had never seen anything like it.'

Saunders was the Fleet Signal Officer in HMS *Nelson* in 1930:

'A debacle occurred when we visited the French Navy at Brest, which was a saluting port, so the international ceremonial consisted of:

1. Nelson fires a salute of 21 guns to France;

2. This is returned by a 21 gun salute by the Fort;

3. Nelson then fires a 19 gun salute to the French C-in-C;

4. The French flagship fires 19 guns to the British C-in-C.

'In the event, Nelson fired her salute to France. Nothing happened. We waited a considerable time, then concluded that the Fort must have returned our salute and we had not seen it. The C-in-C told me to carry on with the salute to the French C-in-C. We had no sooner started this, than the French flagship started firing, followed shortly by the Fort, so all three were banging away simultaneously. A French staff officer came rushing off to us to express his Admiral's deep apologies. What had happened was that the Fort was asleep, and rather than appear discourteous, the French flagship had endeavoured to take the place of the Fort, and was doing so when the Fort woke up. These interchanges may not seem important to the layman, but countries can be very touchy if they feel they have not received the proper

marks of respect, and a diplomatic incident can result.

'When we went to Invergordon for battle practice, I invited a soldier friend, Colin Roff, to spend a few days and witness the firings. The first morning, he appeared on deck just as 'Colours' was sounding off and smoking a pipe! I told him to put it out at once. This he proceeded to do by knocking the contents on to our sacred and immaculate quarterdeck. Poor Colin. I sent him below forthwith. Pongos at sea are all at sea.

'The new C-in-C was Admiral Sir John Kelly. He came up to the Admiral's Bridge. After an hour or so he sent for the ship's painter. The Staff were already there. In Admiral Hodges' day the entire Staff came up, and having nothing to do, smoked and chattered away like a lot of magpies, getting in my way and even in the C-in-Cs. They wondered at the call for the painter. They were soon to learn. He told the painter to paint a broad white line across the middle of the bridge. That done, he informed the Staff that they were to remain behind this line unless they had something to report to him. There was to be no chattering and no smoking. This delighted me. I could now move freely between the C-in-C and my signal communications.

'One of the first signals he made was to Barham, our next astern and too far astern. Instead of the usual curt flag signal, "You are astern of station", he made: "Be a bit more matey!"

'After a marathon race which Rodney won, he dictated the following signal to be sent to the fleet: "I was pleased with the spirit shown in the marathon today and I congratulate Rodney on her win, which I hope to repeat on a future occasion." Quizzically, I asked "Do you mean you hope to repeat your congratulations to Rodney?" He glowered at me and said "There will be a potential widow in Scotland if you don't b....r off!" I replied: "I am not married, Sir." Swiftly came the reply, "I said POTENTIAL!". At that, I b......d off, rewording the signal to make it clear.

'Late one evening the C-in-C came on deck and spotted the Royal Marine Corporal of the Watch leaning against the turret. Joe moved up behind the man, leaned against the turret in the same posture, and said quietly: 'All right, mate. I've got the weight!' The Corporal nearly had a heart attack.

'At the Admiralty in 1933 my job was to start a reserve of wireless operators from the numerous amateur wireless fans in the country. The Post Office, who issued their licences, put me in touch with some of the leading fans, and with them I toured the country, spreading the gospel. They had the most impressive installations and welcomed the *idea of putting them to some useful purpose, with the additional privileges I was able to offer them. And so the Royal Naval Wireless Auxiliary Reserve* [2] *was borne.'*

In 1934 Saunders was in command of HMS *Escapade*:

'A signalman named Jennings was serving in our Flotilla Leader, Exmouth. He was a grand man; no matter how bad the weather, with seas washing over the bridge, he could be relied upon to get a signal through. He was an enthusiastic player of the Highland bagpipes and used to play the ship in and out of harbour. But he had one failing - he would periodically go ashore and indulge in a most terrific blind. His promotion to Leading Signalman therefore never lasted very long.

'One evening the Queen of Spain dined on board and Jennings played the pipes during dinner. The Queen asked if he could be spared to play at a party at the Palace in Madrid. We begged him to behave, the honour of the Navy in his hands, etc. In due course he returned - festooned with cigars, one behind each ear and others stuffed in his jumper. All were agog to hear how he had got on. "Well, Sorr, Her Majesty seemed to enjoy them but some of the Grandees didn'a pay much attention." Knowing it was customary for Royalty to present a small gift, we asked if he had been so thanked. "No Sorr. She thanked me very much, but she did ask me if there was anything I would like." Great excitement - the whole of Spain for the asking! "Well, what did you say?" "I asked her Majesty if she no had a wee drap whisky aboot the Palace."

'On another occasion Jennings came off from shore in the early hours, very, very drunk. He demanded his pipes. The Officer of the Watch told him to turn in. The Quartermaster took him below. A short time elapsed, then the whole ship shook from stem to stern. Jennings had gone to the focs'le and let go the anchor! So once more off came his killick.'

[2] This became the RNV(W)R, which the 1938 Regulations stated was 'to provide a reserve of trained W/T operators for service in the RN in time of Emergency, and to afford opportunities for practice and training ... and to encourage those interested in the transmission of messages by wireless in the morse code.' Divided into nine Districts, the peacetime establishment was stated to be 30 officers and 1,200 ratings.

Lord Louis

During the 1925 long signal course, Mountbatten seemed to burn the candle at both ends, working extremely hard but then going home to practice a new hobby, polo (and to write a book on the subject, 'Polo' by Marco), or up to London to dine and dance, sometimes arriving back in his Hispano-Suiza sports car (with a model of a signalman holding semaphore flags on the radiator cap) just in time to go to work. Despite this daunting regimen, he passed out top, and his fast lifestyle did nothing to alienate the others on his course.

He had a good understanding of technical matters and a love of gadgetry. One invention of his was the Mountbatten Station-Keeper, which was installed in J and K class destroyers, and some others. Having decided that one's ship was a certain distance ahead or astern of station, a dial was turned to the appropriate setting, and the engine room then adjusted the revolutions to bring the pointer back to zero when, theoretically, the ship would be back in station. The author recalls using it in HMS *Kandahar*; there was always the worry that it might get things wrong and it was necessary to keep a very sharp look-out in case one suddenly caught up the next ahead, or was nuzzled by the next astern who might also have been relying on his station-keeping equipment.

Andrew Yates, a contemporary of Mountbatten's, writing to a friend in America during the war, said:

'The station-keeper served him to the last - he was able to stand on it when abandoning ship!' [3]

A particular interest of Lord Louis was the cinema. Most of the big ships had silent projectors for showing locally hired films, but the cost of conversion to 'talkies' was beyond the resources of most canteen funds. Mountbatten enlisted the help of one of his long course students, Lieutenant Mansfield 'Dafty' Robinson (whom he described as a 'brilliant radio amateur') to design a conversion kit which was then built by the Fleet Repair ship *Resource* against repayment of a fairly modest sum, so that the ships were able to turn over to talkies within a few weeks.

Lord Louis always maintained a close connection with the Signal School, regularly attending reunions and other functions; in 1971 the New Entries' division had been named 'Kelly Squadron' after his destroyer and on several occasions thereafter Lord Louis came to inspect their passing out parade, when he would address the young communicators and their parents.

In his book 'On My Way to the Club', Ludovic Kennedy describes his first night at sea as a Sub Lieutenant in HMS Tartar. While being shown various pieces of equipment on the bridge by the first lieutenant, 'he came to some large instrument covered in canvas. I think he was going to pass it by when, to show keen interest, I said:

'What's in there, sir?'

'That,' he said, 'is a thing called the Mountbatten station-keeping gear. It was invented by Lord Louis or his father, I forget which. We keep it covered because the captain finds it quite useless!'

[3] IWM - Papers of Captain AVS Yates

*   *   *   *   *

In 1954 Mountbatten was C-in-C Mediterranean. The new Royal Yacht, *Britannia*, had been completed in time to 'relieve' the *Gothic* for the final leg of the 1953-54 Royal tour. Having disembarked from the *Gothic* in Aden, the Royal party embarked in *Britannia* at Tobruk, being escorted by the 2nd Frigate Squadron of four ships.

Some 200 miles from Malta, she was met by the Mediterranean Fleet, consisting of *Eagle*, three cruisers and eleven destroyers. The C-in-C, in *Glasgow*, led the fleet which approached in two columns at high speed from ahead, cruisers and *Eagle* to starboard, destroyers to port. The columns then wheeled in succession and steamed past the Royal Yacht close aboard on either side.

The FCO, Christopher Wake-Walker, recalls that the fleet was practised in the manœuvres and the sequence of signals was well known; it was the execution of the signals that really mattered.

Prince Louis of Battenberg was appointed First Sea Lord by Winston Churchill, then First Lord, in 1913. One of Churchill's last acts as Prime Minister was to appoint his son to the same post in 1955.

PRECISE MANŒUVRES

COLUMNS EXCHANGING POSITIONS

EA The two columns are to exchange their positions by turning together 90° towards each other, the ships of each column passing through the intervals of the other.

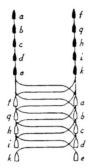

(*a*) Ships turn together 90° inwards and pass so as to leave the corresponding ships of the other column on the port hand, resuming the original course together so as to arrive at their proper distance apart.

The Admiral works the Turning Flag.

(*b*) The ships of the port column commence to turn with tactical rudder when the executive signal is made and at the same moment ships of the starboard column commence to turn with the amount of rudder necessary to turn the ship with an advance of one cable more than that used by the ships of the port column. That is to say, if in a 90° turn the ships in the port column advance 700 yards, the ships of the starboard column should advance 900 yards.

(*c*) **Restriction.**—The distance apart of columns must be great enough to admit of ships being steadied before passing each other.

'*All signals were made by flags and repeated by voice; in the days when TBS sets were worn out and Inglefield clips had a nasty habit of carrying away, such precautions were necessary. I lived in terror that some vital flaghoist would execute itself and ruin the whole show.*

'*Perfect timing was essential and this was a headache for the Fleet Navigator. For instance, the last gun salute had to coincide with the signal executing the wheel of the columns in towards the Yacht. The wheel could not wait for the guns and there was no margin for error at 25 knots with cruisers two cables apart and other ships 1½, except for Eagle at 3 cables. Ships were to pass Britannia at a distance of 100 yards.*

'*Safely back in my office at Lascaris, I was visited by an excited Navigator from the Yacht who said: "C'est magnifique ... never do it again!" The sight of the fleet bearing down on him had been bad enough but as we steamed past he had had to use 25 degrees of wheel to keep the Yacht steady.*

Mediterranean Fleet destroyers carrying out the 'Grid-iron' in 1954

'After the manœuvres were over I said to the Fleet Navigator, well out of the C-in-C's hearing, "I reckon there is only one thing we can do which would be worse and that is a 'grid-iron' ahead of a ship." A few months later we were sent for by the C-in-C who said: "The Emperor of Ethiopia is going from Malta to England in Gambia. I want to do some manœuvres for him and this time we shall do a grid-iron ahead of the ship." We did. It was an 18 ship grid-iron, including four Pakistani destroyers, at 24 knots with ships two cables apart. As the ships passed, the nearest was 3 cables ahead of Gambia. It was fun but I was glad when it was over.'

'Two Toots'

Lieutenant Commander Arthur McCulloch, a Telegraphist in the *Coventry*, RA(D)s flagship in the Mediterranean in 1931 when Mountbatten was Fleet Wireless Officer, insists that the following is true.

'Our transmissions were taped resulting in caustic signals to those not up to his high standard. One 'habit' Mountbatten deplored was the sending of cryptic private messages during the night watches: for example in Coventry we might receive 'INT KYE' from the operator in Bulldog, which meant 'request permission to close down for five minutes to make the cocoa?' If things were quiet the reply would be 'AF'. This procedure would be followed in turn by each ship on the destroyer frequency until all had made their kye.'

Drafted to the *Royal Sovereign*, McCulloch became a watchkeeper on Fleet Wave, a frequency believed to be monitored by Lord Louis.

At a conference for off-watch telegraphists in the Corradino canteen, Lord Louis said that since he had started monitoring, the efficiency of the fleet's communications had improved dramatically, but the making of private messages was to stop. "The sending of one single 'toot' on the key will constitute a private message and the culprit will be severely dealt with.'

That afternoon things were fairly quiet when McCulloch was handed a message to send to *Curacao*. Switching on the transmitter, he sent the signal, then reached behind his morse key to break the heavy duty switch; in the process he accidentally caught his elbow on the key, blasting out a loud 'toot' for all to hear!

'That was bad enough but the operator in Curacao forgot the forenoon's instructions and sent back a cheery 'toot toot'. With hardly a pause, out came a signal from the C-in-C 'Report name and rating of operator of the watch'.

'On the Saturday I felt I had better have a final run ashore, all sorts of dire punishments having been forecast by my messmates. While enjoying a few pints one of my pals saw a poster for the Flagship's Farewell Ball that evening; we decided to join in! The dance hall was packed with officers and men from every ship in the fleet, together with their ladies, and a great time was being had by all. Our chance to join in came with the announcement: "Take your partners for the Paul Jones."

'My third partner was obviously an officer's wife, she was a superb dancer and I said so. Just then Lord Louis danced by and gave her a big smile which she acknowledged with a discreet wave. "I see you know my Chief," I said. "I ought to," she replied, "I'm married to him!" "If you are one of his telegraphists" she went on, "you'll know he is furious with two of you for making 'toots' or something. In fact we've heard so much of these men that we've christened them 'Toots No.1' and 'Toots No.2'". I paused for a moment and then said "I'm afraid I'm Toots No.1". She stopped in the middle of the floor and held me at arms length. "I don't believe it - I'm actually dancing with 'Toots' himself! You must come and meet everyone."

'Having escorted her to her seat, I set off towards the bar. "McCulloch", Lord Louis' voice boomed behind me, "So, you're the culprit are you? What have you to say for yourself?" The ladies of his party caught up with us and Lord Louis introduced me. "Now, what have you to say for yourself?" I explained what had happened: "Bad luck really Sir, particularly coming on top of your lecture." Lady Edwina spoke up: "I'm sure he is telling the truth Dickie, don't be too hard on him." "Fortunately for you, young man, I'm familiar with the layout of the wireless gear and I

*can see how it could have happened. Perhaps I should give
you the benefit of the doubt. I'll write to your Captain before
he sees you, but remember to be more careful in future." I
thanked him and shot off to tell my pals what had happened.*

*'In due course I found myself in front of the Captain.
"Ah! I've had a letter about you. I see you had an interview
with the FWO ashore and he recommends that I give you
another chance. Case dismissed. Don't do it again!" Sad
to say my oppo in Curacao was not so fortunate; his
Commander had been at Jutland and blamed all telegraphists
for allowing the German fleet to escape, so he got a months
stoppage of leave.'*

*   *   *   *   *

McCulloch was not the only telegraphist to suffer a similar experience
as this poem, first published in *The Communicator,* reveals:

A nondescript nonentity, a limb of the oppressed,
I wear no badges on my arm, no medals on my chest,
But though my past is colourless, my future dim and bleak,
I cherish a distinction which is probably unique.

Of all the mass of traffic through the tortured ether hurled,
By all the busy Tels of all the navies of the world,
No morse of mine impinged upon a fellow sparker's ear;
I never sent a signal in the whole of my career.

I used to wonder meekly when control would let me in
To add my little quota to the universal din.
Then realised my destiny, surrendered to my fate,
Eternally to sit and serve by being told to wait.

But once - and only once - I found my baser self constrained
To break the wireless silence I so rigidly maintained.
My weary watch was over, my relief was overdue,
I gently, briefly, pressed the key to see what it would do.

I often sit and wonder where that blameless dot has gone,
If still through endless time and space it hurries bravely on,
Disowned by its creator, and dismissed its parent ship,
Unauthorised, attenuated, lonely little pip.

But though beyond our universe its travels may extend,
It still will bear my fingerprints on reaching journey's end
And beings in some unknown world may trace it back to me,
As surely as the Flagship did in 1943.

Prelude to NATO?

As RAD, Mediterranean, in the light cruiser *Galatea* in 1936, James Somerville found himself at Palma, Majorca, which had declared for the Nationalists in the civil war but which was somewhat isolated. Several foreign warships were there and when the Republicans threatened to bombard Palma, Somerville, as the senior officer present, led the German pocket battleship *Deutschland* (flying the flag of Rear Admiral Carlos), the Italian destroyer *Marcello*, and the British destroyer *Garland* to sea and manœuvred them as a squadron. The bombardment failed to materialise, and on return Somerville signalled:

'*The station-keeping, signalling and manœuvring of the 'international squadron' has aroused my warmest appreciation.*' *The German Admiral replied: 'When all ships of these three navies would be joined in a squadron like that one today, it would be very good in many ways.*'

'*The Fighting Admiral*', by Donald Macintyre

Marching Manœuvres

Michael Chichester attended the 1942 Long Course.

'*Besides mastering the morse code, the colours of flags and pendants, and the basics of wireless telegraphy, we of the Signal Branch had to do our bit of parade ground drill like any other training class, marching, doubling, etc. as we dispersed from morning divisions or shifted berth from one classroom to another.*

'*But not for us the 'gas and gaiters' and loud-mouthed 'bull' which were the traditional accompaniments of these activities. We did it our way by turning drill into a useful training aid in the use of the Fleet Signal Book and the manœuvres set out in that lead-weighted red covered volume.*

'*So imagine a class of aspiring (S) officers, bunting tossers or sparkers paraded in two ranks outside the front door at Leydene on a crisp autumn morning, waiting to move off. Anywhere else it would be 'Class - right turn - double March', but not at the Signal School. The parade ground orders would be replaced by a series of 'flag hoists' initiated by the class leader or instructor, acknowledged by each member of the class holding up his hand, or a small replica of the Answer Pendant, first horizontally ('at the dip'), then vertically ('close up') when the signal was understood. The signal would be executed by the cry of 'Down'.*

'*Thus 'Blue Nine, George One Five' would be the order for 'Right turn, double march,' while 'Freddy Duff' (Stop engines) would bring the class to a halt. More complicated*

According to John Meadows, marching manœuvres used to be put on as a variety turn by Leading Signalmen qualifying courses at dances held at Portsmouth Guildhall, and the records show that they were sometimes used in the early part of the century as demonstrations for VIPs visiting the Commander-in-Chief.

Marching Manœuvres at
HMS *Ganges* between the wars

The 'Admiral' leads the
starboard column.

*manœuvres could be performed if 'a bit of a show' was
thought appropriate. Red or white pendant turns, equal
speed manœuvres and even 'grid-irons' were sometimes
attempted; indeed given enough space the opening moves of
the British battle fleet at Jutland could be played out before
an admiring group of spectators. If collision or disaster
threatened in the shape of a well-kept rose bed 'Emergency
Freddy Duff' would bring the fleet to a shuddering halt.*

*'When King George VI visited the Signal School in 1942
classes were fallen in for inspection and march past. The
Long Course included a Major, Royal Signals, mastering
the art of naval communications prior to joining Combined
Ops. He had donned his best uniform, a well-cut pair of riding
breeches, shining boots, Sam Browne belt, swagger stick
and all the trimmings, topped by a magnificent moustache.
Here was a splendid example of combined services communications, the riding boots turning smartly, not to spur his
steed, but to obey the 'Blue nine' flaghoist, acknowledged by
his swagger stick close up at the starboard yardarm.*

*'A couple of years later when the King visited the Home
Fleet before the D-Day landings, I was then Flag Lieutenant
to CS10 with whom the King was lunching, and asked him
if he remembered his visit to Leydene, and the solitary
soldier. "Yes, of course I do," was the reply, "and what a
splendid moustache".'*

The Telegraphist Air Gunner

The TAG formed a member of the crew of multi-seat aircraft from 1922 when the first course was held at RAF Gosport; they flew in seaplanes from cruisers and battleships, and in carrier borne aircraft. Their training in the early days was fairly short - provided they could maintain W/T (morse) touch with the ground over three or four cross-country flights, they were qualified! They were paid 1/- a day.

In almost all the pre-war aircraft they were in open cockpits, operating equipment which required a novel operation known as 'lickers and tappers' to establish whether or not the receiver was working. This consisted of licking the finger and tapping it on a point fitted on the face of the receiver to produce a clicking noise in the 'phones. In the transmitter, master oscillator and amplifier coils had to be withdrawn and exchanged to set up a new frequency. The aerial trailed beneath the aircraft, being reeled in and out with a small winch in the cockpit.

Signalling between aircraft was usually carried out by 'zogging', a combination of semaphore and morse using the arm, as waving a flag was not practicable. The arm was held upright, then swung down from the elbow, short swings for dots and long for dashes.

From about 1936, with the expansion of the Fleet Air Arm, not enough telegraphists could be spared, and volunteers from other branches joined as Air Gunners. By now flying pay was 2/6 per day.

On 26 September 1939 several Blackburn Skuas from *Ark Royal* met three Dornier flying boats; TAG Bryan Seymour shot one down, the first enemy aircraft to be destroyed in the war.

After the war it was thought that the fashion would be mainly for single seat aircraft, and anyway the guns would be fixed to the airframe and fired by the pilot, so there would no longer be a requirement for a Gunner. However bigger and better aircraft arrived and the telegraphists were called upon again, this time becoming known as Tels (Flying). They were then employed mainly in anti-submarine aircraft. But this phase was short-lived, as Voice took over from Morse, and the training of Tels (F) finally ceased in 1957.

Chapter Twenty One

1939 - 1941

*'His answering pendant should be at the dip before the
flagship's signal reaches the truck.'*

Signal Handbook, 1890

A WRNS Signal Officer at War

Peggy Ahearn (Mrs Morrissey) joined up early in the war as an
'immobile' Wren at Harwich, where she became a Coder in the SDO.

*'One of the finest and most competent people for whom I
have worked was Gerald Affleck-Graves. There I was taught
the basis of a signal officer's trade by retired Yeomen who,
under Gerald, had to operate on us raw girls, and managed
to turn us into cypher officers.*

*'Gerald was relieved by David Bromley-Martin, equally
helpful, who offered a bottle of precious rationed gin to the
person who learned by heart the most instructions in the W/T
manual. I did not get it.*

*'In 1941 I reported for duty at Derby House, Liverpool,
headquarters of the Western Approaches Command. Two
signal officers who had practical experience of headquarters communications requirements, Ridley Waymouth at
Liverpool, and Micky Hodges at the Nore, were confident
that WRNS officers could become competent signal officers
and that we would be needed as more and more RNVR
officers were wanted at sea. Thus volunteers were eventually
called for, and six of us (only two actually volunteers, of
whom I wasn't one!) reported to HMS Mercury for the first
course, which comprised six RNVRs and six WRNS. Our
RNVR colleagues were splendid and promptly apologised
for the fact that each had a single bed while we were put into
double-deckers sharing a cabin!*

*'Morse was my Achilles Heel. The noises I produced
were quite unintelligible until, after patient coaching by two*

From: Admiralty
Following from British
Ambassador, Washington.

President has just heard from
a source in Berlin which he
considers most reliable that
invasion of England is timed
for 3 pm tomorrow Sunday.
= 22.9.40

RNVRs, I correctly tapped out an irreverent message to our instructor, Dicky Courage. In the final test - V/S on the Broadwalk - we all passed, but only with the help of Yeomen hidden behind bushes.

'Four of us went to the Western Approaches headquarters as Assistant Signal Officers, where our lack of V/S was no handicap. and later I moved on to Plymouth. My interest then was in W/T, and with the aid of a splendid publication 'The Band of Optimum Frequencies' and a Chief of Staff who had faith in me, things went well. One task was to make sure that ships of all nations arriving in Plymouth had the means of contacting friendly aircraft; it seemed obvious, but many ships overlooked the need. A standard signal was made to each new ship on arrival, and I earned the name of 'Crystal Packing Momma'.

'The horror of learning morse paid off in 1944, during the pre-D-Day build up, when W/T operators were having trouble intercepting E-Boat signals, and my splendid retired Chief discovered that his signal officer had an ability to 'search and find'.

USN ships arriving in UK waters at this time had great problems - they were not used to the confined sea spaces around the UK, they didn't have time to digest the voluminous

Signalman to WRNS (Ce) candidate:
    'Do you want me to write down what you say, or what he's transmitting?'

The second combined RNVR and WRNS Signal Course, 1943
Back (L to R): Sue Hobson, Peggy Wightman, Geoffrey Crothers, Philip Whipp, David Griffith-Jones, 'Hank' Fahey USN, HL Day, CPO Tel Percy Hancock, Margaret Levick, Phoebe Irwin.
Front (L to R): Evelyn Currie, Elizabeth Hudson, G Oldfield, Dicky Wells (Course Officer), Hayden Thomas, Connie McLelland, Leslie Henry.

No photo of the first course in 1942 has been traced, but Peggy Ahearn, referred to in this article, appears in the photo of the Signal Division in 1945, on page 167.

OVERLORD W/T orders, and they had difficulty with the phraseology. I was given 48 hours to precis about 40 pages into 4 pages of essentials - we used large print and short paragraphs.

'*Two splendid signal officers were attached to Plymouth for OVERLORD, John Meadows and Rupert Bray. One day I told John there was an uncanny silence from Omaha and Utah beaches. John disappeared. 24 hours later we were in communication again. Then he re-appeared, having hitched a ride to the beaches, and gone round marking all the beach parties' transmitters with elastoplast to show the operators where to keep the needle!*

'*In 1944 I joined DSD/DNI 9, the first WRNS signal officer to serve in the Admiralty. DSD9 was Herbert Layman, an apparently non-dynamic person, but who had no equal in the speed with which he could get a docket cleared; when something urgent cropped up he would disappear for an hour or so, re-appearing with the file covered in initials and action approved.*

'*My job entailed working closely with the 'Y' stations, and also with Captain Roger Winn RNVR, later Lord Justice Winn, in charge of the Submarine Tracking Room, whose knowledge of U-Boats and their captains was fantastic. He very quietly did not suffer fools, but I always found him the most generous of men, giving more credit elsewhere than was always due.*'

Black Light Signalling

Between 1940 and 1942 the First Minelaying Squadron of five ships, based at Kyle of Lochalsh, laid the northern barrage of mines between Scotland and north of Iceland. The squadron signal officer was Ian Balfour. They had no VHF equipment, so were committed to strict radio silence. They were, however, fitted with ZAX.

'*ZAX was an infra-red system transmitted from specially adapted 10-inch signal projectors; the receivers were fitted on the mast and connected to buzzers at the 10-inch SP position. The equipment was very reliable, night and day, or even in fog when a sort of 'Are you there Moriarty?' routine was used to find the next in line. No special operator training was needed, other than to learn to train the SP accurately if a range in excess of about three and a half cables was to be achieved.*

'*The squadron of five ships did a good deal of manœuvring, using either V/S or ZAX, because of the need for very accurate navigation, which was aided by taut-wire measuring gear, and because it was anyway inadvisable to lay mines in a line ahead formation! Communication with the close escort, if we had one, had to be by V/S only, until near the end of the operation when the flagship was fitted with VHF R/T.*

'These minelayers were converted merchant ships of 10-12,000 tons - Southern Prince (flag), Agamemnon, Menestheus, Port Napier and Port Quebec. By the end of the operation Southern Prince had been torpedoed, returning safely to harbour at 12 knots with a cement filled forepeak; Port Quebec had been bombed but suffered only superficial damage, and Port Napier was burnt out in harbour (while carrying a full load of mines!). The report of the Southern Prince being torpedoed close to the gap in its own minefield was treated with great derision in the Admiralty until Rear Admiral Minelayers appeared with part of the German torpedo which had landed on the foc'sle!

'The only casualties in the Squadron were two men lost overboard from the last liberty boat.'

Survivor of the *Hood*

Lieutenant Commander Ted Briggs, then a young signalman, was one of three survivors when the *Hood* was sunk by the *Bismarck* in 1941. He had joined the Navy as a Signal Boy aged 15 in March 1938, and after sixteen months at *Ganges*, found himself drafted to *Hood*. The following is taken from his book, *Flagship Hood*.

'As one of my duties I had to set myself up on the forecastle whenever we moored or weighed anchor and signal by flags to the chief yeoman on the bridge the number of shackles of cable on deck or whether the anchor was down, away, clear or foul. To be such an important linchpin in the communication system did my ego the world of good, even though the very information which I was signalling was also being sent to the bridge by telephone!

'I have always had a head for heights and enjoyed climbing the ninety-two-foot mainmast. Because of this I was normally detailed to strike the foretopmast whenever Hood passed under the Forth Bridge. I was also sent aloft when a halyard was lost accidentally by one of my fellow 'bunts'. The masts were not difficult to scale, and only the last six feet, which was a sheer pole, had to be shinned up. One day when a halyard had been blown away on the starboard forward upper yardarm, I was ordered to go up for it. I had inched my way to the end to regain the Inglefield clip when the safety valves in the engine-room were blown. A large cloud of steam swirled up towards me. I clung on grimly

Gadget for recovering a lost hoist showing the Inglefield Clips, one with a swivel which would normally be at the head of a flag, the fixed clip being at the tack.

The clips were invented by Admiral Sir Edward Inglefield, 1820-1894, and allow flags to be bent on rapidly, with little risk of them coming adrift.

but decided that, if it was hot, I would let go and drop into the sea. I preferred drowning to being boiled alive. But by the time it immersed me the steam had turned into a cold shower.

Ordinary Signalman Briggs

'All the boys were subjected to the normal apprentice-type jokes, like getting green oil for the starboard lamps; on 31 August, the day the fleet mobilised, Hood was entering Scapa Flow to join Repulse and Renown. It was a serious - and for me emotive - occasion, until I noticed Yeoman Wright and Ivor Holding, a Royal Marine signalman, directing their binoculars towards the shore. "Quick, there's one over there" shouted Wright. "What is it, Yeo?" I asked. He handed me a telescope: "Just look at them - they're wild haggis. They have webbed feet and are covered in brown fur." I scanned the shore line for several minutes before realising I was 'being had'.*

'At 11 am on 3 September, in company with the Renown and part of the fleet, we were on watch with the intention of shadowing German surface raiders which might slip through the Iceland-Faroes Channel into the Atlantic. I was on the point of making my first signal in a warship. Flag 'E' was hoisted as a preliminary for a general semaphore message, and Chief Yeoman George Thomas ordered: "Briggs, get a pair of hand-flags and get up to the fifteen-inch director and show up 46." It was with a strange sort of pride and yet a sinking feeling in my belly that I spelt out to the fleet; 'Commence hostilities against Germany'.*

'For the next six months Hood's routine became long days and piercingly cold nights at sea ... there was a scramble for the lee side of the flag deck. It was very unwise to be on the weather edge for more than an hour at a time because it took more than two hours to thaw out. One unofficial punishment if we did anything wrong was to be sent to the side which caught the worst of the weather. Another was 'telescope soup' - a sharp blow with the leading signalman's telescope on the elbow or funny bone.'*

In early 1940 Briggs became messenger to the flag lieutenant:

'A plum job for a signal boy. I had to follow Lieutenant Commander J M Villiers at a discreet distance, run his errands and supply him with copies of signals throughout the day. I was given the grand title of 'staff signalman' and felt extremely smug about my position - until one night on Atlantic patrol when I was given a message to take to the Commander down aft. I dashed down the ladder to the admiral's bridge and was trotting across to the ladder to the flag deck when I bumped into a soft body. There was a crash, and a strangled grunt; on the deck I could just make out the stretched-out figure of Admiral Whitworth. I was escorted away by 'Shiner'*

Wright, and was given a rocket by everyone on the bridge from the captain downwards. Rarely does an admiral remember a boy, but Whitworth, who was something of a martinet, was kind enough to remember me more than a year later when we met again in more emotional circumstances.'

In March *Hood* moved from the Clyde to Devonport for refit.

'As one Hood moved out, another moved in. The newcomer was one of Churchill's decoys. We considered ourselves fortunate that we had a 'double', and indeed it served its purpose as it took the people of Greenock several days to tumble to it that the real Hood had gone. My older 'oppo' on the flag deck, Marine Holding, was in trouble with his girl friend too, because she believed the Hood was in port and he had ditched her!'

In June *Hood* joined Force H, based at Gibraltar, and took part in the operations against the French fleet at Oran, flying the flag of Admiral Somerville. Cedric Holland, Captain of *Ark Royal*, who had been Naval Attache in Paris pre-war, and was a fluent French speaker, embarked in HMS *Foxhound* to act as the intermediary with the French Vice Admiral Gensoul (under whose orders *Hood* had been operating only a year earlier in the Atlantic, when she was in company with the battlecruiser *Dunkerque* at the time of the sinking of the *Rawalpindi*). Briggs had a grandstand view of the proceedings:

'First the admiral's barge from the Dunkerque arrived alongside Foxhound; then the destroyer weighed anchor, leaving her motor boat which headed for the Dunkerque. Half way to the mole they were met by the admiral's barge and stopped. The French boat scuttled back and forth.

'Hood was using her 20-inch SPs to keep in touch with Foxhound. The heat was intense. Around noon there was an uneasy calm - "Cooks to the galley" was piped - up came hot soup! While we were eating, the wisps of smoke coming from the French fleet turned into spiralling plumes, bugles sounded, awnings were furled. A flurry of reports indicated that Gensoul intended to sail. Loudspeakers on the flagdeck kept us up to date, but most of us were reading the light messages which were being flashed to and fro.

'Just before 1700 I saw Somerville's messenger, Leading Signalman Lewington, who spoke fluent French, scuttle to the projector: "If one of the British proposals is not accepted by 1700 I must sink your ships." The reply from Dunkerque was in English. Eagerly we all spelt it out on the flag deck. "Do not create the irreparable."

'The flag deck was coming to life now, and a few minutes later Chief Yeoman Thomas called down the voice pipe. Leading Signalman Johns answered and then told us

*to string together and hoist ZTH1 - readiness for instant
action. As the flags fluttered to the starboard masthead I still
could not believe that our fifteen inch guns would be hurling
tons of high explosives - and on helpless friends at that!*

'There was a further burst of searchlight activity -
Holland's final communication "Gensoul says crews being
reduced, and if threatened would go to Martinique or USA,
but this not quite our proposition. Can get no nearer." This
did not reach Somerville until one minute before the deadline ... then Foxhound's boat emerged from the harbour. The
voice-pipe squealed. "Flag 5 - Hoist." We took up the red
and white piece of bunting that signified "Open fire - may be
obeyed as soon as seen." My fingers trembled as I put the
Inglefield clip on the flag's head. The response was immediate - the guns of Resolution and Valiant roared - then came
the ting-ting of our firing bell. Seconds later my ears felt as
if they had been sandwiched between two manhole covers.'*

In the event, most of the French ships were disabled, but the
battlecruiser *Strasbourg* and five destroyers escaped to Toulon.

*   *   *   *   *

*'A personal milestone was reached on 1 March, my eighteenth
birthday, when I had to go through the ritual of requesting
that I be advanced to Ordinary Signalman. My pay went up
from 8s. 9d. to 14 shillings a week, but I still had to wait
another three years before I could draw my tot of rum,
although I was able to drink as much as I liked ashore!'*

In May 1941, *Hood* was back at Scapa and Vice Admiral Lancelot
Holland had taken over from Admiral Whitworth.

*'It was my job to collect messages for the flag lieutenant
- I hurried to Lieutenant Commander Wyldbore-Smith's
cabin in the evening of 21 May with a confidential signal
from the C-in-C: "Raise steam with all despatch ..."'*

HMS *Hood*, in the 1930s

Hood, *Prince of Wales* and destroyers sailed for Iceland, but just before entering Hvalfjord a signal told them that *Bismarck* and a cruiser were at sea, and to patrol southwest of Iceland:

'At 1930 on 23 May the broadcast system spluttered into life: "Flag Lieutenant's messenger report to the SDO at the double!" I was told to rush a message to Lieutenant Commander Wyldbore-Smith in his cabin. This particular signal stated: "From Suffolk - enemy in sight." Enemy reports from Suffolk and Norfolk put the enemy about 300 miles to the North.

'At 0535 the enemy were spotted from the Hood. I did not have any binoculars so could not see the top-masts ... Captain Kerr said "Pilot, make the enemy report." This was passed by voice-pipe to the bridge wireless office - a few minutes later came confirmation that the message had been sent.

'When the range was down to thirteen miles, Holland said quietly "Open Fire." Chief Yeoman Carne shouted to the flag deck; "Flag 5, hoist." From the control tower the gunnery officer bellowed: "Shoot!" Hood's first salvo belched out in an ear-splitting roar. Seconds later a duller boom came from our starboard quarter as Prince of Wales unleashed her first fourteen-inch salvo.

'Suddenly a report from the spotting top said, "We're shooting at the wrong ship. The Bismarck's on the right not the left." Our shells had been falling near the Prinz Eugen which was leading the German force. Holland seemed hardly perturbed and said "Shift target to the right." In the next two minutes, Hood's foremost turrets managed to ram in six salvoes at the Bismarck.

'Then I was flung off my feet ... I picked myself up, thinking I had made a complete fool of myself, but everyone else on the compass platform was also scrambling to his feet. "We've been hit at the base of the mainmast, and we're on fire" reported the squadron gunnery officer. On the boat deck a fierce blaze flared. The torpedo officer reported "The four-inch ready-use ammunition is exploding".

'The range was down to 8½ miles; we had been under fire for just two minutes. It was time to bring X and Y turrets to bear. "Turn 20 degrees to port together." "Two Blue" went up; I remember musing: not everyone on the flag deck is dead then. As Hood turned, X turret roared in approval, but Y stayed silent. And then a blinding flash swept around the outside of the compass platform. Again I found myself being lifted off my feet and dumped head first on the deck. When I got up, the scene was cold and unreal. The ship listed slowly, almost hesitatingly, to starboard. She stopped after *about ten degrees, when I heard the helmsman's voice: "Steering's gone, sir." The reply "Very good" showed no signs of animation or agitation.*

'*There was still no concern on the compass platform. Slowly Hood righted herself. "Thank heaven for that" I murmured, only to be terrorized by her sudden, horrifying cant to port. On and on she rolled. When everyone realised that she would not swing back, we all began to make our way out in single file - it was all done as if in a drill. As I reached the door, Commander Warrand stood aside and let me go first. I looked back and saw the admiral slumped in his chair, while the captain tried to keep his feet as the deck turned into a slide. I picked my way down the ladder ... then the sea swirled around my legs and I was walking on the side of the bridge.*

'*I threw away my tin hat and gas-mask and managed to slip off my anti-flash gear, but my lifebelt was under my burberry and I could not inflate it. The water engulfed me with a roar. The suction was dragging me down ... then a sudden surge beneath me shot me to the surface. Fifty yards away I could see the bows of the Hood vertical in the sea ... it was a vision which was to recur terrifyingly in nightmares for the next forty years.*

'*Fortunately before we left Scapa the ship had been equipped with three-foot-square rafts. There were dozens of these in the sea and I managed to lug myself half on to one .. a small patch of oil blazed. I could see the stern of the Prince of Wales as she pressed on with her guns firing; she was being straddled by shells from Bismarck and Prinz Eugen ... the oil fire instilled a spirit of self-preservation in me and with both hands I paddled out of the brown coating of oil. I still had on my burberry, number three suit, lifebelt, shoes and socks; the cold was beginning to numb my arms, fingers, legs and toes ... about fifty yards away I suddenly saw life on another raft. A figure began to wave at me. Then another raft with a man flapping his arms. I tried to find other signs of life - there was none.*'

Midshipman Dundas, Able Seaman Tilburn and Ordinary Signalman Briggs were picked up by the destroyer *Electra* - the only three survivors.

Swordfish slow the *Bismarck*

After *Hood* had been sunk early on 24 May, *Bismarck* was shadowed by *Prince of Wales*, *Norfolk* and *Suffolk*. *Swordfish* from *Victorious* attacked her just after midnight and scored one torpedo hit, but the damage was not serious except for loss of fuel oil. Shortly after this the shadowing ships lost touch, and *Bismarck* was 'missing' for nearly thirty six hours. However at one stage she broke silence to make a long radio transmission to report her situation; this was DF'd and led the Admiralty to appreciate that she was heading for Brest. Searching forces were re-disposed, and the RAF eventually sighted her again at 1030 on 26 May; this enabled Force H, with *Ark Royal*, coming up from Gibraltar, to get into position for another air strike that evening. Commander Stewart-Moore was then CO of 820 Squadron:

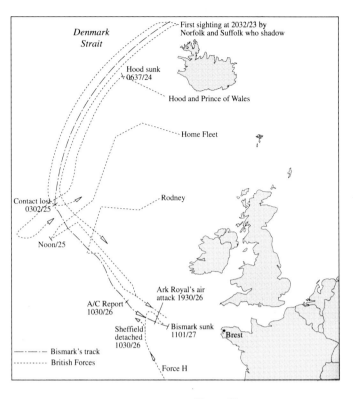

Bismarck's route

'The aircraft next to mine in the leading sub-flight carried one of the first airborne radar sets - ASV - manned by a young sub-lieutenant, Lithgow, and an even younger midshipman, Cooper. The latter's duties included navigation, radar operator, wireless operator and general look-out. After a while I saw Cooper waving to me - he semaphored that he had a radar contact about 20 miles to starboard, We were told there were no British ships in the area so it had to be German.

'We saw what appeared to be a cruiser - we approached above clouds getting occasional glimpses, and decided to attack. After dropping torpedoes my pilot, Hunter, called down the voicepipe "It's the Sheffield." Hunter waggled our wings to attract the attention of other aircraft, but couldn't prevent some of them attacking while we watched from above, horrified and praying for a miracle... for no apparent reason, except for one or two, all the torpedoes (which had magnetic pistols) blew up within half a mile of striking the water. It was a surprising sight.

'We had hardly got settled on our course back to Ark when my telegraphist, PO RH McColl handed me a message: "Operational Immediate - Look out for Sheffield which is in your vicinity." I thought of plenty of rude replies but none seemed helpful, except perhaps 1 Kings 10 verse 7: "Behold, the half was not told me!" I didn't send it.'

Lieutenant Commander E S Barringer, RNVR, also flew in Swordfish. 'Radar - ASV - was a remarkable addition to the old Swordfish which absorbed the equipment in her own inimitable way, just as she coped with the depth charges and rocket projectiles on her wings, spare airscrews, and the odd bicycle tied to her torpedo carrier... the extra aerials on each wing only added to the impression which the Swordfish gave of a very complicated aerial clothes line. The radar transmitter was positioned in the belly of the aircraft, the observer looked into a screen, protected by a black rubber visor... '

Memoirs of Stewart-Moore,
Friend and Barringer are in
the Imperial War Museum

In a subsequent attack on the *Bismarck*, they flew via the *Sheffield*
and were then directed by her. Another Observer on the same
mission, Lieutenant Charles Friend, did the same:

> *'On the second strike, in cloud, the pilot asked me "Where
> is Bismarck?" I said I had no idea, but I did know where the
> Sheffield was. We flew low past her and I made "Where is
> target?" by Aldis lamp. "Enemy bears 185, 10 miles" came
> the reply.'*

At least one torpedo hit was scored which survivors later said had hit
Bismarck's rudder while she was turning, jamming the steering gear
and reducing her speed, so that the fleet was able to intercept and sink
her next morning.

The RNVR and the Signal Branch

Eric Lowe joined the London Division in 1938 as a Probationary
Ordinary Signalman. London tended to specialise in Signals and
Gunnery, and drafting for annual sea-training and for mobilisation
was arranged with Chatham on an individual basis.

> *'After the Munich crisis recruiting increased and an addi-
> tional staff officer, Lt Cdr Longden, was appointed to see this
> through. Office space was rented for extra classrooms near
> HMS President in King's Reach, and early in 1939 the
> London Stock Exchange opened its trading floor to us every
> evening for practical training. My class mustered every
> Tuesday and Thursday; our Yeoman would mount one of the
> Jobbers Boxes, which had been rigged with lights, and put us
> through a standard flashing exercise followed by semaphore
> with hand flags. All around 'the floor' were similar groups,
> altogether probably some 300-400 volunteers under training.*

> *'By late spring 1939 I had become a Signalman QB
> (Qualified in Branch) and was on the way to Trained
> Operator. London Division's complement included a
> Commissioned Signal Boatswain RNVR - Peter Curram,
> who was Postmaster at the House of Commons (he later
> became a Signal Lieutenant Commander RNVR, a pretty
> rare bird). Curram was tasked to find competent volun-
> teers who would be prepared to accept call up ahead of any
> general mobilisation of the Reserves. Needless to say, this
> was 'sold' to us as a great privilege, and as a young
> ingenuous articled clerk I allowed myself to become part
> of Peter Curram's 'private navy'.*

> *'At this time the Defence Teleprinter Network (DTN) was
> coming into commission and there was a shortage of people
> to man it, particularly in the more remote areas. In July 1939
> at the end of my 14 days annual training in HMS Nelson, then*

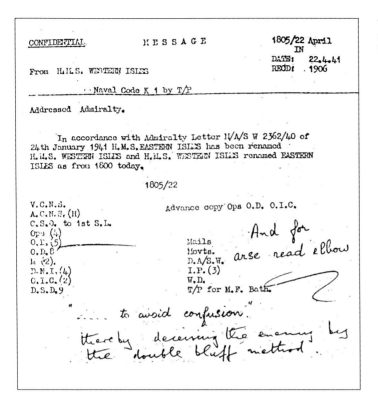

The distributed copies of signals sometimes included apt comments by the recipient

Home Fleet flagship, I was mobilised along with four others and put ashore at Scapa Flow to help man the Lyness DTN telex and telephone exchange. A Leading Tel RNV(W)R was in charge, reporting to the Signal Officer to Flag Officer, Orkney and Shetland, Lt Cdr Lenox-Conyngham.'

Having been commissioned, and after a couple of sea jobs, Lowe qualified (Ce) and, like several other RNVR officers with sea experience, later did the Long (C) course. (His experiences at Greenock and in the Far East were referred to earlier). In 1948 he rejoined the London Division; signals were again a prime training task and Lowe became Head of Department.

'To be sure of being called up into the navy, national servicemen had first to serve in the RNVR for ab-initio training. Being a relatively large Division, London's 'Signal School' repidly expanded to quite a sizeable operation, and was passing on to Chatham a very high proportion of the total national service intake into the Signal Branch. Coding and W/T practical were taught in HMS Chrysanthemum, and W/T also in the tower of the Old Admiralty Building. Typing skills and V/S overflowed into rented office space in the Temple, and two of the 'Trafalgar' tunnels under Whitehall were re-opened for teleprinter training.

'I was supported by three RNVR and two WRNVR (Ce)s; senior instructors were seconded from HMS Mercury, but the majority were RNVR and WRNVR. It was quite surprising how much practical training could be achieved, remembering that it was entirely a spare time job; two evenings a week and a weekend a month was not unusual. Having two drill ships with fully fitted flag decks, and putting teams out on bridges and buildings around King's Reach, one could simulate squadron manœuvres by day and night. The ultimate 'lollipop' for the W/T department would be getting a landline from Chrysanthemum through to Rugby, and then keying the 2100Z plain language news bulletin on 16 KHz. This chance was offered to those who had done well in their W/T2 exams, and was fiercely competed for.'

Coal Burner

Having joined the RNVR before the war, Ronald Aitchison trained as a telegraphist at *Royal Arthur*. Drafted to a coal burning patrol service trawler, HMT *Arsenal*, he arrived on board to find the ship was unbelievably filthy.

'The radio cabin was behind the steering engine compartment; this was always full of oily steam at sea so that it was necessary to hold one's breath when passing through. The steam and smell seeped into the radio cabin and added to the nauseating stench that the general filth had already created. The cabin measured about 3' by 9' with a bench bearing the receiver and transmitter. Communication with the bridge was by means of a voice pipe with one of those lovely old brass whistles in the end. Wedged under the bench was that most essential piece of equipment - a bucket.

'We were often required to keep continuous listening watch. I found that I could sleep with the earphones on and a continuous cacophony of morse and strange noises coming from them, but as soon as our callsign was received I would waken immediately. This accomplishment probably wasn't unique, but I believe another was - the ability to take down a message without error or gaps, while vomiting into the bucket at the same time.'

Despite this unpromising start, Aitchison ended the war as a Lieutenant with a DSC.

From: D of ST
To: PSTO Med

Most Secret

Pass to Master Aorangi from P & O London. Squashes with water to be sold at 3d. per half, repeat half pint. No charge for straws.

232336A

H O Telegraphist

George Greaves volunteered to join the Navy as an 'HO' Telegraphist before conscription was introduced, to avoid being sent to another branch or service. Of his initial training at *Royal Arthur*, he particularly remembers watching the signalmen learning semaphore - a skill which depended on what he describes as 'operant conditioning' (immediate and unthinking response to some stimulus, like typing), which was practised to music. The only two tunes available and suitable (perhaps the only survivors of Butlin's record collection) were 'The Whistler and his Dog' and 'The Teddy Bears' Picnic'.

> *'Even today, if I hear either of them, I have the greatest difficulty in restraining myself from beating out the letters of the alphabet.'*

Because of the tremendous demand for telegraphists, Greaves was 'farmed out' to the London Telegraphy Training College, Earls Court, to learn the primary skills of a radio operator, alongside but separate from Merchant Navy Wireless Operators. This was a welcome change:

> *'To be in uniform in London, billetted in a hotel with little in the way of naval routine and discipline, was little short of wondrous. Then to HMS Scotia to deal with the confidential aspects of the training.*
>
> *'Here, in the seaboots issued to enable us to get about in the mud, we learnt the mysteries of the Fleet Signal Book, Naval Code, 'S' Orders, storage and disposal of CBs, etc. Coding was then totally manual and we learnt the intricacies of decoding the head of a message by reference to the Green Dragon - the book of Address Indicating Groups - and the laborious process of decoding, group by group, by subtracting without carrying.'*

Greaves joined HMS *Saladin*, almost the oldest destroyer in the Navy, at Londonderry, where she was based with five other 'S' class for convoy escort duties. The original radio gear was of museum vintage - a wondrous confection of immense bottle-valves, relays and magnetic keys of steam-engineering size and sturdiness, the whole connected up by yards of highly polished copper bar running round the bulkheads. The control panel of the original transmitter was resplendent with wooden fittings and ivory nameplates. This was augmented for war service by a relatively modern Marconi TW12 transmitter and its associated 349G receiver, and another receiver used to monitor Convoy wave.

> *'Normal day-to-day contact was by V/S but loudspeaker watch was sometimes kept on convoy-intercom (R/T); the CO seldom if ever spoke personally to his opposite numbers, as the COs in the later attack groups did. We used a simple substitution code - Syko or Nyko - for morse communication*

Being handed a round, soft, bun one day, Reg Trudgett had the feeling that 'this has happened before ...' Then it came back to him - first, as a new entry boy, the stand-easy bun; then, in one of the 5th DF 'K' class destroyers, shepherding neutral merchant ships into some semblance of a convoy - but without a common signal book, or a loud hailer:

'I was sent below for a bucket of spuds - the printed orders were buried in the spuds, the captain took the ship hair-raisingly close, and the Yeoman lobbed them over!'

between escorting aircraft and surface ships. It utilised a simple metal frame with columns of vertical letter-slides, with a card of the day, or period, which provided the means of substitution. It seldom worked, whether due to some disparity between us, or by asking too much of someone sitting with the machine on his knee in an aeroplane, I do not know!

'*But for the most part radio communication between base and ships was very effective - we normally read the Area Routine, in our case on Broadcast BN. We only decoded traffic addressed to our convoy or relating to our area (it would have been physically impossible to decode every signal completely), so after decoding the Address we would file it for reference later if needed. If a signal was missed, we hoped to pick it up when next transmitted, perhaps four hours later. One notable memory concerns my monumental blunder one middle watch when I decoded the AIGs with one hand while writing down the message with the other. It was addressed to another escort group and convoy, but I read the whole message (thankfully) and put it in the discard basket.*

'*Some twelve hours later another escort came up by light, enquiring when we, as senior officer, would be detaching the other half of the convoy to their new arrival port. The PO Tel was sent for, so was I ... what had happened was that the signal had been originated shortly before midnight on the 12th, whereas I had used the decode for the time of receipt on the 13th - the time of origin should of course have been used. Dire consequences were threatened, but to my relief nothing more was heard. But I still shudder a little at the responsibility we very young ratings shouldered in wartime - I was getting three and ninepence a day at the time!*'

After *Saladin*, a short spell at HMS *Mercury*, then a draft to Combined Operations meant a trip to the States to pick up a Landing Craft Infantry (LCI), and three months in HMS *Asbury*, a couple of requisitioned hotels on the New Jersey coast near New York.

'*The lack of formality when we commissioned LCI(L)289 was amazing. The skipper signed for it, presumably, and away we went down the Hudson River, with a civilian pilot (in a trilby hat, I remember with horror, on the bridge of a British warship too!).*'

One Telegraphist was carried plus a Landing Craft Signalman - a seaman who had received some training in V/S.

'*The radio equipment was a nice little set made by Collins Radio of Cedar Rapids, Iowa. The transmitter covered 1,500 to 12,000 kHz, with CW and Voice capability, this and the receiver being driven from wet batteries and a rotary converter. The ship boasted a shower for the ratings, fridge, freezer, bunks, and a coffee making machine. The rudder*

'Ah! - Didn't pass it to CinC ...'

indicator for the helmsman - who had a high stool, if you please - was marked Left and Right.

'On the voyage across to Gibraltar, via Bermuda, we kept Merchant Navy single operator periods, on the BAMS broadcast, and as well as our international callsign, GZWF, we were also allocated a special war callsign, more merchant style than RN, which I remember to this day - BQ4EZ.'

A week in Gib, then along the North African coast to the landing craft base at Djidjelli, in Algeria, for a series of landing exercises, and then Operation HUSKY, the invasion of Sicily. This was followed by various landings in Italy, and dummy landing schemes in which radio deception played a part (including, for example, transmissions between two transmitters in the same craft, to try to convince the enemy that they were part of a larger force 'leap-frogging' the front line!).

Greaves ended up at the Combined Operations headquarters, HMS *Hamilcar*, which had moved from Djidjelli to Messina:

'Here I worked in the shore wireless station, a marvel of ingenious cobbling together of RN and Italian equipment, plus the venerable (army) landline scrambler, the Fullerphone, with which we communicated with Catania and other stations (when the local peasants had not dug up the cable to use it for repairing their fences). Here I received my first introduction to the Allies answer to the Enigma - the Typex. During a downpour of rain through the rather ramshackle roof, we discovered that the ink used for printing the setting-up instructions for the machine was soluble in water!'

Liaising with Russians, Poles and Italians

Signalman Jack Thwaite, who joined *Ganges* as a Boy in 1939, then *Impregnable* at Plymouth, recalls that both the heliograph and the morse flag were included in their instruction. Although neither were actually used in anger, he did take a heliograph with him when involved with Special Party 840 for the invasion of Sicily.

Earlier as a Boy Signalman he had been in *Edinburgh* for Operation SUBSTANCE - a fast convoy to Malta, during which he remembers *Fearless* being sunk by bombs. 'I can still see a Signalman standing on the iron deck semaphoring:

"I am abandoning ship apart from a volunteer fire-fighting party. Good luck and safe journey," then he gave a wave, threw his semaphore flags over the side and dived in after them.'

Edinburgh later escorted a convoy to Murmansk; while the ship was in the Kola Inlet, two signalmen were landed each day to man a Soviet Navy signal station.

'We didn't speak Russian and they didn't speak English but

we managed to converse with the aid of their Russian/ English edition of the International Code. We looked up the phrase we wanted in the English section, pointed out the flags, and they then looked up the Russian equivalent. It was a bit laborious but worked very well.'

After the *Edinburgh* was sunk in May 1942, Thwaite was sent back to Kola and spent another month or so at a Russian signal station, where they were linked by telephone to SBNO Murmansk. After this he spent a month in the Polish destroyer ORP *Sorlund*, joined Combined Ops for the invasion of Sicily, then found himself on the liaison staff at Taranto. This led to him joining the Italian submarine *Beneditto Brin* on passage to Colombo, during which they carried out A/S exercises with British and Indian Navy ships. The liaison staff consisted of a Lieutenant RNVR, a telegraphist and Thwaite.

'The Italian signalman was also the ships 'scribe' and his V/S was very rusty, so I did most of the signalling. I had learned the accented letters at Shotley, and although I couldn't speak Italian I could more or less pronounce the words, and if I got it wrong I was soon corrected by the First Lieutenant who spoke perfect English.'

After a period in Ceylon, in August 1945 they returned the submarine to Italy, and Thwaite then travelled back overland to the UK.

Red Sealing Wax

Ivor Saul was an HO Signalman in the flotilla leader *Inglefield* in 1941 and 1942, escorting convoys to Russia.

'We didn't wear gloves or mittens when hoisting flags, and sometimes the cold was intense. The hand-shutter of the 10" signalling lamp was the worst. Your skin could freeze to it, and if you weren't careful, lumps of skin would tear away as you tried to let go. The reason for not wearing gloves was to avoid the risk of wool catching in the pulleys.

'Being leader we sent many more signals than we received. Batches of 'dead' signals were bundled up and sent down to the Admiralty Depot at Deptford when we reached port. Those bundles, neatly secured with red sealing wax, were taken ashore to be posted. But the neatly sealed parcels often served another - quite unofficial - purpose. They were lower deck 'camouflage'. Signalmen used to be detailed as postmen, and while officers doubtless knew that postmen might 'have a jar' while ashore, few knew the other secrets. Quite a number of those red-sealed parcels, neatly labelled for Deptford, were carried past the Dockyard gates containing not

*signals but carefully wrapped bottles of rum or packets of
fags. We already had other labels in our pockets addressed
to sweethearts and wives. A quick substitution was done
between the Dockyard gate and the Post Office!'* [1]

[1] From *'Camera in Convoy'*
by Ivor Saul

'Sink, Burn and Destroy'

Similarly phrased signals tend to recur over the years. For instance:

*'You are hereby required and directed to use your utmost to
take, sink, burn or otherwise destroy all Spanish ships and
vessels as well as ships of war.'*
Admiral Vernon, at sea in the *Burford*, to his Captains,
1 August 1739.

*'Proceed in quest of the Armament preparing by the Enemy
at Toulon and Genoa ... On falling in with (them) ... use your
utmost endeavours to take, sink, burn or destroy them.'*
Admiral St Vincent to Nelson, 21 May 1798, shortly before
the battle of the Nile.

'Sink, burn and destroy. Let nothing pass.'
Admiral Cunningham, to ships on patrol in the Sicilian
Channel, 8 May 1943.

And a particularly straight forward instruction:

From: C-in-C Home Fleet
To: Tartar
Capture or sink every German ship that you meet
= 1331 9 April 1940.

Liaison with the US Navy

In May 1941 (some seven months before Pearl Harbour) a highly
secret joint mission went to Washington to draw up combined plans
in the event of America entering the war. The signal officer was
Commander Peter Dawnay (later Vice Admiral Sir Peter Dawnay),
who recorded the events in some detail. The following are extracts
from his report.

*'Just before we arrived in New York, in the Britannic, we
changed into plain clothes. In the custom's shed, as they
opened our boxes, our uniforms, swords etc., fell out, but the
officers had clearly been instructed to look the other way!
We were told to say, if asked, that we were advisers to the
British Supply Council.*

*'Initially it was purely liaison work that we were doing,
working with our opposite numbers in the Navy Department.*

Before the war no arrangements had been made for secure communications between the RN and the USN. In June 1941 one of the RNs reserve Naval Cypher basic books plus long subtractor tables were issued for use by the RN, USN and RCN in the Atlantic. Initially it was used without some of the improvements made to other cyphers to improve their security, and for most of 1942 and the first half of 1943, when the system was carrying a lot of traffic, the Germans were able to read a large proportion of the messages. A new and secure re-cyphering system was introduced in June 1943 by the RN and RCN, and in January 1944 by the USN.

By this time the Admiralty and Navy Department had concluded a British-US Signalling arrangement so that the two navies could signal to each other in a better form than the International Code - it was fairly elementary but included a high grade cypher.

'Not long after our arrival we were given a British room in the Navy Department where we kept a sort of watch-keeping arrangement. For some time this room played a role out of all proportion to its size and one for which it was not strictly intended, for the operational side of the Navy Dept. at that time was completely undeveloped. They had no operations or war room, didn't know where their ships were - "Not our business, we leave it to the C-in-C" - and a tiny little communications set-up with only three or four teleprinters. "Put it on Washington Fox" was the answer to almost everything!

'When they did get going, their Ops Rooms etc. were manned with very inexperienced personnel and watch-keepers who lacked initiative. So we were continually giving advice and exerting an important influence, far beyond what was intended. Indeed this advice was often eagerly sought. However, like so many things the Americans did, when they got things going they were on a gigantic scale, employed hundreds and were wonderful affairs.

'Soon after Pearl Harbour, the Combined Chiefs of Staff organisation came into being, based in Washington (Combined meaning Anglo-US, while Joint referred to the three British Services). Amongst the many committees was the Combined Communications Board - like the other committees the members were the appropriate Director (ie DSD) and his opposite number, but of course DSD was normally represented by myself.

'The Canadians, Australians and New Zealanders had small staff missions in Washington (South Africa an Attaché only), but they conceded to us the job of carrying out the higher direction of the war on their behalf, although they needed to be kept in the picture - not without difficulty as the Americans regarded them as 'Colonies' and were loth to allow some of the Top Secret stuff to be given to them, even though they might be directly affected.

'The British Admiralty Delegation (BAD) grew to something like 500 at its peak, in fact a miniature Admiralty. The CCB itself sprouted some 42 committees and sub-committees - e.g. Codes & Cyphers, Signal Security, Wireless Procedure, Combined Ops Signalling, and so on. At one time I sat on, I think, 21. One trick of the Americans was to throw off Working Groups at the slightest difficulty appearing

in a Committee; this was all right for them with the whole of the Navy Dept. behind them, but quite a different matter for us! The CCB was probably quite the most explosive and turbulent of all the Combined Committees - not surprising really, partly from its size and also because if you mess about with a Service's communication system which is built up like a jig-saw, you may tear the guts out of it. To do so in wartime is a very difficult and dangerous affair. Admiral King's influence [2] *was bad and showed itself by suddenly throwing out at the last moment a solution on which weeks had been spent in getting agreement. Unfortunately his Signal Officer disliked the Americans having to change anything, and would go to King and say something like:*

'"This British proposal coming up in the CCB will slow down our communications in the Pacific." "Throw it out," King would reply.

'Then it would either be put back to the CCB for another shot, or another Committee would get it, usually with the same British representatives as before, and as a last resort it was referred to the CCS. This was hardly ever done in practice and was a catastrophe if it happened; the Combined Chiefs were anyway even less capable of solving some technical difficulty! The W/T Procedure argument was a classic case. After about eight months wrangling, and with a sharp jab from General Eisenhower from North Africa, this frightfully involved and technical 'dog's breakfast' reached a deadlock and appeared before the CCS! Can you imagine their feelings seeing this paper before them? But Admiral King had smuggled in his Signal Officer (no others were present) who suddenly sprang up and waved a signal which had taken twelve hours to come from Gib. "Terrible, terrible" everyone muttered. "Tell them to produce an agreed procedure within a month." So back it came to the CCB. (Looking into the Gib signal later, I found that it had come by cable!).

'In fact the original US-British Naval Signalling Book which came out in June 1941 was 100% British, [3] *so some swing away from that was only to be expected. Anyway, pre-war the three British Services had never been able to agree on common signalling systems, so it was quite an achievement to arrive at US-British inter-service systems.*

'Our naval signal organisation in Washington was in the CCS building, manned by Wrens with Canadian typists and teleprinter girls. We were connected by direct T/P to the Admiralty. In addition to the very heavy BAD traffic we also handled all the JSM and its Committee traffic. The other signal organisations in Washington were somewhat

[2] After Pearl Harbour, Admiral King was brought in as Commander-in-Chief of the US Fleet (COMINCH) inside the Navy Department, while Admiral Stark continued as CNO. King had an anti-British reputation, not undeserved. Dawnay comments:

'The confusion his arrival caused within the Navy Department had to be seen to be believed - no one knew who was responsible for what. Eventually King assumed the dual role of CNO and COMINCH. He undoubtedly made it difficult for the CCS to function smoothly and his suspicion of the British had a bad effect as it permeated downwards. But he was tough, which was what the USN needed; he knew what he wanted, and usually got it. However everyone in the Navy Dept, from Admirals down, were scared of him, as once the 'man in the green suit' (he had at one time worn a green uniform) had said something was to be done, nobody dare approach him however wrong they knew the decision to be.'

[3] This presumably refers to the Cypher System, mentioned above

jealous of us in this respect, particularly as it took us to all the conferences in North America, and everyone tended to use us as a sort of post box for the whole country. This could be a tricky problem, as a boy on a bicycle from Washington to Seattle hardly fitted the picture! We had to employ an elaborate courier system, and used US Navy facilities when suitable.

'*Providing the communications for the 'summit' conferences between Churchill and Roosevelt was complicated by the secrecy surrounding them until the great men actually arrived. For the Quebec conference, for example, the whole of the enormous Hotel Frontenac was taken over (it normally holds 1,100 people) and the inmates were only given 24 hours notice to quit and were out just 36 hours before the PM arrived. We had to set up a comprehensive communications office alongside a US Army counter-part, with book and machine cypher offices, registry, and teleprinter rooms, and our normal Washington-London links had to be switched to the Frontenac. Because of the security problems, I made most of the arrangements at a highly secret conference closeted in a New York skyscraper with the US Army Deputy Director of Signals, the President of AT & T and a high-up Western Union official.*

'*To deal with the hiatus that occurred between the PM's party landing at Halifax from the Queen Mary and arriving by train in Quebec, we took up from Washington a small cypher staff of fifteen WRNS officers and some T/P operators to handle traffic until the UK cypher staff arrived. Just as the traffic was being switched from the QM to Quebec a white faced senior WRNS officer rushed up to say: "Something terrible has happened - we've left the Typex Indicator book behind!" This meant we could not start to unbutton a single Typex message. There was nothing for it but to use our T/P link with Washington to get the answer in each case until I could borrow a copy from the Canadians, and then get ours flown up.*

'*The arrival of the UK party meant a hectic time for the signal staff, as they had hatched up dozens of long messages during the train journey, and their Defence Registry could not digest the piles of 'In' messages we had accumulated for them. So for some time the staff could not understand why they were receiving no signals!*

'*We had moments of great stress when we got overloaded, and as everything was Most Immediate and required a reply within a few hours, we did not like getting behind. As the deadline for meetings approached, we would be rung up to enquire about replies, and one would wonder if anything had gone wrong with the 'Out' message - bad for the nerves and morale! The worst panic I remember was over Mrs Churchill's shoes which had gone missing, and from the amount of abuse I received you would think I had lost them!*

'*The end of a conference was the period of greatest activity however. I remember at Yalta getting a document of 24 closely typed pages all to go in one time pad book cypher as it was to be published, with a long list of who was present including many Russian names which all had to be spelt out. It came to some 25,000 groups and was sent in about 50 parts. This was followed by trailers giving instructions about publishing it, and other people's famous last thoughts!*'

MESSAGE   II

UNCLASSIFIED   171955Z February

From: Radio Port Lyautey   Date: 17.2.62.

                                                Recd: 2107Z

To: 67 ARS Prestwick
        57 ARS Lajes

Info: USCOMEASTLANT
        Comdr. H.Q.s Atlantic Air Rescue Centre
        Admiralty
        COMFAIRMED
        All U.S.S. Ships copying this Broadcast

EMERGENCY

        Following received 500 Kcs.

        Begins.

        XXX XXX XXX CNP CNP CNP IE KKMX KKMX MEDICO RUSH HR MEDICO 1 CK NC
S.S. EMMA/KKMX 17 1935 G.M.T.

        Radiomedical Casablanca Radio.

        Patient white male 34 years MLD at 0830 G.M.T. 16th pulse 115 errat
temperature 101.8 respiration normal. Occasional stomach pains. Recurr
illness from same two weeks ago. 0730 G.M.T. T. 99.4 degrees respiratio
normal. At 1500 man got up and shaved and at 1645 G.M.T. temperature
jumped to 103.2 degrees pulse 100 respiration normal. Man complains of
cold feet and hot head, am using ice pack on head and hot water bottle o
feet and aspirin for fever. Vessel stopped at 34 54 N. 11 09 W. with
engine trouble. Expect to use engine within two hours. Please prescrib
Master.

                                                171955Z

This should even him out!

Chapter Twenty Two

1942 -1945

*'A Signalman should not let the officer of the watch or any
other officer have time to call attention to a signal flying,
he should see it before the officer as it is his exclusive
duty, whereas the officer of the watch has many other
affairs to attend to ... There are a great many officers
who take great interest in the signals and will embrace
every opportunity to see a signal before the signalman.'*

Signal Handbook, 1890

Escape from Java

Captain Peter Reid was Chief Signal Officer to General Wavell in the
ill-fated ABDA Command at the time of the fall of Singapore. [1]

[1] This story was recounted by
Admiral Sir Peter Reid to
Vice Admiral Sir Louis Le Bailly;
the Engineer mentioned is
Vice Admiral Dick Wildish

ABDA:
American-British- Dutch-Australian

*'One day in 1942 I was sent for by Wavell's Chief of Staff,
Lt Gen Sir Henry Pownall, and told in confidence that we
had orders to pack up and go. "As you are the only sailor
here you must arrange for a ship to get us out." We had a
British Naval HQ at Batavia and I got hold of a little ship
called HMS Kedah. She had been taken over by the Navy
with an RNR Commander in command. Not very suitable for
a long voyage, but she was said to do 17 knots and she was
the best I could get.*

*'While I was fixing this, a tall rather elderly RNVR Sub-
Lieutenant walked in, having somehow just arrived by air,
and said 'Hallo Gaffer'. I told him to go at once to the port
of Tjilatjap from where I hoped we would be able to sail in
Kedah. He was known as 'Foxy' and I arranged a little code
with him so that we could communicate by phone.*

*'We loaded up early one morning and drove over the
hills to Tjilatjap where we found the Kedah and crowded
aboard. Just as I hurried off to arrange for two US destroyers
to escort us out of harbour the Major in charge of the Royal
Corps of Signals asked me if he could bring on board an
Army wireless transmitter together with the 50 large cells
which powered it. I agreed so long as he was quick. We
sailed just before dark - everyone very relieved as we knew
the Japs could not be far behind.*

The C-in-C returning the call of Vice Admiral Peter Reid, second-in-command Mediterranean Fleet, in HMS *Gambia* (Captain Peter Gretton) in 1954

Admiral Sir Peter Reid, who played an important part in writing the new RN Signal Books after the war, was a most successful Controller of the Navy from 1956 to 1961. An important project during this time was the building of the first British nuclear-powered submarine, HMS Dreadnought. Vice Admiral Sir Louis le Bailly, in his book 'From Fisher to the Falklands', quotes Admiral Rickover, who ran the US Navy's nuclear submarine programme for many years, as saying that there were only two British Admirals who had the brains to understand what he was doing - Mountbatten and Reid!

In 1961, when Reid and Lord Carrington, then First Lord, were returning from a visit to Brest in the frigate Rhyl, it is believed they had the distinction of flying the flag of the Lord High Admiral at sea for the last time as members of the Board of Admiralty, before the Queen assumed this office in 1964.

Admiral Reid served in the historic office of Vice Admiral of the United Kingdom and Lieutenant of the Admiralty for many years; this office is held at the time of writing by another signal officer, Admiral Sir Anthony Morton.

'Some of the ladies (cypherers from Singapore) were given cabins; the men found a bit of deck to lie on. In the night I realised the engines had stopped. I nipped up to the bridge and told the Captain we were a sitting target for a Jap submarine as there was a full moon and we were making smoke. He said that the boilers seemed to be in a very shaky condition and some burst tubes were being plugged. We were lucky as we were obviously not spotted by the Japs and we got going again. By next morning we had got well clear of Java but we had to start to ration water for drinking (washing in salt water) as there were 450 on board ... Then we broke down again; I found there was a naval Lieutenant (E) on board, a real engineer, and I got him to take some Marines down to the boiler room to help. But we only kept going in fits and starts.

'Next morning when we were again stopped I went up to see General Pownall and suggested we were now far enough from Java to take the risk of disclosing our position by using our wireless. I told him we would never get to Colombo without help. Then we heard a heavy tread on the ladder up to the bridge; this was the Chief Engineer whom we were seeing for the first time. "Well, sir, this time we're bitched." He was right - Kedah's engines never worked again that trip. The General agreed with me to get an accurate position (by sun sight) so that we could signal to Colombo for help. We told the Captain who looked at us as if we were very stupid ...

'He said the ship had only one steam dynamo and, as we had lost steam for good, we could no longer transmit a signal for help. This was serious - we were miles from

From: COIS
To: C-in-C Med

Operations report that Egyptian Camel Corps at Berg El Akab have sighted ten Italian submarines off Abu Suir at 1730 today. Consider this should be treated with reserve although Egyptian CO is certain.

anywhere, no one knew where we were and we had not much water left. Then I remembered those Army cells. So we sent for the Major who luckily brought his signaller Sergeant Major with him. We told him it was vital to use his cells to power the ship's wireless set. He looked glum and said he was very sorry but their orders were to empty out the acid before taking them on board and so they were no good. Then the Sergeant Major cleared his throat and said: "Well, sir, there wasn't a lot of time." The Major was annoyed and said: "What, didn't you carry out my orders?" "Well, sir, I'm not sure as how we emptied them all." So I said "Let's go and see." And we found that by wonderful luck they had not emptied any!

'We got them all joined up to provide 100 volts onto the ship's set. Meanwhile the cypher ladies had cyphered up our call for help. When we were connected up I pressed the key and, to my great relief, the needle of the 'aerial ammeter' came up. It now remained to tune the transmitter to the frequency of Colombo. I found a little wavemeter - like a church collection box with a torch lamp, which glowed when you were right. Eventually I got it to glow, and we called Colombo. To my great surprise Colombo came up and answered. Then - bit by bit - we cleared our message, which not only gave our position but also our estimate of how we were drifting. Later we got a signal to say that HMS Dragon was coming. It was only later that we learnt that there had been a naval battle in the Java Sea when the Japs sank all our ships except for the Dragon. We waited another day - and then the cruiser found us - in the dark!'

Ludovic Kennedy

Sub-Lieutenant Kennedy had been on a course for handling balloons which were planned to be attached to ships as protection against air attack, before attending a short signal course.

'After Cardington, we were sent to Portsmouth for a week of practical balloon handling. A balloon had been set up on the dockside close to Nelson's flagship at Trafalgar, the Victory, and we took it in turns to take charge of it during the night and to sleep in one of the officer's cabins. I was told that my cabin had formerly been occupied by Lieutenant Pasco, Nelson's flag-lieutenant ...

'To acquaint us with the meaning of flag signals at sea, we were drilled on the parade ground as though we were ships. Instead of being ordered, 'About turn!', the flags for 'Turn together 180 degrees to starboard' were called out,

*and in place of 'Halt!' we got 'Stop engines!' At the end of
the week we expected to receive orders to join balloon units
in ships of the fleet; but were not altogether surprised, or
disappointed, to be told that the Admiralty had now
concluded what we had suspected all along, that the scheme
was wildly impracticable and had been cancelled.'*

Kennedy joined the Tribal class destroyer *Tartar*.

*'When I came on watch next morning I was met by an
impressive sight: all around us the ships of the Home Fleet
which we had joined during the night - steaming south-
eastwards at high speed in search of the German fleet. But
the sea remained empty ... Yet the sight of our own ships -
and there must have been some forty - manœuvring at high
speed as one unit, many of them shipping green water over
their bows, their halyards billowing out a succession of
brightly coloured flags, was a heartening spectacle. From
the turn of the century, such fleet manœuvring was common-
place; after 1945, it never happened again on such a scale.'*

*   *   *   *   *

*'I had the first watch that May evening (in 1941) a day out
from the Clyde. With Somali, Eskimo and Mashona we were
escorting the troopship Britannic and the battleship Rodney
westwards across the Atlantic. It was, as I recall, an uneventful
watch (until) I heard the buzzer from the wireless office.
Signalman Pearson, with whom I was sharing the watch, a
barrel-shaped fellow partial to chocolate 'Nutty', thrust his
fist into the voicepipe and hauled up the signal box.*

"U-Boat Disposition Report, I expect," *he said.*

*'He unravelled the signal, scanned it, then handed it to
me. It was prefixed Most Immediate, came from the cruiser
Norfolk, and went something like this: 1BS 1CR 66.40N
28.22 W Co 220 Sp 30.*

"Pearson,' I said, "does that mean what I think it means?"

"Yes, sir. One enemy battleship, one enemy cruiser,
position sixty-six forty North, twenty-eight twenty-two West,
course 220, speed 30 knots."

"Christ!" I said, and pressed the captain's buzzer.'

*   *   *   *   *

*'At the end of the month, in company with a cruiser and our
sister ship Bedouin, we sailed for the Arctic in search of an
enemy weather-reporting trawler called the Lauenberg. DF
had placed the ship in the general direction of Jan Mayen
Island ... the force was spread five miles apart to widen the
area of search, and in Tartar the first lieutenant promised £1*

From: Cossack
To: Maine

For Surgeon Commander from
Surgeon Lieutenant.
RPC Cocktails 1945 tonight =
1400K

From: Maine
To: Cossack

For Surgeon Lieutenant from
Surgeon Commander.
Your 1400K. MRU. Have just
received a case of leprosy =
1405K

From: Cossack
To: Maine

For Surgeon Commander from
Surgeon Lieutenant.
Your 1405K. Bring it over.
We drink anything. = 1415K

to the first man to sight the enemy. Within a short time a sailor in the crow's nest started shouting and waving, and, hoisting the signal 'Enemy in sight' the captain went on to full speed ... we came alongside and the boarding party searched cabins and compartments for whatever they could find.

'In the next forty minutes they returned with armfuls of papers ... meanwhile Bedouin had lowered a boat and sent over an RNVR lieutenant called Bacon from naval intelligence, an expert on German naval documents, who had been specially embarked for the operation. During the return to Scapa, Lieutenant Bacon hardly moved from the captain's cabin. We all hoped he was having a happy time there, though we rather doubted whether the pickings from a little weather ship in the Arctic would reveal much ... But Lieutenant Bacon was bringing home the bacon; for what none of us knew were the efforts then being made by the Admiralty to crack the German naval ciphers, and the imperative need to obtain, as opportunity offered, whatever scraps of intelligence they could. It wasn't until long after the war, when the secrets of Ultra were finally revealed, that I learned that codebooks and signals found in Lauenberg, plus a set of rotor arms discovered in the trawler Krebs during the Lofoten raid, plus material taken three weeks earlier from another weather ship, München, and finally and most important of all the Enigma machine and codebooks captured from the U-Boat U-110 all, when pieced together, enabled the Bletchley Park codebreakers to penetrate the principal German naval cipher and continue to penetrate it, with a few breaks, until the end of the war. This penetration, in conjunction with High Frequency Direction Finding and other factors, was what enabled us to win the U-Boat campaign - a campaign which, had we lost it, would also have lost us the war.' [2]

[2] From Ludovic Kennedy's book *'On My Way to the Club'*

Leander in the Indian Ocean

Jack Harker, a Telegraphist in the RNZN, joined the cruiser *Leander* in 1939. He served in her in the Indian ocean, Mediterranean and Far East, until she was damaged in action off the Solomon Islands and paid off in Boston, USA for repairs in 1943.

'Since we 'Sparks' carbon-copied all signals, a source of reliable information became available, thanks to the cypher staff of officers using our coding office in which to work. They naturally told us nothing of the purport of the signals handled by them but, being co-operative, we set out new carbons and therein lay our secret. Hurrying off in pursuit of the Captain with the decyphered message, the officers often crumpled the carbon paper into our confidential waste

*paper basket for burning. No sooner was a cypher officer
out of sight than the carbon would be retrieved and carefully
flattened for perusal in front of an electric light, and
provided very precise information about our future movements. This was kept strictly to the few men on watch since
any leakage would be traced straight back to us.'*

In the Indian Ocean in 1940 *Leander* flew the flag of the Senior Naval
Officer Red Sea Forces (SNORS), Rear Admiral A J L Murray, who
had been DSD from 1932 to 1934, and was again to be DSD, up-graded
to Rear Admiral in wartime, from 1941 to 1942. Harker describes the
shore-to-ship signal procedure, an elaborate form of the 'I' Method:

*'In the Main Office we sweated watch about as signals were
intercepted from routine transmissions at Bombay Naval
Radio. Aden repeated the transmission back to Bombay who
corrected any errors before Aden sent the same message to
Colombo who repeated back to Aden. Finally Colombo
transmitted to Mauritius; Mauritius relayed back to Colombo
and that message was considered delivered to a ship in any
part of the East Indies Station, Red Sea or Persian Gulf.*

*'One night while escorting a convoy from Aden to India,
a look-out detected a darker patch than usual; "Action
Stations" sounded, guns loaded and swung to the target ... an
operator sat in the Main W/T office, our high power transmitter running. On his desk lay a signal, coded for transmission
to C-in-C East Indies. It told of night action and gave our
position (but only to be sent when we received the order from
the bridge). "Searchlights!" Gunners tensed for the "Open
Fire". Down below, the operator flexed his fingers as Chief
Tel Joe Crouch fingered the tumbler-switch in readiness for
transmission, and the bridge signalman flashed the challenge. Back came a reply, swift and correct. We relaxed and
regretted; too many of these false alarms. The Westbury
wished us "Good Hunting". "Bon Voyage" we replied.'*

Rear Admiral A J L Murray

Murray became Captain of the
Signal School in 1937 and was
quick to press for more priority to
be given to the development of
radar. He had been Director of the
Signal Division from 1932-34, and
was again DSD, as a Rear
Admiral, from 1941-42.

Hunting raiders in February 1941, *Leander* was steaming along the
equator, practising damage control arrangements, and rigging spare
aerials, when a ship was sighted on the horizon. It took some time to
overtake her; for a merchant ship flying the Red Ensign she was
doing a surprising 20 knots which gave rise to some suspicion. On
being challenged she hoisted the signal letters for the British vessel
Grosmont Castle, not known to be in the area.

*'To the secret challenge she made all manner of remarkable
replies. An indefatigable student of ships' profiles and photographs of foreign vessels, our Chief Yeoman, 'Yum' Ackerley,
loudly voiced his opinion, correctly as it turned out, as to who
the ship was. But - Red Ensign - so Leander nudged closer to
within 3,000 yards. Down came the Red Duster, passing the
Italian Ensign on the way up. Fore and aft, guns swung*

towards Leander as flaps dropped and twenty-one rounds crashed and banged. Projectiles aimed at us had landed in between, and ricochetted overhead, others passed ahead or astern ... there was one ragged hole in the funnel.'

Fire was immediately returned and several hits scored. The raider's crew soon abandoned ship, which had caught fire, and before long her magazine exploded and she sank. The crew were rescued. She turned out to be the *Ramb I*, which had been fitted out at Massawa with four 4.7 inch and several AA guns. She met no merchant ships during her short cruise. [3]

[3] From Jack Harker's book
'Well Done Leander'

'Subtract Without Carrying... '

The method of encrypting a message in a book cypher system was first to convert the plain text into groups (usually four or five figures) from the Basic Code, then to subtract these from the groups in the cypher table 'without carrying'. For example:

Plain text:	Proceed	to	Scapa
Groups from Cypher table:	3821	7345	1904
Groups from Basic Code:	4271	8892	6457
Encrypted message groups:	9650	9553	5557

The reverse process took place to decrypt the incoming message, the received groups being subtracted from the cypher table groups, again 'without carrying'. Thus:

Groups from Cypher table:	3821	7345	1904
Received groups:	9650	9553	5557
Groups from Basic Code:	4271	8892	6457
Plain text:	Proceed	to	Scapa

Cypher tables were composed of groups made up of 'random' numbers. In most cases the groups could be used more than once, e.g. with the wartime stencil frame, when sheets might be in force for days or weeks. If traffic was heavy this made messages vulnerable to be broken by cryptanalysis.

Complete security could be achieved by using one-time-pads when the cypher groups were used once only, and then crossed out and the pages subsequently destroyed. But since each ship or authority had to have its own 'unique' set of pads (and those of the 'other end'), this meant an enormous production and distribution problem, so that it could only be used in limited circumstances, e.g. as an 'out' system to all ships, or from Admiralty to certain flag officers, and then only for messages for a high security classification.

The Basic Code had little intrinsic security, being designed primarily for the conversion of words into figure groups, and was only changed very infrequently. Special groups, sent at the beginning of a message, indicated the cypher table in use and the place to begin decryption.

Machine Cyphers such as Typex, CCM and Enigma converted plain text into groups digit by digit, the revolving rotors and plugboard settings making different electrical circuits for each digit. Even then it was not possible to prevent some repetition if the system was heavily used, and these machines could be vulnerable. As described in Chapter 11, the Enigma system was broken by Bletchley, but the Germans made no serious attempt to break either CCM or Typex (the latter was not used at sea during the war).

Modern electronic equipment can generate truly random streams of cypher key. Any weakness in the security of modern systems is likely to be due to human error.

Evacuation of Greece and Crete

Ian Robertson had joined the Combined Ops set-up at Inverary to train RN Beach Signal Sections, and in 1940 when some of the Commandos were sent to the Middle East he found himself on the staff of Flag Officer Attached Middle East (FOAM), Rear Admiral Baillie-Grohman, at Cairo. [4]

[4] Robertson's story is taken from his autobiography *Renegade Signalman RN'*

In April he went with the Admiral to Athens, to plan for the evacuation of the British Army.

> '*I discovered that there were just three sets of the British Naval cypher, the only secure means of communication for the British since both the Army and the RAF seemed to have lost theirs. I commandeered a couple of lorries and sent one set ahead with a beach signal officer, an RNVR Lieutenant, retained one copy and burnt the third in the hotel we were occupying as the RN headquarters. I also retained one lorry with a wireless set and four ratings to man it.'*

Southern Greece and Crete

After dinner in the restaurant, and cheering the head waiter with the news that he would have plenty of Germans to cater for the next night, Robertson got away just in time to cross the Corinth Canal about 1½ hours ahead of the German parachutists.

> '*After a brief rest in an olive grove, we proceeded south to report to Admiral Baillie-Grohman who was at a temporary Army headquarters; also there was the King of Greece.*

```
         MESSAGE              IN


UNCLASSIFIED              182255Z NOVEMBER

FROM:  KENT              DATE:  19.11.63

TO:    ADMIRALTY         REDC:  0735Z

INFO:  C. IN C. HOME FLEET
       A.S. PORTSMOUTH




      EXPERIENCE OF STRONG BEAM SEA CAUSING ROLL AND LIST
TO STARBOARD HAS RESULTED IN C.P.O. AND P.O. HEADS
BECOMING UNUSABLE, SOIL DISCHARGE THROUGH INBOARD WC PANS
TO DECK AND UNPLEASANT SITUATION AGGREVATED BY OVERFLOW
TO BATHROOM AND PASSAGE OWING TO LACK OF SCUPPERS.

2.    URINALS SUFFER FROM SAME DEFECT.

3.    REQUEST EARLY ACTION TO BE TAKEN TO ALLEVIATE HARDSHIP
TO SENIOR RATINGS BY MODIFICATION TO SOIL PIPE OR
ADJUSTMENT TO LEVEL OF WC PANS.

                182255Z


CONTROLLER
4TH SEA LORD (2)            You can't whack
V.C.N.S.
D.C.N.S. AND 5TH SEA LORD (2)   a life at sea.
A.C.N.S.
U.S. MAT.
D.T.O.D. (8)
D.C.
D.G.S.
D.G.D. AND M.
D.G.W. (2)
D.G.P.S. (S) (3)
```

Inside my lorry were an RAF transportable GP set and several telegraphists. The HQ was not far from Nauplion, a useful deep-water port which enabled cruisers, destroyers and the Glengyle to take off a good portion of the army. Two LCAs were left behind, and later these put the admiral and signal personnel ashore in the very south of the Peloponnese. Communications between the GP set and the fleet were pretty good on the whole. I remember an amusing incident when a signal had been dictated by the Admiral, handed by his signal officer to a telegraphist who retreated to the wireless set at the other side of the olive grove, stepping over the long legs of the Admiral, at which point the latter exclaimed irascibly "Go round the other way, can't you see this is my cabin?". The cabin, needless to say, consisted of an army bedding roll and a Gieves burberry! (The telegraphists and I were dressed in khaki which we had had the foresight to bring with us, but the Admiral was still dressed as by Gieves, with a blue burberry which made him a conspicuous target for the Luftwaffe which flew over us two or three times a day).'

After the King of Greece and others had been evacuated, the Admiral and his staff were embarked in *Hotspur* and taken round to a beach near the small port of Ythion, where they spent three or four days with no form of shelter other than a blanket each.

'The naval wireless maintained communication with the fleet throughout so that as the beach filled up with weary troops, mostly Australians and New Zealanders, we signalled for destroyers to come in on the following night. I went out in an LCA to guide them, one standing off on each side of the little peninsular, Baillie-Grohman acting as beachmaster on the North side and myself on the other.'

Robertson acquired a discarded tommy gun before himself being evacuated with his team.

Arriving in Cairo, he was told to go to Alexandria to be briefed for another job, as naval liaison officer to General Freyberg in Crete, in order to improve communications between the fleet and the shore. Sporting his tommy gun, he reported on board the flagship, HMS *Warspite*.

"We know the invasion of Crete will take place on Sunday. You will proceed there tonight (Friday) in HMS Fiji taking with you nine telegraphists from the fleet to set up three wireless stations (with RAF GP sets) ... you will arrange always to be in direct touch with the fleet and if you fail to do so, you will be court-martialled on return!"

'*My bed and breakfast consisted of a blanket on a hillside above headquarters CREFORCE and bully-beef sandwiches for lunch, tea and dinner. I worked at CREFORCE advising on the naval aspect, occasionally getting on a motor-bike to visit Captain Morse, NOIC Suda Bay. But before reaching CREFORCE I had distributed to each military command one naval beach signal section (one P O Tel and three Tels), retaining my Warrant Tel alongside me in case of emergencies. In fact the emergency arose fairly soon as the decision was taken to use Sphakia as the evacuation port. I sent the Warrant Tel there by ML to establish a fourth naval communication facility, but the ML was intercepted by the Luftwaffe and sunk with all hands who were machine gunned in the water.*'

Soon the retreat started and Robertson commandeered a lorry to visit the naval camp which had been evacuated the previous night by HMS *Abdiel* (which had brought three Commandos to Suda), suspecting that there would be valuable documents and signal books which ought to be recovered or destroyed, although the camp was now in the midst of the ground battle.

'*There I met a section of Maoris fighting a rearguard action, but they paused long enough to fill a large iron pot suspended over an open fire with about a hundred raw eggs. This turned out to be one of the best meals I had had for days.*'

On the way back, stopping frequently to pick up British or New Zealand stragglers, there was a shout of "aircraft".

'*I saw four ME-110s racing at nought feet up the road, so jamming on the brakes, I pulled off into the scrub - everyone was scrambling out when all hell was let loose and the air was blue with incendiary bullets, unfortunately killing the cox'n and getting me in the thigh - a bullet had penetrated an artery after passing through my silver pencil, and I was bleeding like a pig.*'

Luckily their plight had been seen, and an over-crowded ambulance took them over the mountains to Sphakia, where they found Captain Morse. 'If your signals work, you will have a destroyer to take you off tonight" he said. They did, and the party was taken off in a pulling whaler, Robertson appropriately in a Neil Robertson stretcher, to the *Napier*, and eventually to the hospital ship *Maine* in Alexandria, and thence back home. Recovery took some months, but he remained associated with Combined Ops for most of the rest of the war, first commanding the Combined Signal School, HMS *Dundonald II*, at Troon, and then as Chief Signal Officer at COHQ.

From: 66 Gen Hospital
To: C-in-C Med.

Able Seaman Larkins on seriously ill list ... eleven stab wounds right chest left neck and rupture of liver. Accident.

The Navy in the Western Desert

After being sunk in *Kelly* in May 1941, 'Dusty' Dunsterville found himself dealing with the Base communications at Alexandria.

Captain ETL 'Dusty' Dunsterville, who was DSD 1958-1960

'*Sandy Gordon-Lennox had made a first-rate W/T organisation out of nothing. The main transmitters of the depot ships were used, remotely controlled from the receiving station at Ras-el-Tin. We had one transmitter ashore, I think it came from a submarine, and was permanently on 8,290 kc/s, the favourite ship-shore frequency. We had no handbook for this set and dared not touch it; it worked beautifully, despite having some strange unconnected wire hanging loose.*

'*We then got permission to build a proper transmitting station, having bought 30 acres of land and rented an old Egyptian cinema in the middle of Alex. SWB8 and SWB11 transmitters were duly delivered, set up and checked in the cinema before being taken to the new transmitting station. As soon as power, a plinth and aerial were ready, the transmitter was installed and immediately went on air. We had no engineering help from the UK at all.*

'*This was just in time, as Rommel advanced to Alamein and the fleet disappeared, leaving the Admiral and myself as the only two naval officers in Alex!*

'*To cope with the little W/T stations we had along the coast at Mersa Matruh, Sollum, Tobruk etc., I devised a shore-shore system based on the well-tried ship-shore organisation. Having reported details to the Admiralty, I was later surprised to find my plan incorporated in a CB to do with the latest technical advances. Anyway, it worked successfully, and I introduced the same system later in the East Indies to replace the existing fixed service arrangement.*

'*The desert war was more like a war at sea than on land, and the normal Army staff organisation and consequential signal arrangements with signals being routed down from Army through Corps, Division, Brigade and finally to Battalion, and vice versa, was quite unsuitable, when the need was for each unit to receive a signal at the same moment. Tank recognition signals, for example (usually two flags of different colours on a pole), had to be capable of being changed instantly. So I joined the Royal Corps of Signals and we fitted out about twenty 15-cwt vehicles with a naval MF receiver, each truck manned by a P O Tel and two Army Signallers. Battalion headquarters had one each, and kept constant watch on an MF broadcast from Alex. At first the navy keyed the transmitter from Ras-el-Tin (morse at 16 wpm) but as things progressed the Army took over.*'

Royer Dick

To: Admiralty
From: C-in-C Med

Be pleased to inform Their Lordships that the Italian Battlefleet now lies at anchor under the guns of the Fortress of Malta. = 111038B Sept 1943

Rear Admiral Royer Dick, then Chief of Staff to Admiral Cunningham, annotated his copy of the message:

> *'This signal was one which I drafted and suggested to Admiral Cunningham that he should send to mark an historic event. Rather to my surprise he accepted it verbatim. The original draft had 'beneath', changed for paraphrasing reasons.'*

Paraphrasing was carried out in certain circumstances when a message was encrypted in two or more different cypher systems, or if a plain language copy of the message was to be circulated or released to the press, to reduce the risk of a cypher system being 'broken'; thus the wording of the distributed copies of a message could differ slightly.

Commodore (later Rear Admiral) Royer Dick, Chief of Staff to C-in-C Med., at his desk in Algiers after Operation TORCH

*   *   *   *   *

The following draft signal was found in Admiral Royer Dick's papers [5] - but was it ever sent?

[5] Rear Admiral Dick's papers are in the National Maritime Museum, reference MS91/006

From: C-in-C Med
To: Admiralty

I wish to draw attention to the lamentable situation as regards the facilities for the reproduction of signals. Despite all endeavours to obtain necessary material, that now available is so meagre, inefficient and worn out that it is no exaggeration to say that only some 50% of messages can be read by the recipients.

To add to the inconvenience in order to obtain even this degree of legibility messages are reproduced in an insidious and loathsome compound which leaves marks for life on the person, clothes and temper of the recipient.

Not the least satisfactory feature is that our antiquated and clumsy methods make us the laughing stock of the Americans who have the misfortune to have to read our effusions.

St Nazaire

On 28 March 1942 HMS *Campbeltown*, one of the US lend-lease destroyers, rammed and blew up the dock gate of the large 'Normandie' dock at St Nazaire to ensure that it could not be used by the *Tirpitz*.

In his book *The Greatest Raid of All*, C E Lucas Phillips wrote of the moment when German coastal defences challenged the ship as the force approached.

'Two German signal stations, their lamps winking through the blaze of light, at once challenged - one from right ahead in the dockyard area (in fact from a Sperrbrecher [6] moored off the East Jetty), the other from a position on the port beam. At the same time a few bursts were fired at the van of the force from the Bofors gun at positions M16 and M17 at Ville-Martin.

[6] 'Mine-exploding' vessel

'Now was the moment for Leading Seaman (sic) Pike to play his part. For this critical eventuality Ryder had made careful preparation and had given Pike instructions before-hand how to act. He was to transmit in German a long, delaying message and to give 'Morsename' or callsign of one of the German torpedo boats on that coast, of which we knew several from documents found on the Vaagso raid ...

'What Ryder had not been prepared for, however, was being called up by two stations simultaneously. He would have to think fast. Pike, who had been quick to grasp what was needed of him, was standing ready with his night signalling lamp, as the harsh white light burst on them, and Ryder told him to answer first the station abeam of them. "Make the callsign and then the delaying signal." "Aye, aye, sir."

'Pike complied. Standing up very prominently on the bridge and wearing a petty officer's cap which at that distance might give him an outline similar to a German's, he aligned his lamp on the challenging station, made the Morsename and then began the bogus signal: "Proceeding up harbour in accordance with orders ..."

'It worked like magic. At the same moment, quite unaccountably, Mecke was advised by the Harbour Com-mander that the convoy was after all, German. Firing stopped at once and several of the searchlights switched off. All hands on deck could see the German station acknowledging the pre-arranged signal, however it became imperative to deal with the Sperrbrecher station ahead, which continued to challenge. Ryder therefore interrupted Pike and ordered: "Make the signal to 'wait'."

'Pike, cool and steady, complied, making 'EB' followed by the Morsename.

"Now the station ahead. Callsign and same signal."

'*With some searchlights still glaring at them, Pike turned his signal lamp to the Sperrbrecher. He had scarcely begun, however, when the ships were again fired on, but still with obvious hesitation. Once more Ryder interrupted Pike and ordered him to make the signal for "ship being fired on by friendly forces." This Pike made by directing the lamp vertically upwards, making two short flashes repeated three times, followed by the Morsename. On board the Campbeltown Beattie made the same signal.*

'*Again the firing ceased. Four precious minutes had been won. It was 1.27. Scarcely a mile to go. In another six minutes Campbeltown would be home.*'

Leading Signalman Pike was awarded the DSM.

Coastal Convoys

J W Booth joined HMS *Royal Arthur* at Skegness in February 1942 to train as a Convoy Signalman.[7] There he learnt the International Code, flashing at 10 wpm and semaphore at 20 wpm. He spent much of the war on East Coast convoys between Portsmouth and the Firth of Forth.

'*I never had occasion to use semaphore at sea as it was virtually unknown in the Merchant Navy ... The Navy has a thing about junior ratings moving at the double. The rules excluded POs and above, and they jealously guarded the privilege. I remember hearing of one Chief Yeoman of a battleship who was down below when a signals panic broke out on the bridge. The officer of the watch sent the bridge messenger to tell him to come up at the double. Assured that those were the officer's actual words, he told the messenger: "Go back to the bridge, at the double, and tell the officer of the watch that the Chief Yeoman is coming up at the quick. Tell him my doubling days are over." The OOW duly apologised!*'

Coastal convoys were assembled at the Southend anchorage and sailed daily to the Firth of Forth and twice a week to Portsmouth. Once clear of the Thames Estuary they formed two columns, the Commodore leading the port column and the Vice Commodore the starboard. The Commodore had one Leading Signalman and two Signalmen, the Vice-Commodore one Signalman, the latter working daylight hours only. In the Commodore's ship the Signalmen worked four on, four off, with the Leading Signalman as required.

'*As it got light on Christmas eve 1942, approaching the Tyne where we were to spend Christmas, the leading escort hoisted, not a white ensign, but a huge flag bearing the slogan "Guinness is good for you." At the same time she ran up the signal "Happy Christmas. The convoy will proceed at 30 knots." We would have burst a few boilers at 8!*'

HMS *Cardiff* was anchored in the Clyde off Greenock early in 1944 when half a dozen US escorts arrived. The Captain decided to invite a few officers to drinks - two from each ship. John Waugh, the ship's signal officer duly wrote out the signal:

'*RPC two officers each ship 1800 tonight.*'

No messenger being handy, he telephoned it to the signal deck, confirmatory copy to follow. Soon after 1800 several boats drew alongside and a large number of USN officers arrived on board, and drank Cardiff dry. Needless to say, the signal had been sent as:

'*RPC to officers each ship ...*'

On leaving the senior US officer asked if he could do anything in return. '*No thank you*' said the Captain, thinking of the dry USN wardrooms.

'*Well*' chipped in Waugh, '*if you have any spare magazines - Time, Esquire, that sort of thing, they would be very welcome*'.

Just before the US ships sailed, a launch drew alongside and a large bundle of magazines was thrown on board. And for the rest of the year, a selection of magazines arrived every week or two direct from the publishers.

[7] Memoirs - IWM 91/17/1

'Between convoys we were apt to be put on shore duties or jobs on harbour craft operating around Southend. One of the least interesting chores was 'back door sentry' at the base at Royal Terrace. The sentry was duly equipped with belt and gaiters, the traditional gear that indicates that a sailor is going to play at being a soldier. The Chief Yeoman read the standing orders, including the requirement that the sentry should walk to his post in a seamanlike manner. The Chief said that from what he had seen this should mean half-seas over with his cap flat-a-back, but it didn't!

'Harbour duties were rather more entertaining. There were a number of Thames tugs with civilian crews. a Sub Lieut RNVR, R/T operator (a seaman) and a signalman, patrolling the Barrow Deep and ushering convoys in and out. Sometimes they performed a trick called 'buttoning on' which involved going alongside ships of an incoming channel convoy, swapping over their papers, and tacking them on to a north-bound convoy. In windy weather this could be exciting stuff.

'One of our R/T operators asked for leave because his wife was expecting their first child, but this was refused. Later we heard the Wren base R/T operator pass him a routine message and add at the end "a girl - out." The new father came on in great excitement: "Hallo 32 - 32 - say again last word!" The Wren did so but was overheard by the PO Tel and put on a charge for passing a private message. The crime having been described in detail the First Lieutenant asked her: "Is this true?" "Yes, sir" replied the Wren. "Very well - Case dismissed!" Collapse of miserable old bugger!

'Another job was to put a signalman on board an outgoing destroyer for an educational trip. This was usually abandoned in bad weather but I was on a tug once when the officer insisted on trying it on a very rough morning. As we closed, the signalman grabbed the destroyer's guard rail and hung on as the tug rose and the ship dropped away leaving him standing on his hands with his feet in the air. Before he could fall to almost certain death between the two vessels, a couple of heroes on the destroyer grabbed him by his clothes and hurled him inboard.

'We saw little of the real Navy but a great deal of the Merchant Navy, often being in as many as fifty ships a year,

MESSAGE.
1340/28. February.
IN.
From Iceland.
Date. 28.2.41.
Rec'd. 1357.

Addressed, Wick.

IMMEDIATE.
S.O.S. DE RICHMOND HILL.
Position bearing due South from Vik. Commodore broken down, require assistance. T.O.R. 1115. Ends.
1340/28.
Advance copies sent to O.D., Trade,
C.C.R.T. Cdr. Holbrook.
+ Vik. King Island.
V.C.N.S.   D.T.D. (M)
A.C.N.S. (H)   D.N.I. (4)
A.C.N.S. (T)   O.I.C. (2)
C.S.C. to 1st. S.L.   Cdr. Holbrook.   *He's not the*
Ops. (4)   Press Division.   *only one either -*
O.D. (5)   D. of Salvage.
D. of S.T.   C.C.R.T.
I.P. (3)   Hydrog.
D.S.D. 9.   W.D.
D.T.D. (4)

though only a few days in each. Some of the small coasters, which the Commodores chose because their officers knew the routes thoroughly, were usually uncomfortable, having no spare accommodation. They had little time for signalmen, with whom they were regularly lumbered, and never quite knew where we fitted in. In the Merchant Navy Sparkers are officers, V/S is done by deck officers or apprentices, and there are no signalmen as such.

'One tanker running regularly up the coast still had a full complement including apprentices. She was bitterly disliked by signalmen because she not only had the largest and bleakest bridge on the coast but also a very unpleasant First Officer and a senior apprentice to match. Most apprentices were eager to assist the signalmen and pick up knowledge for their Mate's exams, but this one was superior to all that. One windy morning the signal staff were a bit pushed and the Commodore, a kindly man who had been a liner captain in peacetime, hauled down a hoist of flags himself. The wind got hold of them and the ship's captain arrived on the bridge to see him struggling with the stream of bunting while the apprentice looked on with his hands in his pockets. A lifetime at sea had equipped the captain with the right vocabulary for dealing with that situation and we saw little of the unfortunate lad for the rest of the trip.'

Socotra W/T

After training as a Telegraphist at HMS *Scotia*, Oliver White was sent out to Aden in 1943 where he found himself detailed off to join a party destined to set up a small W/T receiving station on the island of Socotra.

'There was considerable U-Boat activity in the Indian Ocean, and we were to mount continuous watch on Commercial wave, 500 kcs, to listen out for 'SSS' signals from merchant ships being attacked. This was because reception at RAF Khormaksar at Aden was difficult due to interference, and it was thought that Socotra would prove better.

'At Aden we learnt that we would be the first naval party to visit the island this century. The four of us were transported by the RAF and lived at the small RAF base by the airstrip on the island. Our link back to Aden was via the RAF fixed service.

'We worked 8-hour watches continuously for a year, using B.52 receivers, and picked up at least one distress signal which we understood resulted in the sinking of a submarine by aircraft.'

Chapter Twenty Three

Life at Leydene

'Start fattening calves and decanting the wine,
The Lords of the Ether are coming to dine ...'

Leydene House and Lady Peel

Lady Peel's father, James Williamson, was the son of a linoleum manufacturer, and as well as running the business he became a Liberal MP; when he retired from Parliament he was created a peer and became Lord Ashton. His daughter, Eleanor, married William Peel, grandson of the famous Sir Robert, and son of the first Viscount, Speaker of the House of Commons. Her father's main wedding gift was a settlement of £800,000, probably an ingredient in an 'arranged' marriage. William Peel was a Liberal Unionist MP and held several ministerial appointments, including that of Secretary of State for India twice, in 1922 and again in 1928, and was created the first Earl Peel. When her father died, Eleanor became the governing director of the linoleum company, with her husband as chairman.

The Peels decided to build a splendid country house, regardless of cost, in Hampshire. They wanted a site from which no other building would be visible, and eventually found this just below the crest of Hyden Hill which they judged to be perfect. They employed the Hooydonk Brothers who, as 'Decorative Artists', prepared elaborate interior schemes for the homes of the 'moneyed classes'. Work started in 1914 but was held up by the war, and the house, christened 'Leydene' after the hollow to the south called Leydene Bottom, was finally occupied in 1924, though not completed until 1925. Another two years were required to lay out the gardens.

The house has a magnificent domed hall, with a gracious figure-of-eight mahogany self-supporting staircase (see Plate III), built in Gosport and believed to be a copy of one in Bruges, together with spacious, elegant reception rooms with moulded 'Georgian style' ceilings. From 1927 onwards brilliant weekend parties were held, once including Winston Churchill whom Lady Peel described as 'a very rude man'. Pheasant shooting took place in the winter, with lunch in a rustic timber lodge in Hyden Wood, until this was burnt down through the excessive enthusiasm of a footman sent ahead to get a warm fire going. Another feature was the large rose garden on the south side of the house, laid out in the pattern of the best selling linoleum design. In fact Lord Peel was rarely seen at Leydene, living mostly in London but with frequent trips to Scotland for the shooting; he died in 1937.

Eleanor Peel had inherited an active brain and financial acumen, but she became extremely reserved, even reclusive, disliked children (her grandson, Brian Blacker, only met her once, and then only by cornering her one day on her Scottish estate; the short interview lasted less than five minutes!), and she had a profound antipathy towards local authorities. In 1928 she was at war with the Petersfield Rural District Council whom she sued for £7.17s.7d. being, as the local paper recorded, 'the estimated cost of keeping six visitors for four days in excess of their invitation' through the council's failure to clear snowbound roads!

A story often attributed to Lady Peel but which actually involved her daughter, Lady Blacker, told of a couple who had been to stay for the weekend and subsequently received a letter asking them to return the sheets they had apparently taken with them. They found composing a reply somewhat tricky, as they had been too embarrassed at the time to tell her that there had been no sheets on their beds!

The following appeared in daily orders on the occasion of a visit to Leydene by the Chaplain of the Fleet:

'0800 Holy Communication'

The Piggery

A feature of life at Leydene in the 1950s was the Pig Farm. This came within the responsibilities of the First Lieutenant, though the subject had not been covered in his Long Course. Fortunately he was able to delegate this to a splendid professional pig man by the name of Bert Thatcher. Bert was backed up by one or two Sigs or Tels who fancied mucking out the pigs rather than whatever part-of-ship job might otherwise come their way.

Pigs were money - with only one paid hand and fine pigswill, something like £2,000 per annum profit could be made - and that in 1950s money. This went to finance many worthwhile projects in and around Leydene - playing fields, squash courts and the rifle range were all subsidised by the pigs.

Duncan Knight, First Lieutenant at the time, remembers that the pigs were bred from Sows named Duchess, Countess and Lady, while others were bought in for fattening up. The population was generally some 100 piglets, most ultimately destined for Wall's sausages.

Visiting admirals, in the middle of carrying out the detailed programme arranged by the Training Commander, would suddenly exclaim "Do I smell pigs?" "Yes Sir", Number One would quickly reply, "Would you like to see them?" They would, and did. As the admiral leant over leisurely scratching a pig's back with his walking stick and discussing the relative merits of Landrace and Saddleback,

Duncan Knight, First Lieutenant

the Training Commander would have to send messengers flying off to the various classes with instructions to 'keep typing', or whatever. The programme rarely got back on track.

For various reasons, the Piggery became less economic over the years, and was finally closed down in the early 1970s.

The Shoot

The Leydene Shoot was very much part of the scenery in the early days. The 'guns' seemed to be chosen in strict order of seniority - Captain, Commander, Training Commander and then Lieutenant Commanders. The cost was £10 p.a. and until the Peel family sold the land there was good shooting - good enough to ask the Commander-in-Chief up once a year. When the land was sold, a shoot had to be rented from local farmers at double the cost for less suitable land. At least there was no shortage of volunteers to act as beaters.

On one occasion the C-in-C fired at a passing pheasant when a hound appeared out of the woods, followed shortly after by an irate huntsman. The latter, the Master of the Hambledon Hunt,

The Hambledon Hunt meeting in front of Leydene House, 1971

'A fox was found in Hyden Wood but owing to a misunderstanding between the huntsman and the field this fox was never really hunted' said the local paper
   A communication failure, in other words!

proceeded to give the C-in-C the biggest dressing down the great man had received in years. There was acute embarrassment all round when the Master discovered the identity of the object of his wrath. The Captain was, thankfully, out of earshot, but it was the last time that particular C-in-C came to shoot at Leydene.

Despite this incident, the Hambledon Hunt did meet at Leydene from time to time. On one occasion the Captain, who was an inexpert horseman, appeared suitably attired and more or less strapped on to his horse; however he arranged with one of his officers, a keen rider, that as soon as the hounds moved off, they would meet behind a nearby tall hedge where they would change over. The Captain then sneaked off home while his 'relief' enjoyed a good day's hunting.

Navigators and HMS *Mercury*

In 1903 Commander H F Oliver (later Admiral of the Fleet) advocated that Lieutenants carrying out Navigation duties should undergo proper training courses with exams. Previously those wishing to specialise in Navigation were appointed to small ships for three years to learn the tricks of the trade, followed by a *viva-voce* exam before a Fleet Board. After an enquiry it was agreed that a Navigation School should be set up and Oliver, about to be promoted to Captain, was given the command.

As there was no provision in the Naval Estimates for a shore establishment, Oliver was given the 25 year old light cruiser *Mercury*, 3,370 tons, then awaiting disposal. (He was also given a flat-iron gunboat, the *Plucky*, for pilotage and compass instruction).

During this time the *Mercury* was temporarily used as a yacht for the visit to Portsmouth of Prince George and Princess Mary (later King George V and Queen Mary), who had been invited by the C-in-C, Admiral Sir John (Jackie) Fisher. Oliver relates that on the day it was blowing rather hard and the Princess and Lady Fisher did not go to sea (though the Misses Fisher braved it). He says:

> *'I knew there would be a lot of signalling, so I took the C-in-Cs signal staff from Victory out with the spare flags and other gear. At one time when a lot of signalling was going on, Fisher said to me that he didn't think much of my signal staff, and I was able to say that they were his own. The Prince said, "He rather had you there, Fisher!"'* [1]

[1] Quoted in *'A History of HM Navigation School 1903-1968'* by Captain A W Clarke CBE, DSO* RNM 1348/82

After two and a half years in the *Mercury*, the Navigators moved ashore to the new Navigation School, in the old Naval College in Portsmouth Dockyard, which opened on 1 January 1906. They

The twelfth *Mercury*, launched 1878

stayed there until evacuated to Southwick House, commissioned as HMS *Dryad* in 1941.

In 1977 the (N) specialists found themselves back in HMS *Mercury* once more, at Leydene, *Dryad* being overloaded with the expansion of other training facilities, and having also become the home of the School of Maritime Operations. The Navigators remained at *Mercury* until the Signal School moved from Leydene to HMS *Collingwood* in 1993, when they returned once more to *Dryad*.

*   *   *   *   *

Earlier, while the Navigators were still at *Dryad*, they invited the officers of HMS *Mercury* to dinner, apparently with some apprehension:

> Start fattening calves and decanting the wine;
> The Lords of the Ether are coming to dine.
> The pillars of fashion are donning their best
> To visit the Wreckers who dwell Sou-Sou-West.
>
> Let's set about writing some singable staves,
> Extolling their genius at ruling the waves;
> Let's put them to music and code them in morse,
> And buzz them through dinner, one verse to each course.
>
> Let's think up some off-colour stories, and let's -
> On suitable circuits, waves, channels or nets -
> Transmit them discreetly, addressed to the men,
> But close down on pow'r if DF'd by a Wren.
>
> We'll talk scramblers with soup, ACPs with the fish,
> TBS with the entree and then, if they wish,
> Devote both the sweet and the sav'ry as well
> To consigning the Yanks to a Signalman's Hell.
>
> But that still leaves us time to discuss with dessert
> That divine Victor Stiebel's bolero and skirt,
> Which bolster the bosom and flatter the hips,
> And at Leydene are fastened with Inglefield clips.
>
> For we're nothing if not up-to-date with the shop
> That Mercury mutters when munching its chop;
> And we will, if it kills us, disprove that to log
> Is a vital requirement for putting on dog.
>
> So hold fast, fellow-wreckers, and see that your socks
> Are close-up, and your made-up black ties are two blocks;
> The Signal contingent are ready to slip:
> God knows what's in store, but we're all at the dip!

The Royal Naval Communication Chiefs' Association

In 1965 the first annual reunion of past and present Chief Communicators was held at the Signal School, and in 1968 at the suggestion of ex-Chief Tel Bill Barnden it was decided to put the reunion on a more formal basis by forming an Association. The incoming President of the Chief's Mess, Dennis Alderson, set up a committee to organise this, and the Association was formally inaugurated, and granted official recognition by the Ministry of Defence, in time for the 1969 Reunion.

Vice Admiral Sir John Parker accepted the invitation to become President of the Association, and guests at the annual Reunion or Dinner have included two MPs (both with naval interests), Lord Mottistone (himself a Signal Officer, better known as David Seely), and Admiral Mountbatten, who was made an Honorary Life Member.

The Association provides an opportunity for those with a common interest to meet annually and to keep in touch with one another by means of a regular Newsletter. The 'common interest' was defined by Dennis Alderson as 'comradeship, esprit-de-corps, unity, loyalty and pride of service - characteristics which tend to be lacking in some quarters today.' The importance of the Association to the Communicator was emphasised in 1975 when the Communications Branch became part of the new Operations Branch.

At the 1978 Royal Naval Communication Chiefs' Association Reunion

Front (L to R): Capt Roger Morgan, FCCY Terry Hankey (Chairman), Vice Admiral Sir John Parker (President), Rear Admiral Sir Peter Anson, Capt Barrie Kent, and CCY Ted Palfrey.
Back (L to R): CRS John Maye, CRS Ken Taylor, Lieut (CS) Dennis Alderson, CRS Ron Strangeway (Treasurer), CRS Charlie Tinkler, CYS Jeff Farnell, CYS Bill Bugg (Secretary), CYS Gordon Lester, CRS John Hilder and FCCY Les Murrell.

The first elected officials were Palfrey (Chairman), Tinkler (Hon Treasurer) and Bugg (Secretary), all of whom served in various capacities for many years.

'Sammy' Woods and Rev. John Scott

Vice Admiral Alexander Woods, DSO*, known in the navy as 'Sammy', was Fleet Signal Officer to Admiral Jellicoe, C-in-C Grand Fleet. He won his first DSO at Jutland, and the second in command of HMS *Topaze* in 1917, when he led a landing party to silence Turkish shore batteries at Salif in what is now the Yemen.

After he retired in 1931, despite suffering greatly from muscular dystrophy, he was ordained and became Assistant Curate at St Paul's, Whitechapel, the 'Dockland Church', and Chaplain at the Merchant Seamen's Home in Lemon Street. He was also for a time Honorary Chaplain to the London Division, RNVR.

In 1934 a young insurance clerk, John Scott, met 'Father' Woods at the Seaman's Mission, and was taught morse and semaphore by him to qualify for his Scout and Sea Cadet signal badge. Scott was thinking of leaving his office desk and was undecided whether to go to sea or become a priest. 'Combine both vocations' was Woods' advice, 'become a sailor and a naval chaplain.' With Woods' encouragement Scott joined the navy in 1941, started training as an Ordinary Telegraphist, but a few months later had the opportunity to take his final exams for ordination. He became a Chaplain in the Royal Navy, and will be well known to many communicators, as he served for some years at the Signal School, and became Honorary Chaplain to the Royal Naval Communication Chiefs' Association.

The Long Arm ...

From the 'Portsmouth Evening News':

'William W——, serving in HMS Vanguard at Malta, was fined 2/6d by the Havant Magistrates yesterday for permitting a chimney at his home in Emsworth to catch fire.'

Bird Class Carrier

Centaur and *Eagle* decided to exercise 'search and strike', and *Eagle* went off to be the enemy. In due course *Centaur* sent off the appropriate search aircraft, and when the target was located, mounted a strike. On completion, *Centaur* signalled to Flag Officer Aircraft Carriers 'Have struck one bird class carrier'. *Eagle's* operator unfortunately read an extra 'dot' so that the signal was received in that ship as 'Have struck one third class carrier'. Restoration of normal relations between the two ships took a long time.

Centaur was also involved in co-ordinating the ceremonial arrangements for a Trade Fair in Lisbon. It was planned that the appropriate national flag would be broken on a series of masts when the national anthem of each country was played.

The British Ambassador suggested that international goodwill would be generated if signalmen from different countries broke each flag, rather than their own. The SCO, Ronnie Graham-Clarke, strongly advised against this change in plan but was over-ruled.

As each anthem was played, the faces of the signalmen, who were not entirely *au fait* with the relevant tunes, developed looks of bewilderment and then panic. The result was complete disaster.

Moral: Don't change plans at the last minute; or perhaps in a similar situation dress bandsmen as signalmen!

G3BZU - The Royal Naval Amateur Radio Society

An Amateur Radio Club was first set up at the Signal School in 1947 when the callsign G3BZU was allocated by the GPO. The early years were the subject of mixed fortunes, depending on the availability of a spare nissen hut in which to operate, and a licensed member of the staff who could hold the club licence. But it survived, and members of the staff and long courses going through were encouraged to join as a means of improving their prowess at morse.

At Kranji W/T in 1957 the Officer in Charge, Dickie Richardson, gave Radio Supervisor Mike Matthews permission to start a local Radio Club. Matthews was serving on the committee of the Malaysian Amateur Radio Society at the time, together with members of the RAF Amateur Radio Society, and he realised that the RAF had a number of clubs around the world which were supported by their Signal School. Back in the UK, he drew up proposals, with the help of George Tagg (G8IX), a telegraphist who had served at Newfoundland W/T during the first war, for the setting up of a navy-wide Society. It was expected that this would ease the way for amateur radio enthusiasts to operate at naval establishments, and would benefit the service by encouraging a hobby allied to their profession. A list of some 150 names of those with naval connections who would be interested in becoming members was compiled.

With the help of Lieutenant John Riggs, then running the *Mercury* Amateur Radio Club, a proposed constitution was drawn up. This was approved by the Captain, John Henley, and on 25 June 1960 the inaugural meeting of the Royal Naval Amateur Radio Society was held in the cinema under the Chairmanship of George Tagg. Matthews (G3JFF) became the first Secretary, and Riggs Treasurer. Subsequently both Matthews and Mick Puttick (G3LIK) had much to do with the running of the Society for many years.

A generous grant from the Nuffield Trust helped to equip the station with modern transmitters and receivers, and soon the callsign G3BZU was being heard around the world on a regular basis. Publicity in radio magazines resulted in new members, many from overseas, and the Society regularly exhibited at the London radio shows. The first Society Newsletter appeared in 1964 - a six page affair edited by Sub Lieutenant Dave Davies (G3SJQ), who continued the task by post when he was appointed to a new job in Malta. This has now grown to a 64 page tri-annual newsletter featuring articles from members around the world.

One of the Society's earliest undertakings was to provide morse code transmissions to assist those who had just passed the GPO morse test (12 wpm) to increase their proficiency, but also to allow other amateurs to maintain their standard at speeds up to 40 wpm. In fact the first run had to be abandoned; scheduled for January 1963, which it may be remembered was a particularly cold winter, the QRQ Manager, Dave Pilley (G3HLW), and Mike Matthews were caught by snow drifts several feet deep on the road up from Clanfield. This

During a mock encounter with the French Mediterranean Fleet, the British aircraft carrier squadron was taken by surprise when the French Admiral led his forces undetected round the van of the British and launched his attack from a totally unexpected direction. The British Admiral, gallantly conceding defeat, congratulated the French Admiral by signalling:

'Vous m'avez attrappé avec mes pantalons en bas!'

The RNARS Stand at the 1968 Radio CommunicationsExhibition

CRS Mike Matthews (G3JFF) and RS Bill Metcalfe (G3TIF) with visitors reading code proficiency transmissions at speeds between 20 and 40 wpm. These transmissions were also transmitted weekly from HMS *Mercury* (G3BZU).

set-back did however result in considerable publicity with beneficial results in terms of membership. The QRQ run is still transmitted regularly, modern computer equipment having replaced the old Creed and GNT autoheads and paper tape, and the RNARS Code Proficiency Certificate is a much sought after award in the amateur and professional radio fraternity.

A regular event has been the annual Mobile Rally, held in early June on the playing fields at Hyden Wood. From small beginnings in 1965 when some 150 attended, this has grown into a major event on the UK amateur radio scene with attendances of as many as 3,000.

In 1973 the Society was invited to put an amateur radio station on display in the Admiral's Bridge in HMS *Belfast*, as part of the diamond jubilee celebrations of the Radio Society of Great Britain. The success of this activity resulted in permission being given to the RNARS to set up a permanent radio presence on board, the callsign GB2RN was allocated, and visitors can now hear the sounds of morse emanating from the open W/T office door. This was the first of a long line of ships which followed suit, such as the *Warrior* at Portsmouth (GB4HMS), *Alliance* at Gosport (GB0SUB), *Plymouth* at Birkenhead (GB0PLY), HMAS *Castlemaine* at Melbourne (VK3RAN), *Diamantina* at Brisbane (VK4RAN), HMCS *Sackville* at Halifax (VE1RCN) and USS *Olympia* at Philadelphia (WA3BAT).

A permanent headquarters for the RNARS was built in to the new P & RT centre in *Mercury* and formally opened by Captain Derek O'Reilly in 1976. From Nissen hut to relative luxury in 29 years!

Coming of age was celebrated in 1981 with a dinner at *Mercury*, and in 1985 Lord Mottistone, an early supporter of the Society, became its Patron. With the move of the Signal School to *Collingwood* in 1993, a new home is being prepared and the future of the Society seems assured.

In the Caribbean

Commodore Cameron Rusby, Senior Naval Officer West Indies, was being relieved by Commodore Bryan Straker and, accompanied by the SOO-cum-Flag Lieutenant, Peter Abbott, this trio of signal officers was crossing the Great Sound at Bermuda in the barge, dressed in '4Ws', to make official calls in Hamilton.

'We suddenly came across a dinghy in distress', recalls Abbott, 'and Commodore Straker immediately stripped out of his ice cream suit and sword and went to the rescue with

great flair and panache, putting his miserable Flag Lieuten-
ant to shame!'

As Abbott said, life in the Caribbean was often stranger than fiction. At Bequia, just south of St Vincent, he went to collect four lunch guests. The first two, the local Canon and his wife turned up on time, but there was no sign of the others.

'Having given them 20 minutes, I co-opted the local police-
man for lunch and we headed back to Mohawk. The leading
yachts of the round-the-island race arrived at the finishing
line as we approached the ship; the third yacht seemed to be
crewed by a couple of children with no clothes on. We
chugged on, drawing closer, when the yacht suddenly tacked
and all was revealed. Yes, they were naked! No, they were
certainly not children, but very well developed young ladies!
The Canon's wife giggled and blushed, and the Canon
muttered "Damn disgusting, man".

'At the reception ashore that evening conversation
centred on the streaking ladies, but sadly the only people
who had witnessed the incident were the Canon, his wife and
the Flag Lieutenant. Another good day in the Caribbean!'

Basegram Hall

Geoffrey Willans, an RNVR (Ce) officer, who qualified during the war, had a number of articles about life at Leydene published in Punch. The following is a sample:

Every so often, in words dripping with honey, the Admiralty invites officers to apply for Courses, and all officers who have had a row with the Captain that morning invariably apply. Courses usually require a knowledge of higher mathematics, calculus, a sound knowledge of physics ... It is only very rarely that a Course demands 'no technical knowledge whatsoever', and when this happens there is a tendency to apply rashly without further thought. Which, roughly speaking, was how twelve of us came to be learning Morse at Basegram Hall.

Morse, as you know, is a series of dots and dashes inextricably mixed. You can make Morse with a light, which is called Flashing: or you can make it on a little machine screwed to a table, which is called Buzzing. In certain circumstances you can make it on a ship's siren, when you get a series of bubbles and a rush of gurgling hot water that drenches everyone on deck.

In any case, Morse is useless unless you can read it.

Every morning at Basegram Hall they make us put on our headphones and Petty Officer Postagram gives us our buzzer exercise. For years he has been making Morse, and he can actually read it faster than he can write it down. When he makes Morse he sits with one hand on the key and with the other he scratches his nose while gazing wistfully out of the window. He is a kind and friendly man, however.

Not so our Instructor, Lieutenant Lumping. When he makes Morse he really means business. He grits his teeth and hammers the key like a man possessed. Not only does he expect you to read what he makes, he actually wants you to reply. This is fairly easy, actually, because after a few minutes' silence you are aware that Lieutenant Lumping is glaring at you and you know it is your turn to answer.

It has not taken our Course long, in fact, to realise that there is more to attaining proficiency at Morse than merely making stern efforts to read it. You can, for instance, take a look at what the man next to you has written. This is all right because you know he is looking at what you have written and that the chances are that both of you are wrong...

But you must not think we do not take our Morse seriously or that we are all equally inefficient. Lieutenant Lanyard, for instance, has been able to read Morse for years, ever since he was a Boy Scout, and each mistake he makes is like a drop of blood to him. He even remembers particular letters that have been made early in the exercise and says to himself: 'That's funny.' When he makes a mistake there is nothing underhand about him. He takes the direct line.

'Look here,' he says, 'you gave me dar-dar-dee-dar.' 'No Sir', says the Petty Officer. 'Dee-dar-dee-dee - that's what it was.'

'Dee-dar-dee-dee?'

'Yes Sir.'

'I could have been certain' says Lieutenant Lanyard, 'that it was the dee-dar-dee-dee just before the dar-dar-dar.'

He makes the alteration firmly but regretfully. I don't suppose it matters, because Lieutenant Flake says we have only been selected for the Course for social reasons. He doesn't suppose we shall need Morse to arrange an Admiral's dinner-party or dance attendance on his daughter.

*   *   *   *   *

We have now been here for twelve buzzer exercises, and our Course is even beginning to look like a conglomeration of Signal Officers. The point about Signal Officers is that, in company with Gunnery Officers, Navigation Officers and Torpedo Officers, they consider themselves the cream of the Service. But you need special knowledge to pick out a Signal Officer.

There are small points to be observed - the top button is left undone, the white handkerchief shows brazenly from the breast pocket, and the hair is worn long. But the real, infallible sign, is the Signal Officer's waistcoat. For weeks this may lurk modestly beneath the monkey jacket, until suddenly the coat is thrown open and there, like a primrose is the waistcoat - trim, brass-buttoned, the ultimate sign.

No one on our Course, not even Lieutenant Flake, has dared to buy a waistcoat yet, but we watch our instructors enviously and wait for the day.

Tone, you see, is the watchword of the Signal Officer, and we are fortunate in having a fitting abode in Basegram Hall. There can be little wrong when we receive instruction in a room marked 'Walnut Suite' on the door, even if the naval authorities try to call it 8AB.

This relic of past splendour has problems. Lieutenant Flake, whose cabin is called 'The Tassel Room' is all right; but what of Lieutenant Copping? He inhabits the Third Footman's Bedroom.

$$* \qquad * \qquad * \qquad * \qquad *$$

The scene is the stone-balustraded terrace of Basegram Hall. Above us, full of clickings, buzzes, oscillations, wiring diagrams and Wrens broods the Hall itself, casting a shadow over the summer day. Small wonder that we look so dejected. We are still on our Course and we are doing an SFX.

The trouble is you do things for weeks before you know what they are. So with an SFX. I did one every day until a careless word revealed to me that it was a Standard Flashing Exercise.

Flashing (or 'Bobbing' if you wish it to appear that you have been in the Navy for some years) is the process of making Morse by light. It is of course extensively employed at sea, where it is rarely seen by signalmen until the Officer of the Watch says 'Bobbing Bunts', and then turns away (if he can't read it himself) or tries to correct the signalman (if he can).

Once the signalmen are aware that a ship is calling they spring to an enormous lantern which is almost invariably placed behind an even larger obstruction, and beat up and down on the handle like a tom-tom. The Yeoman watches them for a minute or two, mouthing oaths to himself, then says: 'Come along. Get him on the six-inch, then.'

In 1947 Duke of York, the Home Fleet flagship, was anchored off Kristiansand (S) on Midsummer's day.

At midnight she gave a firework display surrounded by most of the local population in their boats. Then, on the spur of the moment, the flagdeck staff hoisted the Norwegian Ensign and floodlit it with ten and twenty inch signal projectors.

The result was astonishing - hundreds of Norwegians stood up in their boats and sang their national anthem, a most impressive sound as it floated over the still water.

This is a smaller lantern which can always be seen perfectly, but when wanted it is always stowed in the wheel-house or signal office.

Eventually communication is established on a very small lamp indeed, and the signalmen, who have been cursing each other, now send a steady stream of oaths towards the sending ship. They curse it for having too bright a light or too weak a light, for making the message too fast or too slow, for making bad Morse, for directing the light badly and for making the signal at all.

The contents of the message are called out in a strange language: 'From Charlie in Chokey. Detach and proceed. Time from orange 1717 annie rotchet.' This has the great advantage of meaning little to anyone but a signalman.

However all this is fairly advanced technique. At Basegram Hall as we read our SFX our concentration is so great that none of us has any idea what any signal is about. It is not only that the eyes water and bulge from the head, but the least sound becomes an intolerable distraction. And the terrace is full of sounds, chiefly those of birds. A signal should read somewhat as follows:

> *'HMS Caustic tweet-tweet from Captain miss. miss again. Damn. Tweet-tweet. Blast. Something boats crews are to, cow shifting in a field, unless crews are, tweet-tweet. miss. and now we have music while you work once again. miss. something rig of the day. ends.'*

During an SFX the class divides into pairs, in which one victim reads the signal and the other writes it down. The one who writes has his back to the light and the pairs are spaced so they cannot hear one another. It is quite a shame that the system has flaws. These are that the man writing down gets interested in the bird-life in the valley and forgets to write down, while a hundred yards would be too little to avoid hearing what Lieutenant Copping is saying. This would be fine if Copping was a good reader of Morse, but unfortunately he isn't. If he says it's B for Baker you can be fairly sure it's F for Fox, or L for Love if he has recently taken a Wren to a dance. The only person who is totally undisturbed is Copping himself - as befits a man who has been known to read a volume called *The Keen Boy's Guide to Wireless*.

Since all our exercises are marked it may be wondered how the confusion affects our percentages. But there is no need to worry. The Yeoman collects our papers and bears them off to some fastness, where he has a system of working out marks that transforms the worst exercise into immediate respectability. When he returns your copy is still the same and very depressing - but scrawled across it is the magic symbol 75%. We think he does it with a slide-rule.

In any case the SFX represents the end of a working day. We walk down the hill and turn in to the hospitable parlour of 'The George.'

'Ah, Yeoman' we say, 'What's yours?'

Perhaps, you never know, that has something to do with our marks.

Signal Ties

The Signal Branch has several ties. The Signal Officers tie, dark blue and grey stripes, first saw the light of day in 1947. Lord Louis used to claim that he had designed it, saying that he wanted the colours to be subdued so that it would be suitable for wearing with a business suit in the Admiralty, the blue representing the sea, and grey the ether; a more popular version is that the colours represent blue blood and grey matter. Others say Lord Louis was consulted but did not actually design it!

The Royal Naval Communication Chiefs' Association has two different designs. One is fairly subdued - blue with a small motif of a sparker's and bunting's badge surrounded by a laurel wreath and surmounted by a crown; the other is a much 'louder' version with alternate sparker's and bunting's badges on a blue background between the normal red and white naval stripes. The most prominent badge, in the centre, may be either, and the idea is to choose the tie that emphasises one's own specialisation!

'One in the Bucket...'

Hugh Lee operating a long-standing and effective means of communication
- a container for messages on the end of a piece of string, hauled up the voicepipe
from the wireless office to the bridge. In big ships (this was in *Illustrious* in 1950),
the system would be between the Remote Control Office (RCO) and the bridge.

Chapter Twenty Four

The Colours of the Fleet

*'It is a well known fact that there is scarcely any
undertaking of note carried out in the Navy without a
Signalman being required to assist in it.'*

Signal Handbook, 1890

The Union Flag

England's national flag, the Red Cross of St George, was in use in
ships as early as the 13th century, though sometimes combined with
other devices, when the red cross was usually in the upper canton.
The White Cross of St Andrew (known in heraldic terms as a
'saltire') was probably used by Scotland from a very early date, but
the earliest Scottish records were lost at sea in the ship which was
bringing them home after they had been carried off, together with the
Stone of Destiny, by Edward I. The background colour varied at first
but was established as blue after about 1540.

Ireland never adopted a common national flag, although the red
saltire, originally the arms of the Earl of Kildare, was 'most prominently
displayed by the representatives of the English government in
Ireland and was, for a political purpose, used by them as an Irish
emblem under the name of St Patrick's cross.' [1] It became the badge
of the Order of St Patrick and was, conveniently, incorporated in the
eventual Union Flag.

On the accession of James I in 1603, bitter disputes arose
between English and Scottish seamen, previously 'foreigners' to
each other, as to the precedence of their national flags (at this time
the national flag was also used by ships as what would now be termed
an ensign). In an effort to settle this, James issued a proclamation in
1606 which read, in part:

> *'Whereas some differences hath arisen between our Sub-
> jects of North and South Britain, travelling by seas, about
> the bearing of their flags: for the avoiding of all such
> contentions hereafter, We have, with the advice of our
> Council, ordered that, from henceforth, all our Subjects of
> this Isle and Kingdom of Great Britain and the members*

[1] *'A History of Irish Flags from the
Earliest Times'*, by G A Hayes-McCoy

thereof, shall bear in their maintops the Red Cross, commonly called the Saint George's Cross, and the White Cross, commonly called Saint Andrew's Cross, joined together, according to a form made by our Heralds ... and in their foretops Our Subjects of South Britain shall wear the Red Cross only, as they were wont; and Our Subjects of North Britain in their foretops the White Cross only, as they were accustomed.'

This new flag, known originally as the British flag, was intended to be flown by both warships and merchantmen. However in 1634 a further proclamation directed that the Union flag, as it was now being called, was to be flown by ships of the Royal Navy only. This was necessary because foreigners were not paying the proper marks of respect to ships of the Royal Navy, and used the excuse that until they were shot at they had no idea that they had encountered the King's ships! Another reason for the restriction was that merchant ships sometimes masqueraded as warships to avoid the payment of pilotage and harbour dues.

The new 'British' flag of 1606

During the Commonwealth both countries went back to their old national flags since the union of 'crowns' no longer existed, but the State's Navy used what became known as the Commonwealth Jack, the St George's Cross with the yellow harp for Ireland in the fly. When the two countries were again united, the Union Flag was reinstated, for a short time with the Irish harp in the centre.

The Union flag was also used for signalling purposes, for example to call officers on board, being hoisted in different positions to denote the rank of the officer required. Hoisted superior to a three figure group it denoted the ship's number from the List of Navy, while at the fore top-gallant masthead it was the signal for a pilot. Marryat also used it to identify warships, and to request a pilot, despite the 1634 ruling. Their Lordships were concerned at this and in 1823 ordered that this be stopped 'for any purpose whatsoever ... the Signal Jack to be hereafter worn by merchant ships should have an entire white border ... and should also in future be used as a signal for a Pilot ...' [2] This wording unintentionally gave the impression that the white bordered flag could be used as a 'Jack' in the bow of merchant ships, a practice sometimes adopted although prohibited by the Pilotage Act - 'If the master of a vessel displays ... any of the pilot signals for any other purpose than that of summoning a pilot ... he shall be liable to a fine not exceeding £20.'

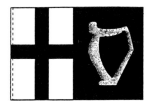

The Commonwealth Jack

[2] *'London Gazette'* of 8 July 1823

It was only when the 'Pilot Jack', as it came to be known, ceased to be a signal for a pilot in 1970 that its use as a Jack was no longer illegal. A house flag, or a square red or blue ensign, perhaps with the appropriate badge, is now commonly used. The white-bordered union flag was nevertheless used in the RN code (as the 'Screen' flag) until it disappeared in the changes introduced in the 1950s, and a version is still used as the flag of a Queen's Harbour Master - in this case it has at the centre a crown above the letters 'QHM' in a white circle.

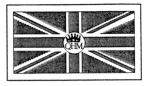

The Flag of the Queen's Harbourmaster

On 1 January 1801, as a result of the Union of Great Britain and Ireland, a proclamation stated that the Union Flag was to consist of the Cross of St George conjoined with the Crosses of St Andrew and St Patrick. To avoid one of the saltires hiding the other, they were 'counterchanged', that is divided on each leg with white above red in the hoist and red above white in the fly. With the red cross and red saltire being 'fimbriated' (edged in white), this resulted in the uneven appearance of the flag but it had the desired effect of giving the white saltire of Scotland the 'senior' position, Scotland having joined the Union first.

In 1908, in response to a Parliamentary question, the Government confirmed that the Union flag should be regarded as the National flag.

For many years the RN used the Union Flag at Dockyard ports to denote ships entering or leaving harbour. This could lead to a somewhat absurd situation, as when the *Inflexible* was seen in Portsmouth flying two Union flags, at the fore and the main, the former indicating that the ship was leaving harbour, the latter that an Admiral of the Fleet was on board!

When the Union flag is worn at the jackstaff it may be referred to, correctly, as the 'Union Jack', or more usually as 'the Jack'. The term is sometimes said to refer to James (Jacques) the First, but it probably derives from the fact that the 'Jack' is smaller than the ensign, 'jack' being a naval colloquialism for 'small'.

The Union flag as it finally became

Red, White and Blue Ensigns

The red, white and blue ensigns were used for many years to distinguish ships belonging to different squadrons or divisions of the Fleet. A manuscript dated 1627 describes a typical organisation under the Duke of Buckingham:

> *'The Duke, now lying at Portsmouth, divided his Fleete into Squadrons. Himselfe Admirall and Generall in Chiefe went in ye Triumph bearing the Standard of England in ye main topp, and Admirall particular of the bloody colours.*
>
> *'The Earle of Lindsey was Vice-Admirall to the Fleete in the Rainbowe, bearing the King's usual colours in his fore topp, and a Blew Flag in his maine topp, and was Admirall of the blew colours.*
>
> *'The Lord Harvey was Rear Admirall in ye Repulse, bearing the King's usual colours in his mizzen and a White Flagg in the maine topp, and was Admirall of ye Squadron of white colours.'*

In this instance the blue took precedence over the white, but in 1653 the precedence was changed to red, white and blue. At that date the white ensign was a plain white flag with a red St George's Cross in the first quarter or upper canton, but in 1702 it was altered by the introduction of a second, large, St George's Cross in the same position as it is today. On the Union with Scotland in 1707, two new white ensigns were produced, one with the crosses of St George and

St Andrew combined on a blue ground in the upper canton of a plain white flag, the other, known as the White St George's ensign, with the large St George's Cross in addition. In 1801, on the Union with Ireland, it achieved its present form.

The variety of ensigns could cause confusion, particularly in action, when the darker red and blue ensigns could be difficult to distinguish in the smoke, and they sometimes looked too much like foreign flags when not flying clear; because of this, before the battle of Trafalgar, Nelson, who was Vice Admiral of the White, ordered the ships of all three squadrons to wear the white ensign.

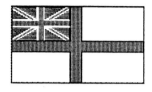

The White Ensign

As fleets got smaller the need for distinguishing colours became less important, while the frequent change of colours was inconvenient, and was often puzzling to foreigners. By Order in Council in 1864 it was directed that the white ensign only should in future be used by warships; as the Order said: '... each vessel (has to be) supplied with three sets of colours, and the frequent alterations that have to be made when the Fleet is distributed as at present, under the Orders of many Flag Officers, is attended with much inconvenience from the uncertainty and expense which the system entails.' This Order also established the practice whereby the blue ensign, with the appropriate badge in the fly, should be worn by ships in the public service, and by merchant ships commanded by Royal Naval Reserve officers, subject to certain conditions and to the issue of an Admiralty Warrant. The red ensign was to be used by all other British ships and vessels.

All Commonwealth navies wore the white ensign originally, usually with their national flag as a 'Jack', but in recent years they have all adopted new naval ensigns. Those of Australia and New Zealand are white, with the union flag in the upper canton, and their stars in the fly (blue stars for the RAN, red for the RNZN), but with no St George's Cross. In Canada, all forces use the same ensign, white with the national flag in the upper canton, and the armed forces device in the fly. The Jack is similar, but with the 'maritime' insignia in the fly.

The Australian Ensign

Certain yacht clubs also have the privilege of flying special ensigns - the White ensign exclusively by the Royal Yacht Squadron, Blue or Red ensigns 'defaced', ie with the club badge in the fly, by others, again under the authority of an Admiralty Warrant.

A ship is said to 'wear' a suit of colours, while the Admiral 'flies' his flag in HMS *Nonsuch*. It is obviously not a good idea to suggest that an Admiral 'wears' his flag!

The New Zealand Ensign

The Queen's Colour is a silk white ensign, with a crown and the Royal Cypher, encircled by the Garter, and with a red, white and blue silk cord and gold tassels; the size is 3' 9" by 3'. Formerly only carried by the Army, in 1924 this was extended to the Royal Navy. Queen's Colours are held by the principal naval commands and RN College, Dartmouth; also by certain Commonwealth navies.

The Colours are paraded when a Guard of Honour is mounted for the Queen or a member of the Royal Family, for foreign Heads of

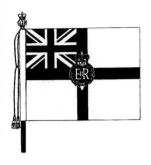

The Queen's Colour

[3] *'Sea Flags'* by Commander Hilary P Mead. Retiring after the war, Mead wrote extensively on Signal matters, and from 1946 to 1953 he edited the Mariner's Mirror, the journal of the Society for Nautical Research

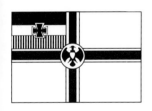

German Naval Ensign, 1914

At a distance, this could be mistaken for the White Ensign.

State, at parades to celebrate the Sovereign's birthday, and on other important ceremonial occasions. When paraded, it is given the same marks of respect as if the Queen was present. At the Jubilee review in 1977, the Queen's Colour of the Naval Home Command was paraded in *Vernon*, that of the Submarine Command in *Dolphin*, and that of the Fleet in *Ark Royal* when *Britannia* left Portsmouth Harbour to review the fleet.

Battle Ensigns

It is usual for a ship to wear at least two White Ensigns in battle, to ensure that if one is shot away it does not look as if the ship is surrendering!

Nelson set a precedent in a Memorandum dated 10 October 1805 which, as mentioned above, not only directed all ships to wear the White Ensign when in the presence of the enemy, but also that '... a Union Jack is to be suspended from the fore top-gallant stay.'

In the Grand Fleet during the 1914-18 war, some curious arrangements along the same lines were ordered and re-ordered, as recounted by Hilary Mead [3], who was the signal officer in HMS *King George V* at the time.

Mead recalls that at the Battle of Heligoland Bight in August 1914,

'A sense of confusion and bewilderment prevailed, intensified by low visibility, complicated manœuvrings and the occasional appearance through the mist of a warship, whose identity, due to the similarity of silhouettes of friend and foe, was doubtful and therefore a source of dangerous, if momentary, hesitation. Added to these troubles was the resemblance of the German Imperial naval flag to our own White Ensign.'

As a result, the C-in-C signalled on 1 September that a Blue Ensign was to be hoisted as well as the White Ensign when going into action or approaching a suspicious vessel. Three days later, says Mead, the Admiralty revoked this order; instead, HM Ships were, 'during the present war', to fly at least one Union flag in a conspicuous position on or near the foremast, but not at the actual masthead except in destroyers. A few days later destroyers were told to fly it at the yardarm instead. These arrangements were confirmed in a Grand Fleet signal order dated 19 September, which added that in two-masted ships the Union Flag was to be hoisted at the main. However, only two months later the rules were changed again, presumably because the arrangement was thought to have become well known and therefore compromised; on 16 November the Admiralty issued a confidential order to the effect that the Red Ensign was to supersede the Union Flag.

This arrangement lasted for just over a year, until in January 1916 the Union Flag once more replaced the Red Ensign, but '... it was not to be hoisted in sight of land or of merchant shipping, only when meeting a man-of-war or when in action'.

Finally, in May 1918, the practice of flying a distinctive flag seems to have lapsed, the Admiralty saying that the previous instructions were cancelled. Since then the general practice seems to have been to fly at least one additional White ensign. The present instructions [4] state that, in wartime, '... the White Ensign is to be worn day and night at sea, and in action two ensigns are always to be displayed in a conspicuous position without interfering with signalling'.

[4] BR 20, Article 9132

Half-Masting Colours

In a Minute dated 10th March 1952 the Flag Lieutenant to the Board of Admiralty said that the Palace had asked for information on the origin of the custom of half-masting colours to signify a death. The Archivist, Peter Kemp, Minuted: [5]

[5] PRO reference ADM1-23597

> *'The earliest record we have of the lowering of a flag to signify a death was an occasion in 1612, when the Master of the Hearts Ease, William Hall, was murdered by Eskimos while taking part in an expedition in search of the North West Passage. On rejoining her consort, the vessel's flag was flown trailing over the stern as a mark of mourning. On her return to London, the Hearts Ease again flew her flag over the stern and it was recognised as an appropriate gesture of mourning.*
>
> *'It was the habit, after the restoration of the Monarchy in 1660, for ships of the Royal Navy to fly their flags at half-mast on the anniversaries of the execution of King Charles I in 1649, and it is from this custom that, so far as we can trace, the present practice of announcing a death by the flying of a flag at half mast has evolved. The earlier practice at sea was to fly a black flag or to set a black sail.'*

In a further minute Kemp added:

> *'It is very difficult to substantiate 'why' a particular custom was adopted in the Navy. We know that the hoisting of black sails was a sign of mourning from the very earliest times. The black sail was superseded by the black flag, probably because it was a nuisance to have to carry black sails for use only on rare occasions. It was probably the position, rather than the colour, that caught the attention, particularly at a distance.'*

A lower deck story, recorded [6] by Signalman Knight serving in the *Sheffield* in 1941, was based on the idea of the captured ship, the ensign being lowered to half mast to leave room for death's invisible ensign to be hoisted superior, indicating that the angel of death had made another capture!

[6] IWM 87/15/1

Admiral's Flags

The first mention of the flag of St George as a distinguishing flag for admirals appears to be in the *Book of Orders for the War by Sea and Land*[7] drawn up by Thomas Audley in about 1530, in which the admiral was to fly two flags, a Standard at the maintop and 'one flag of Saint George crosse' at the foretop.

[7] British Library, Harl. MS.309

From the middle of this century, when ships of war generally had three masts, it was usual for the 'Admiral' or senior officer to fly his flag at the maintop. The Lord High Admiral, as the Sovereign's representative, would fly the Royal Standard; in the seventeenth century this changed to the Union flag, which eventually became established as the flag of an Admiral of the Fleet.

If there was more than one Admiral in the fleet or squadron, the flag of the second-in-command or Admiral of the Van, was flown at the fore, and that of the Admiral of the Rear at the Mizzen. The actual flags used varied, but sometimes included the St George's Cross in the canton.

The use of the St George's Cross by an Admiral of the White was formally established in 1702; in fact the Union flag was allocated initially, but a few weeks later, after complaints that this was unsuitable for the Admiral of the second squadron, the order was rescinded and he was given the St George's Cross. Different ranks, whether for admirals of the Red, White or Blue, continued to be indicated by the mast from which the flag was flown.

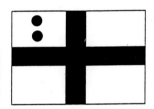

However this was no help in ship's boats with only one mast, for which the system of differencing by 'balls' was introduced for vice and rear admirals. Vice Admirals of the Red and Blue were given one white ball in the hoist, and Rear Admirals two white balls diagonally, on red or blue flags. The same applied initially to Vice and Rear Admirals of the White, the white balls being placed on the Union flag. However, as mentioned above, the St George's Cross was substituted for the Union flag almost immediately, and the balls were then placed in the upper canton, one for a vice admiral and two for a rear admiral, the colour being changed to blue.

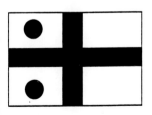

These were the first special designs for vice and rear admirals. In 1864, when the White Squadron's colours were introduced for the whole fleet, the White design for admiral's flags were adopted for all Boat flags, but the colour of the balls was changed to red.

Top: Boat Flags for Rear Admiral of the White, 1702 (balls coloured blue); Rear Admiral from 1864, (balls coloured red).

*Below:*Rear Admiral from 1898, for all purposes

From 1898, with the demise of three masted ships, it became necessary to indicate rank in ships as well as boats, and the 'boat' flags were adopted for both purposes, the balls being increased in size and, for a rear admiral, the second ball placed in the lower canton.

In two masted ships, Admirals of the Fleet, Admirals and Commanders-in-Chief fly their flags at the main, other Admirals at the fore.

Commodores fly a broad pennant, white with a red St George's Cross and one red ball, as did a Commodore 2nd class before 1st and 2nd class commodores were combined in 1958; the broad pennant of a Commodore First Class, who wore the uniform of a rear admiral, was then white with a plain red cross.

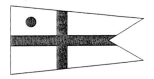

Commodore's broad pennant

In boats nowadays, on ceremonial or other official occasions, an admiral's flag, commodore's broad pennant or masthead pennant (for an officer in command) is flown in the bows. Otherwise, when on duty, a circular red disc with a white St George's Cross is displayed for officers entitled to fly a flag or broad pennant, and a blue disc by other Flag officers, Commodores, Commandant WRNS or the Matron-in-Chief. On informal occasions a white disc with five black crosses may be used, when courtesy salutes only will be accorded.

Commonwealth navies broadly followed suit, but recently there have been some changes. In the Canadian Armed Forces, for example, Flag Officers and Generals fly the same flags - white with the national flag in the upper canton, but with no St George's Cross; for a Rear Admiral/Major General this is a burgee, while the Commander of the Canadian Fleet, and Commodores, also have burgees but of a somewhat unusual shape.

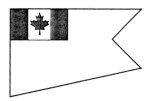

Canadian Commodore's burgee

*   *   *   *   *

When HMS *Edinburgh* was torpedoed in the Barents Sea while escorting convoy QP11 in May 1942, the ship's company were taken off by two of the escorts, *Halcyon* class minesweepers. As Admiral Bonham-Carter stepped on to the quarterdeck of one of the sweepers, her commanding officer saluted.

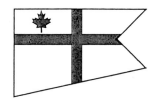

Commander Canadian Fleet's burgee

'*Everything correct, sir. Your flag is hoisted.*'

The Admiral looked up. Flying at the masthead was the Cross of St George, with red balls in the upper and lower cantons. Its ragged edge suggested that it was a senior officer's pennant from which the tails had been cut, and the red balls looked as though they had been hastily daubed on with red paint. But there was no mistaking it for anything but a Rear Admiral's flag.

*   *   *   *   *

At the time of the Dunkirk evacuation, the C-in-C Portsmouth was Admiral Sir William ('Bubbles') James. His son, Kit, later to qualify as a Signal Officer, was driving an MTB based at Gosport. At very short notice the Admiral decided to visit the beach-head in his son's boat. Overnight, with a pot of paint and a steady eye, Kit turned the wardroom mess tablecloth into an Admiral's flag which was flown successfully throughout the trip.

An old custom, periodically revived, involves dipping an Admiral's flag to salute a senior Admiral as their ships pass, usually when the latter is leaving the station or is about to haul down his flag.

Senior Officer's pennant

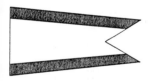

Squadron Command Pennant

[8] Defence Council Instruction RN3/1986

Senior Officer's Pennants

Over the years a variety of devices have been adopted to indicate the senior officer's ship when no flag officer was present. In 1864 the position was regularised:

> *'When two or more of Her Majesty's ships are present in Ports or Roadsteads, a small Broad Pendant (white, with the St George's Cross) is to be hoisted at the mizzen top-gallant masthead of the ship of the Senior Officer.'*

This was modified in 1906 to read:

> *'... in ships with less than three masts this pendant should be hoisted at the starboard topsail yardarm.'*

In 1913 it was further modified to indicate that if a Commodore, junior to him on the list of Captains, was also present, the Senior Officer should still hoist this pendant, this time 'at the masthead.'

The current rules are broadly similar, but the starboard pennant is used instead of the original design; it is hoisted at the starboard yardarm of the senior officer's ship as a distinguishing flag in addition to the masthead pennant, provided that the ship is not already flying a flag or broad pennant. However, when in company with warships of other NATO nations, it is to be flown in addition to any flag or broad pennant (each NATO senior officer present will do the same).

Another distinguishing flag is now flown by all Captains D and F, and other Squadron Commanders, because of the decision in 1984 to abolish black funnel tops 'to achieve a more effective all-grey fighting livery.' [8] This Squadron Command Pennant is a short white swallow-tailed pennant with a red border along the top and bottom edges. It is worn at all times at the starboard yardarm, at the foremast in a two masted ship; it does not displace the masthead pennant, nor is it displaced by an Admiral's flag or Commodore's broad pennant.

Masthead Pennant

All HM ships in commission, commanded by a Royal Navy or Royal Marine Officer appointed in command, and not flying a flag or broad pennant (or indeed a Standard or Admiralty Board flag), fly a masthead pennant at the main, day and night.

Streamers or pennants of various coloured designs have been flown from the earliest times, either as a form of decoration or identification; the length varied but at times was so great that it reached the water. In the 17th century, according to Pepys, a masthead pennant was flown primarily to distinguish men-of-war from merchant ships, and the colour corresponded to the red, white or blue of the squadron colours. When the white ensign was adopted for all warships in 1864, the white masthead pennant came with it. Thus it has a St George's Cross at the hoist and a white fly.

When ships are about to pay off, they substitute a long 'paying-off' pennant. There is no firm rule about the exact length, but for a normal commission it is customary for it to be the same length of the

ship, and somewhat longer if the commission has been extended. Since it is in effect a glorified masthead pennant, it can be argued that it should not be worn if the ship is flying an admiral's flag. Another story is that it originated in the 19th century when all cleaning rags were tied together and hoisted as a sign that they were finished with.

Sometimes when an Admiral was leaving the station in his flagship, especially if the latter was going home to pay off, he was presented with an extra large Admiral's flag to fly. This occurred, for example, in 1902 when Rear Admiral Lord Charles Beresford was leaving Malta in the *Ramillies* and was given a large silk flag (see photograph on page 343), and in 1932 when Admiral Chatfield, C-in-C Mediterranean was leaving in the *Queen Elizabeth*; in the latter case the ship's company gave him a 32-breadth 'paying-off flag' (24 by 36 feet).

The Flag of the Lord High Admiral

The anchor seems to have been used as the badge of the Lord High Admiral from an early date, and it was in use in the 16th century as a mark placed on ships or goods which had been arrested by the Admiralty Court. The earliest instance of the anchor in a flag occurs in an engraving, supposed to be of the *Ark Royal*, Lord Howard's flagship, in 1588, which shows the anchor in the head of a streamer flown from the foretop. However, as mentioned earlier, the Lord High Admiral was permitted to fly the Royal Standard, except when the King was present, when he flew the red flag with a yellow foul anchor, and this custom continued until 1702 when it was stopped by Queen Anne.

A survey of flags at Deptford in 1633 included a silk 'red ensine with ye Lo. Admiralls badge'. Over the years various designs seem to have been used, including one with three anchors, vertical.

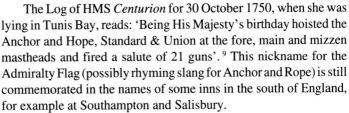

[9] Quoted in *'Flags of the World'*, edited by E M C Barraclough, which covers the history of the Admiralty Flag in some detail

The Log of HMS *Centurion* for 30 October 1750, when she was lying in Tunis Bay, reads: 'Being His Majesty's birthday hoisted the Anchor and Hope, Standard & Union at the fore, main and mizzen mastheads and fired a salute of 21 guns'.[9] This nickname for the Admiralty Flag (possibly rhyming slang for Anchor and Rope) is still commemorated in the names of some inns in the south of England, for example at Southampton and Salisbury.

W G Perrin, Admiralty Librarian for many years, recounts in his book 'British Flags' (1922), how in 1869 the First Lord, Mr Childers, embarked in HMS *Agincourt* and took command, first of the Reserve Fleet, and then of an experimental squadron, under the Admiralty Flag. He was accompanied by the First Sea Lord, Vice Admiral Sir Sydney Dacres but, says Perrin:

'This proceeding gave rise to much comment, but since the Letters Patent appointing a Board of Admiralty give power to "any two or more" of the Commissioners to exercise all the functions of the Lord High Admiral, the action of Mr Childers does not seem to have been ultra vires, though it is not one that is likely to be repeated.'

The current rule, which derives from the Letters Patent, is that the Admiralty Board Flag may be flown when two or more members of the Board are embarked, but even the naval members are unlikely to use their authority to take command of the fleet or squadron, though they would no doubt ask the senior officer to 'carry on, please'!

An oil painting by Van der Velde the Younger of the Royal visit to the Fleet at the Nore in 1672 shows the *Royal Prince* flying the Admiralty Flag at the fore, the Royal Standard at the main, and the Union Flag at the mizzen. The design of the Admiralty flag is of a yellow horizontal 'foul anchor'. When James II ascended the throne in 1685 he assumed the office of Lord High Admiral, although a new Patent was never issued, but he placed the anchor vertically and surmounted it with a crown, '... as being himself his own Admiral'.

Parliament was not entirely happy with this, and in 1688 when James II was deposed, a fundamental change took place in the relationship between the Sovereign and the Navy. From then on, Sovereignty resided in Parliament (technically 'the King or Queen in Parliament') and only with the consent of Parliament could the Sovereign displace the Lord High Admiral or take back any of his powers, placing him beyond the Sovereign's control. Thus the Admiralty Flag became a bone of contention between the Sovereign and the Admiralty, the former contending that, as the source from which the Lords of the Admiralty derived their power, he or she should have the right to fly the Admiralty Flag. Their Lordships on the other hand insisted that theirs was the sole right, as they were in control of HM ships, a contention that was upheld by the Law Officers of the Crown when, in 1833, William IV endeavoured to legalize his right to 'the Anchor Flag of the Admiralty'.

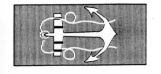

The Flag of the Lord High Admiral

It has been customary since early in the 18th century for the 'Admiralty Flag' to be flown on warships during the launching ceremony.

However an Admiralty Board Minute dated 3 July 1833 laid down that the flags to be flown by any ship in which the Monarch was embarked were to be the Standard at the main, the flag of the Lord High Admiral at the fore, and the Union flag at the mizzen. In any case it was generally recognised that the Admiralty flag could be used by the Sovereign, and this was insisted upon by Queen Victoria after an incident in 1854 when she embarked in the *Victoria and Albert* to review the Fleet before it proceeded to the Baltic for operations against the Russians. The Admiralty Flag was not flown, nor was there one available on board the Royal Yacht. The Queen asked Captain Denman, in command of the Royal Yacht, to make a general signal of good wishes to the Fleet from Her Majesty. It is said that she noticed that instead of doing so, the Captain passed the message only to the Admiralty Yacht, the *Black Eagle*. The Queen demanded to know why her orders were not being carried out; Captain Denman is reputed to have replied that as the Lord High Admiral's flag was flying in *Black Eagle*, indicating the presence of the Board of Admiralty, it was for that ship to make the general signal. [10]

[10] Recounted by Admiral Mountbatten in a paper dated 1962. He says that his father told him that Queen Victoria believed the absence of the Admiralty Flag was intentional, and that she instructed the Keeper of the Cabins to see that one was available in future.

From about that time the Admiralty accepted the anomaly of both the Board and the Sovereign flying the Admiralty Flag, the design of which had reverted to its original, horizontal, form in the reign of William III.

Having flown over the Admiralty in Whitehall since 1850, the Admiralty Flag was hauled down at sunset on 31 March 1964 when the Board of Admiralty ceased to exist, and the affairs of the Royal Navy came under the control of the Defence Council of the new Ministry of Defence. The Queen then formally assumed the office of Lord High Admiral, and thus now flies the Admiralty flag in her own right when embarked, while the flag has resumed its original name as the Flag of the Lord High Admiral.

This left the Board without a flag of their own for some years, but in 1977 one of the old versions, with three vertical anchors, was brought back into use as the Admiralty Board Flag, and was flown for the first time on 28 June 1977 when the Admiralty Board embarked in HMS *Birmingham* for the Jubilee Review of the Fleet by the Queen.

Before this, in 1957, the National Maritime Museum had been authorised to use the three anchor version as the Museum's flag. When the Admiralty Board adopted this, the museum's flag was modified to include two sailing ships above the anchors.

The Admiralty Board Flag

The Shape and Design of Flags and Ensigns

The dimensions of the Union Flag are in the proportion 1 to 2, as are those of our ensigns, and this was copied by most nations of the British Empire, and some others. However many nations use the proportion 3 to 5 which is sometimes considered a more attractive shape. The flag of the Lord High Admiral is 1 to 2, but the Admiralty Board flag is 2 to 3, and this shape is also used for Admiral's flags, Royal Marine Corps and Commando flags, Joint

*Ramillies leaving Malta in 1902
flying the large silk rear admiral's
flag presented to Lord Charles
Beresford on his relinquishing the
appointment of second-in-command
of the Mediterranean Fleet*

[11] Based on a paper by Commander
Bruce Nicolls, President of the Flag
Institute

The Flag of the
National Maritime Museum

Service flags, the NATO flag, and many others.

The reasons for this confusing state of affairs has been explained by Commander Malcolm Farrow, a noted vexillologist: [11]

'This is simply the result of sloppy staff work and attention to detail some 300 years ago. The aim in designing a rectangular flag should be to make it the most pleasing shape consistent with its design. The universally agreed formula for achieving this is based on the Golden Ratio, which produces an aspect ratio of 1:1.6180339, which matches closely the ratio of 5:8. Flags in this proportion, or close to it, are common the world over and this is the most attractive shape for most flags. (The ancient Greeks understood this ratio, and built the Parthenon using it.)

'In 1687 Samuel Pepys issued a table of sizes and shapes for Ensigns and Jacks of the Royal Navy. He directed that: "It is in general to be noted that the bewper of which Colours are made being 22 inches in breadth, and the half of that breadth, namely 11 inches going in ordinary discourse by the name 'Breadth' when wrought into Colours, every such Breadth is allowed about half a yard for its fly." *In other words the proportion of flags and ensigns were fixed in 1687 at 11:18 or very nearly 5:8; Mr Pepys knew what he was about!*

'Early in the 18th century the breadth of bewper, or bunting as it came to be known, was reduced from 11 to 10 inches but no alteration was made to the specifications for flags, hence the proportion altered to 10:18 (or 5:9). Around 1837 the breadth of bunting was reduced once more, this time to 9 inches. As before, no action was taken to alter the specifications for flags so the proportion changed again, this time to 9:18, or 1:2, the ratio in which the Union Flag, Ensigns and Jacks are made today.

'Interestingly, in 1938 Garter King of Arms issued
guidance that flags on land (he did not seek to usurp
Admiralty authority over flags at sea) should be in the
proportion 3:5, which is a very close approximation to the
ideal of 5:8.'

Ensigns and flags are still measured by 'breadths' of 9 inches (23 cm); thus a six breadth ensign will be 4' 6" by 9', and a six breadth Admiral's flag will be 4' 6" by 6' 9".

*   *   *   *   *

Much thought was given to the best shapes and colours of flags as the new signal books were developed during the late eighteenth and early nineteenth centuries. [12]

From the earliest days it was generally recognised that the best colour combinations were red and white, blue and white, and blue and yellow. Red, white and blue stripes showed up well, though Kempenfelt suggested that vertical stripes were better than horizontal. Popham, writing in 1812, made the same point, commenting that the French and Dutch flags were both good designs. Flags with white against the skyline were avoided.

Red and blue were rightly considered a poor combination, though one such flag has been used for many years (now Flag E). In this case, and some others, Howe substituted black for blue in his codes. Captain Young, who served as Rodney's flag-captain, wrote on 31 July 1780 to Sir Charles Middleton:

'Chequered flags should be abolished. Quartered, halved,
three-striped, striped corner-ways, half up and down, and
pierced, are the only ones that are properly distinguished at
a distance.'

Kempenfelt first introduced triangular flags, to indicate squadrons, in 1780, and as the requirements for new designs increased with the introduction of vocabulary codes it became difficult to avoid more complex designs and less good colour combinations. New shapes that made their appearance included the burgee (swallow tailed) and pendants, initially pointed, but later with the fly squared off.

Sir Samuel Hood was enthusiastic about Popham's designs; writing to him in 1814, Hood said:

'The flags have been selected with great circumspection.
When a possibility occurs of the colours being mistaken, the
shape gives sufficient distinction. The Broad Pendants
(burgees) ... give great relief to the observer; the flag
wafting out with every change of view, the colours are more
perfectly distinguished. There certainly is not that advantage in triangular flags; they are in general difficult to
discern. But in your code the colours are so few and so well
varied that they cannot be mistaken.'

The Royal Standard followed the same trend; the early Royal Banners were square, or nearly square (a suitable shape for representing heraldic arms), but they gradually changed until in 1837 Queen Victoria's Standard became 1:2. As Commander Nicolls, President of the Flag Institute, has pointed out:

'This has had the effect of stretching the English lions beyond reasonable limits, while the Scottish lion is over fat, and all feet.'

Flag dimensions are now normally stated as width before length, although as Nicolls says, it is perhaps easier for an Englishman to remember the old way of length before width, or LBW!

[12] An article by Captain (later Vice Admiral) Lancelot Holland, reprinted in the Mariner's Mirror, Vol. 39, Feb.1953, covers the development of flag signalling and the design of flags in some detail. Admiral Holland was lost in the Hood in 1941. His collection of Signal Books, many of them 17th century French books in which he specialised, is now in the National Maritime Museum.

The burgees however did not prove so popular - the five in the signal book of 1816, had all disappeared in that of 1827. However two burgees reappeared in Marryat's code (flags zero and five), and as many of Marryat's designs were adopted for the International Code in 1857 these two have survived, as 'A' (though white and blue instead of Marryat's yellow and blue), and 'B' (red). Triangular flags also survive, as substitutes, and for some special naval purposes.

Marryat had tried to avoid trespassing on naval designs, and thus the international code tended to do the same, resulting in the very large number of flags and pendants that had to be carried by warships until the advent of the NATO signal books in the 1950s.

Various people designed codes using shapes or symbols which could, theoretically, be recognised easily. Popham for example used a ball to indicate 'thousands', but generally shapes were not a success. The Admiralty copy of one such code, designed by Sir Charles Ekins in 1838, contains the manuscript comment:

> *'In the trials the symbols were unfortunately treated like flags and placed between two swivels, and quite surprised the signal officer by turning round so fast that they could not be made out.'*

Signal flags are now generally in the proportion 4:5, though there are some variations.

The Royal Yacht

Ceremonial in the Royal Yacht, established over many years by tradition and custom, has to be meticulously observed.

As mentioned above, when the Queen is embarked, the Royal Standard is flown at the main, the Flag of the Lord High Admiral at the fore, and the Union Flag at the mizzen.

When a member of the Royal Family, other than the Queen, is embarked, his or her personal Standard is flown at the main. The flag of the Flag Officer Royal Yachts will be flown at the fore, and usually the white ensign at the mizzen. However there are exceptions - the Duke of Edinburgh, as an Admiral of the Fleet, flies the Union Flag at the fore, and has the choice of several flags for the mizzen, for example that of an Elder Brother of Trinity House, Grand Master of the Honourable Company of Master Mariners, or the Admiral's flag of a yacht club. Similar arrangements can apply to other members of the Royal Family. [13]

When a foreign Monarch is embarked with the Queen, his personal Standard will usually be flown alongside the Royal Standard at the main. An unusual occasion occurred in 1984 at the 40th anniversary of the D-Day landings, when the Royal Yacht was anchored off Caen, and four foreign heads of state were embarked. The solution was to fly two standards on the starboard and port halyards on the foremast and two on the mizzen, in order of 'seniority'. This resulted in the Standards of King Olav of Norway and King Baudouin of Belgium being hoisted on the fore starboard and port halyards respectively, while those of Queen Beatrix of the Netherlands and The Grand Duke of Luxembourg were on the starboard and port mizzen halyards.

During Cowes week in 1989 the yacht *Scorcher* sailed too close to *Britannia* and the top of her mast got entangled with the 14 breadth ensign, the ensign staff snapped and the yacht proceeded into harbour with the ensign and staff hanging from her mast!

The Yacht is normally dressed overall when on Royal duty in harbour. Dressing ship in *Britannia* can be a tricky business; the 'fore-to-main' spreads both ways from the funnel, where it is stowed prior to the evolution. Not only is this uncomfortable for those stationed in the funnel, but the hot gases tend to eat into the kevlar with which dressing lines are made these days; indeed on arrival at Civitavecchia in 1992 the fore-to-main snapped on being hoisted, the sort of disaster dreaded by those involved. It was rapidly replaced and dignity restored, but the kevlar has now been reinforced with wire!

On another occasion some years ago, the personal Standard of a head of state was hoisted alongside the Royal Standard, ready to be broken out when he stepped onboard; when this was done, to everyone's horror it was seen to be upside down. It turned out that it had been manufactured that way; unfortunately, and unusually, it had not been checked by the signal staff before hoisting.

The Royal Yacht carries no saluting guns; the escort returns any salute. No bugle calls or pipes are made onboard, all orders being passed by word of mouth. Only the Queen and the Duke of Edinburgh (when in uniform), are piped over the side, except that this may apply, with the Queen's consent, to foreign sovereigns who are Honorary Admirals in the Royal Navy, and to certain other Heads of State.

Aiguillettes and Flag Lieutenants

The Aiguillette is of feudal origin, used as a badge of office by retainers. The horses of the 'Chief' (and no doubt the camels of the Sheikh) and their immediate entourage were picketed close to their tents, and when camp was struck it was the duty of a retainer to take up the picket ropes and pegs, and carry them until they were next required. The ropes were worn round the body with the pegs hanging down, and the Chief could easily be located by the proximity of his henchmen who were thus attired.

The present form of aiguillette seems to have been adopted in the nineteenth century. In 1879 it superseded the sash which until then had been worn by Naval ADCs to Queen Victoria.

In 1890 Admiral of the Fleet HRH the Duke of Edinburgh chaired a committee on naval uniforms, which recommended that aiguillettes should be worn by Admirals of the Fleet, who should also receive a baton, and by officers on the staffs of Commanders-in-Chief. Except for the baton, this was approved but extended to include officers on the staffs of all Flag Officers and Commodores, namely Captains of the Fleet, Chiefs of Staff, Flag Captains, Flag

Commanders, Flag Lieutenants and Secretaries. In 1905 Engineer Officers on the staff were added. This list was later reduced to Flag Lieutenants and Secretaries, but aiguillettes are now also worn by Naval Members of the Admiralty Board, and by Attachés on the staff of British Ambassadors.

ADCs to Royalty, Governor's General, and Governors wear aiguillettes on the right shoulder, all others on the left. Royal aiguillettes are of plain gold, and they have the Royal Cipher on the shoulder board. Lord Louis liked to point out that his had three ciphers - E VIII R, G VI R and E II R, and also that the gold braid used for Admiral's stripes worn by Royalty was slightly wider than normal! Naval aiguillettes are blue and gold, Army red and gold, and Air Force pale blue and gold.

The official appointment of Flag Lieutenant did not appear in the Navy List until 1814, although an Admiralty minute of 14 December 1805 mentions the appointment of 'Sub-Lieutenant Augustus Parkyns on board of the *Savage* Flag Lieutenant to Vice Admiral Sir John Warren ...to join the *Foudroyant* without delay'. At this time there would normally be nine Lieutenants in a flagship, eight in other 1st-rates. All the Lieutenants of a flagship received sixpence a day extra pay, supposedly because they were expected to be rather better dressed than their opposite numbers in a private ship. One Lieutenant would be detailed to supervise signals, and he was the only one who had any claim to being a specialist, since he had to become familiar with the signal books of the day. Gunnery was looked after by the Gunner, Navigation by the Master, so there was

Flag Lieutenants on Duty

Peter Anson and Barry Miller escorting Princess Elizabeth who was presenting a new King's Colour to the Mediterranean Fleet in 1951. With her are the Duke of Edinburgh and the C-in-C, Admiral Sir John Edelsten (who qualified in Signals in 1918).

"THE RAKE'S PROGRESS"

THE SIGNAL OFFICER

1. COMPULSION

Mid. J. R. P. Brown, R.N.V.R. (c.e).

2. INSPIRATION

Succumbs to indoctrination becomes R.N.

3. AMBITION

Top of Long 'c' Course, 195*.

4. SUCCESS

Lt. 'J. R. Ponsonby Browne, Flag Lieut. to C. in C. Me*ite**an*an.

5. TEMPTATION

Fails to marry Admiral's daughter.

6. DOWNFALL

Returns to Mercury as *1.

7. RUIN

Lt. Cdr. J. R. P. Brown, R.N. (Ret.)

no equivalent of a Lieutenant (G) or (N). In the *Victory* John Pasco even had an assistant, a junior Lieutenant named George Browne, who would understudy when Pasco was sick or ashore. Midshipmen and other junior officers were often assigned signal duties as part of their training.

John Henley was Flag Lieutenant to Admiral Binney, who complained that he was bullied into entertaining people he disliked - particularly men with beards, which he hated. When Henley was re-appointed, Binney wrote in his 'flimsy':
'... during which period I have, I hope, conducted myself to his entire satisfaction.'

The 'Signal Officer' at this time was not on the Admiral's staff, and did not mess at the Admiral's table. Nevertheless, as signalling systems and signal books developed during the 18th century, it became necessary for him to be in close 'attendance' on the Admiral when manœuvring or in action, and he would have access to him at all times on signal matters. Thus he gradually became a sort of personal assistant, and when the post was formally established as a member of the Admiral's staff, it was logical that he would become known as the Flag Lieutenant.

The Guide to the duties of a Flag Lieutenant, issued by the Signal School, says:

> *'There are no rules for Flag Lieutenants. Your only purpose in life is to make the way smooth for the Admiral, and to help others in their dealings with him ... there is no job where personalities count more - the Admiral's and yours.'*

The tradition of the Flag Lieutenant being a signal specialist was maintained until the 1939-45 war when this was not always practicable, but until quite recently it still applied to sea-going flag lieutenants, those ashore having more of a need for what might be described as a 'Social Flags', which left the signal specialists free to deal with the complex communications systems and vast amount of traffic at a modern shore headquarters; this arrangement tends to apply at sea too nowadays.

*   *   *   *   *

When the American battle squadron joined the Grand Fleet in World War I, the Americans had some difficulty in mastering the British signal books. One day when the whole fleet was at sea, a 'Turn' signal was hoisted. When hauled down, the British ships turned one way, the Americans the other. The US Admiral turned to rend his aide, who forestalled him with: 'Sorry Admiral, I guess I told you wrong!'

This has since been quoted as an example of the perfect relationship between Admiral and Flag Lieutenant.

Pendant Boards

'Pendant Boards' were lists of ships showing their pendant numbers and funnel markings. The main fleets issued their own markings, often duplicating those in another fleet, but the Signal School had an advisory role and also looked after allocations for vessels operating locally, or not in a main fleet.

The role of the Signal School is illustrated by an Admiralty letter of 25 March 1907 to the C-in-C Portsmouth:

> '...to acquaint you for the information of the Superintendent of Signal Schools that, owing to the revision of the Signal Books, the corrrect flags which should appear in the design of the new china (flag pattern coffee cups etc.) which is being ordered for His Majesty's Yacht Alexandra are uncertain. I am to enquire whether the Superintendent of Signal Schools is able to state what combination of flags will be used to denote Alexandra.'

The reply, from the 'RN School of Signalling, HMS *Victory*' stated that:

> '...the new "List of Navy" signal for this yacht will be YBH.'

Funnel bands were originally used to indicate individual ships, not Flotillas, as became the practice later on. Admiralty letter of 23 June 1910 listed a whole lot of new allocations, for example:

Apollo	*1 white band on foremost funnel*
Brilliant	*1 white band on each funnel*
Melpomene	*1 red band on after funnel*
Terpsichore	*2 red bands on each funnel*

The Gin Pennant

The origins of the Gin Pennant are uncertain but it seems to have been used since the 1940s and probably earlier. The distillery manager of Plymouth Gin was quoted some years ago as saying that the firm started supplying gin pennants in the 1950s, but usually they were made up on board ship. Some remember using a small green triangular pennant emblazoned with a white wine glass, hoisted rather inconspicuously on an inner halyard. More usually, the green-white-green Starboard pennant (the old Pennant 9) was used, and no doubt still is, with a green glass in the centre.

The Gin Pennant

Commissioned Signal Boatswain Bill Trotter remembers making one up for some RNVR officers when he was a newly fledged Signal Boatswain in HMS *Blenheim* in 1943, and since his RN Captain didn't go much on it, wonders whether it was 'a myth invented by the RNVR in wartime'.

This is certainly not the case - the author amongst many others used it quite regularly in the 1950s, without any prompting by Reserve officers!

The signal means that the wardroom invites officers from ships in company to drinks; it naturally tends to be used when not too many ships are actually present!

A miniature gin pennant is often hoisted above the bar to signify that drinks are 'on the house', or on someone's wine bill on the occasion of their birthday or promotion.

Colours and Sunset

How often have Signal Officers, Chief Yeomen and Signalmen down to the most junior 'bunting tosser' writhed in agony during those ceremonies of Colours and Sunset? To the casual observer this is a simple matter of hoisting or lowering an ensign, but in practice any number of dramas are likely to occur. Consider:

1. *The PREP may be hoisted too early, too late, not at all.*

2. *The above may occur because the duty Signalman is too keen, adrift, the MCO clock is wrong or has stopped.*

3. *The Ensign and Jack may be at the wrong ends of the ship.*

4. *The Ensign or Jack may be hoisted upside down.*

5. *If the ceremony should be carried out with caps on, the Signalman may have his cap off, or vice versa, depending on the orders in force which 'No one is quite sure about, Sir'.*

6. *If it is wet and the Signalman arrives in his oilskin, the sun may suddenly come out and he will then be invited to remove his oilskin to reveal that he is in plain clothes or his underwear.*

7. *If a band is present, the Signalman may hoist the ensign at the wrong speed, thus achieving 'close up' as the band reaches the half way mark, or he has to finish as if hoisting a manœuvring signal.*

8. *If wet, the lacing or runners may stick and refuse to move either up or down. Eventually the 'Carry on' is sounded, fury descends from on high, and the Signalman has to shin up the ensign staff to sort out the shambles.*

9. *The clocks are put back during the night and the whole ceremony takes place one hour early.*

Even when the ceremony is over and the halyards are firmly secured with umpteen turns, a voice will cry: 'The ensign is at half-mast; get it close up!'. The Signalman undoes the knitting, jiggles the ensign up and down, secures it exactly as it was before, and is told 'That's better'.'

"I'll give 'im 'alyards flapping!"

Signal!

Appendices

Appendix 1

RN Signal Officers

The first recorded Signal Long Course was held in 1905, although as the 1911 course is described as the ninth on the photograph at the Signal School, and there were two courses in 1909, there may have been earlier courses, or more than one in other years.

Signal Officers were first designated (S) in the Navy List in January 1907 (previously the designation (S) had indicated the Surveying Service). A number of the (S) officers then listed had not attended a Long Course, having usually been a Flag Lieutenant or been on the staff of the Signal School; furthermore, a number of officers never designated (S) had also in effect become signal specialists in earlier years - a classic example is Allan Everett, who served as a Flag Lieutenant to three admirals, and was twice Captain of the Signal School and a leading expert in signal matters.

Until W/T training was shifted from HMS *Vernon* to the Signal School in June 1917, a number of officers on the Torpedo Long Course, including Royal Marines, became wireless specialists, and many of them held important 'Signal' appointments, as did a few other specialists and 'salt horses'.

In 1944 when (S) was allocated to Paymasters, Signal specialists found themselves designated (C) for Communicator.

Conventional Long Courses ended in 1972 when the Warfare Officer concept was introduced. After a short gap specialist courses were restarted in 1975, when some Warfare Officers returned to the Schools for a relatively short course of about three months. The (C) specialists became known as Advanced Warfare Officers (C) or AWO(C). From the early 1980s specialisation, totalling some 15 weeks in the case of the communicator, took place during the Warfare course, reverting in effect to a form of Long Course, and the title was changed to PWO(C).

In 1927 Signal Officers on the active list subscribed a sum of £280 to institute a prize for officers qualifying as Signal specialists, to be known as the 'Jackson-Everett Prize', after Admiral Sir Henry Jackson, whose early experiments led to the development of wireless for the Navy, and Admiral Sir Allan Everett, referred to above. The income from the fund provides a sum of money (£35 in 1992) for the purchase of instruments or books.

The 'Dagger' course, described as an 'Advanced W/T course', was introduced at Greenwich in 1921. Previously † denoted officers 'qualified in Signals *and* W/T'.

Note:
* = Top of Course (From 1914) or Jackson-Everett Prize (from 1927)
† = Advanced ('Dagger') Course

'Signal Officers' not designated (S), with seniority as Lieutenant		Wireless Officers ((T) specialists) with seniority as Lieutenant					
				GC Candy	15.8.04	A Cochrane	30.6.96
				RL Nicholson	15.8.04	HW Osburn	30.6.96
				GW Halifax	15.1.05	CH France-Hayhurst	1.10.96
				WB Mackenzie	30.3.05	JA Ingles	31.12.96
				AJL Murray	30.7.07	DM Hamilton	1.4.97
LG Tufnell	10.8.81	HB Jackson	27.10.77	JWS Dorling	30.7.09	HM Edwards	22.6.97
H Evan-Thomas	31.12.84	FL Field	1.4.93			LN Turton	22.6.97
DRL Nicholson	1.4.89	CR Payne	14.10.95			H Escombe	22.6.97
EM Phillpotts (G)	1.2.91	JD Allen	14.6.96	**(S) Officers - pre-Long Course, with seniority as Lieutenant**		MA Kennard	22.6.97
HGG Sandeman	1.4.91	RS Phipps Hornby	9.7.96			CD Roper	31.12.97
AF Everett	30.6.91	HK Kitson	1.10.99			CM Crichton-Maitland	31.8.98
JWG Innes	31.12.95	RM Groves	15.2.00			AW Kerr	31.8.98
AK Macrorie	30.6.96	R Fitzmaurice	15.3.01			WL Allen	31.12.98
RM Burmester (G)	1.4.97	JK im Thurn	15.1.02	HF Shakespear	30.6.91	HB Mulleneux	1.10.99
LG Preston	1.4.97	JSC Salmond	15.9.03	AP Davidson	30.6.91	NH Carter	31.12.99
C Seymour	1.8.98	CE Kennedy-Purvis	15.1.04	HB Robinson	15.8.95	RF White	31.12.99
CE Collins	31.1.05	JF Somerville	15.3.04	CM Staveley	1.4.96	G Sowerby	31.12.99

Long Signal Courses

1904-1905
LM Darbyshire
FC Fisher
WSF Forbes
EJ Hardman-Jones
SAG Hill
MD McNeile
BWL Nicholson
HE de P Rennick
HP Smyth-Osbourn
RHD Townsend
ARW Woods

1906
AEF Bedford
H Boyes
N Burge RM
MB Birkett
B Buxton
PD Campbell
CD Fenn
C Goolden
RC Mayne
BR Poe
HGL Oliphant
FP Saunders
HL Shephard

1907
EG Cheesman RM
RF Eyre
HFD Jeff
JB Kitson
A Marsden
GFLL Page
WD Phipps
JM Pipon
JH Smith-Wright
GB Villiers
HW Wyld

1908
CHA Cartwright
CC Dix
HBB Denniss
RDF Forbes
RL Hamer
P Noble
LG Shiell
HH Tatham
FB Watson

1908-09
AE Evans
A d'A Punnett
BH Ramsay
MC Romford
SPB Russell
GWS Seton
FWD Twigg

1909
RW Blake
MA Blomfield
MES Boissier
GE Cumming
LG Foote

HB Robinson
WJ Whitworth

1910
EO Broadley
JHK Clegg
EW Money
ELB Oliphant
ATL Wilson

1911
RHL Bevan
EBC Dicken
H Fitzherbert

1912
V Alleyne
Hon G Fraser
R Lister-Kaye
L Ormsby-Johnson
Hon HA Pakington
AM Peters
SD Spicer
EWP Westmacott

1913
HS Bowlby
FPO Bridgeman
F Cadogan
Hon CA Colville
ARJ Southby
PA Warre

1914
AWJ Finlayson
WT Makeig-Jones*
FR O'Reilly
H Pott
ENL White

1915
I Cowan
RE Jeffreys*
DNW Joel
HP Mead

1916
FC Bottomley*
RHV Buxton
WA Floyer
CS Holland
LV Morgan

1917
PW Bowyer-Smith*
AEMB Cunninghame Graham
LCA StJ Curzon-Howe
MOD Elwood
CB Graham-Watson
ERB Kemble
DC Lang
Hon H Legge
JP Money
GC Muirhead-Gould

1918
RV Barton
Hon HMA Cecil
GCH Clayton

CS Daniel†
JH Edelsten
RR Stewart*
GH Warner

1919
Hon JB Bruce*†
C Buist
C Caslon
PF Glover
Hon C Roper-Curzon
HR Sandwith

1920
JH Bowen†
WR Brinton
NB Deare
KRD Fawcett*
EHN Harvey
JHC Minter†

1921
KB Best
CAH Brooking
RM Dick
MH Evelegh
LAL de L Evans
WD Fairbairn
CRW Gairdner
WGB Hartley†
JM Howson
WW Jacomb
WS Mann
BGH Phillips
LS Saunders
BR Willett*†
PBRW William-Powlett
FJ Wylie†

1922
CJW Branson†
PWB Brooking*†
GC Congreve
HSL Ewart†
JRS Haines
LD Jones
ATGC Peachey
VJ Robinson
GA Worth RCN

1922-23
E Dangerfield*†
DH Everett
JP Gornall
EH Kitson
JB Newman RAN†
CV Robinson†

1924
JHF Crombie
MG Edwards
RF Lawson RCN
EH Mainguy RCN
AVS Yates*†

1925
GF Burghard†
AM Knapp
Lord Louis Mountbatten*†

AG Rodger
HM Waller RAN†
EP Young

1926
CL Firth†
FL Houghton RCN†
HFH Layman
AK Scott-Moncrieff
GR Waymouth*†

1927
FHG Allen†
WAC Binnie†
RAB Edwards
StJAD Garniss RIM
G Munos (Chile)
ICR Macdonald RAN*†
FB Tours†
G Trudgett (Chile)

1928
CS Bushe
AD Casey RAN†
JD Crossman†
DO Doble
B de L Faunce
C Loehnis†
H St A Malleson
D Mckenzie RAN
J Quicke
JPL Reid*†

1929
EWJ Bankes *†
P Dawnay
EF Evered
M Hodges†
CFW St Quintin†
Hon A Pleydell-Bouverie
JDM Robinson†
LC Sinker
RG Swallow
RS Young

1930
RS Brown
FG Johnstone
J Liddell*†
H Kingsley RCN
Hon NAJWE Napier
K McN Walter

1931
JAS Brame
FH Dunlop
LG Durlacher
D Grove-White†
CM Jacob†
PH Matheson
HD Smallwood
BT Turner*†
HD Wyldbore-Smith

1932
CD Bonham-Carter†
DE Cox
JGT Inglis
AD Lenox-Conyngham†

NA Mackinnon
FD Miller
HN Reid
EO Unwin*
N de G Waymouth†

1933
FWB Edwards
S Francis
WS Handcock
A Kennett
JRB Longden*
JW McClelland
MH St L Nott RIN
TA Pack-Beresford
IG Robertson
JM Villiers

1934
JL Bath RAN
HC Bird RIN
CB Brooke
Hon DC Cairns*†
CJM Eliot
JMA Ennion
DRH Ferguson
JCG Martin
EA Nicholson
NJ Wagstaff
CR Wood

1935
G Affleck-Graves
GM Bennett
RH Courage
AT Courtney
EW Finch-Noyes RCN
JSH Lawrence
RT Paul*
JC Stopford
HEF Tweedie

1936
MJW Barttelot
RW Briggs
GGAΓ Butler
ETL Dunsterville*
WGC Elder
JP Gunner
H Pasley-Tyler
Sir MGC Warmington Bt

1937
TP Aubrey
CPW Cross*
KCM Fleetwood
AHC Gordon-Lennox
JAC Henley
JC Mansell RIN
LF Manton
JR Olive
JR Phillimore
RFT Stannard
CR Williams

1938
R Gibb
P Hankey*
RW Hughes

Viscount Kelburn
A Nolan
RF Phillimore
RF Wells

1939
G Bailey RIN
IM Balfour
DE Bromley-Martin*
RF Colville
BD Gallie
IH Macdonald RAN
RLW Moss
RJ Robertson RAN
PG Sedgwick
CMW Thomas

1940
JOH Burrough*
PWW Graham
JN Kennard
CP Mills
JA Phillips
JE Poulden
PT Williams

1941
GHH Culme-Seymour
RIT Falkner
NLT Kempson
MH Lethbridge*
RW Murdoch RCN
WJ Parker
T Sheppard
MG Sterling RCN
P La B Walshe
R Wrightson

1941-42
EGN Bremner
JL Buckeridge
DA Forrest
FH Foster RNZN
A Gray
JD Hanron
PN Howes
GA Milward
A Phipps
GDW Ram
KA Seddon RAN
AAT Seymour-Haydon
JRG Trechman*
DC Wells RAN

1942
JA Charles RCN
MG Chichester
RG Dreyer*
CA James
EH Lee
AG McCrum
JC O'Brien RCN
RB Richardson
EM Shaw RIN
JAF Somerville
GAB Sutherland R Sigs
J Wood

1942-43
RT Bett

J Fahey USN
DAK Finlay*
JBR Horne
P Keith-Welsh
SN Kohli RIN
PG Loasby
MT Marwood
PDL Milligan
M Phipps
CW Robertson
KM Teare RIN
WB Willett

1943 (1)
RWD Bray*
WG Crabbie
JR Jamieson
WF Paterson
IF Sommerville

1943(2)
RG Addis RNVR
SM Ahsan RIN
EB Ashmore*
AR Barrow
H Jeary RNVR
Marquis of
  Milford Haven
DV Morgan
GE Sampson
WR Wells

1943-44
MA Buxton RNVR
ZS Janowski PN
IC Macintyre
HH Ridler
GM Rocke RNVR*
JH Toon
RWP Yates RIN

1944 (1)
NB Beale RNVR
ATJ Cole RIN
J Durnford RIN
DF Goodale
JN Hutchinson RNVR
DD Knight*
FRS Pearce RNVR
KJ Slater RNVR

1944 (2)
DRE Calf
R Cassey RNZNVR
P Davie
J Dennitts RNVR
TH Hornyold-Strickland
EN Lowe RNVR
J Meadows*
RAH Panter
JE Pope
DVB Unwin

1944-45
W Alder
KJ Ball
AD Black RAN*
AVM Diamond
Hon JC Edmondson

WR Grieve RNVR
ECS Macpherson RIN
IR Mason
JC Rushbrooke
Hon DP Seely
BG Vann
CBH Wake-Walker
ML Woollcombe

1945
DJ Cronin SANF
RH Kilburn*
JK Laughton
RRB Mackenzie
GS Martin RNVR
JB Paterson
JD Williams

1945-46
SF Berthon*
NEF Dalrymple-Hamilton
N Fitzherbert
JRH Haddow
JR McKaig
RC Morgan
M Mosberg R Nor N
DR Sheppard
O Wivestad R Nor N

1946
JA Buchanan-Wollaston
RF Buller
AEP Deane
R Durnford*
PT Edwards RIN
LL Grey
KMH Milburn
AC O'Riordan
RAC Owen
PH Page
DC Pelly
R Pitt
DL Syms

1947
JS Austin RAN
LG Carr RNZN
DO Dykes
PW Dolphin
RSI Hawkins
WL Irving
J Kane
BH Kent
AS Morton*
JSK Oram
AM Ralph
PW Spencer

1948
HV Bruce
JW Daubney
DC Douglas
CJ Hines
RE Lesh RAN*
JBD MIller
MR Simpson
EC Thorne RNZN
KA Townsend-Green
CC Wake-Walker

1946-47
(Air Signal Officers'
Conversion Course)
A Aitken
RDB Birch
WAB Bland
PC Brooker
CG Bush
HA Cheetham
CC Ennever
GHP Hunt
TA de V Hunt
D Jackson
FD Kelly
RB Knight
PT Lawman
DR Lewis
PD Lloyd
JC Newing
GD Nutt
C Pain
DA Poynter
PB Schonfeldt
HK Sergeant
LJ Smith
JA Shuttleworth
PJ Warrington

1949
P Anson*
CK Anthony
R Brokenshire RAN
JRJ Cowlin
RD Franklin
DA Loram
WHM Mackilligin
GH Mann
WTT Pakenham†
C Rusby
PJ Rushbrooke
JS Wilson

1950
HS Bennett
PJ Brooks
W Fitzherbert
J Goldsmith
HR Keate
WP Main
PC Prince
BK Shattock
RC Swan RAN*
GB Thrum RAN

1951
GAF Bower
IW Broben RAN
HR Cornell
JD Gresson RNZN
MI Hosegood
AJS Knocker*
GC Lloyd
GM Lloyd
JD Macpherson
DB Sanders
PED Stearns
JA Stroud
ME St Q Wall

1952-53
RHE Byrne
JAN Cuming
MG Evelegh
RW Graham-Clarke*
PGM Greig
NEC Hammond
JM Jessop
RB Montclare
JA Robertson RAN
WRD Robson
NTJ Skitt

1953
RI Atkinson
HJC Bridger
DJ Cheney RNZN
CG Cronin SAN
NF Fawcett
MJL Freeman
LRD Mackintosh
AMS Macklow-Smith
P Martineau
JMH Millington-Drake
W Nippierd*
WL Payne
PM Rees RAN
EV Stevens RAN

1954-55
R Bennett
AA Browne
DH Cremer*
St JH Herbert
GFN Knox
GW Lowden
EJ Melzer RAN
IH Nicholson RAN
DAP O'Reilly
JB Rumble
BJ Straker*
P Troubridge

1955
BAN Buckley
AH Dickins
RJ Green
PJ Hall
TM Laing*
HB Parker
CDM Ridley
IS Sandeman
ES Spencer

1956
HJP Adams RAN
JF Van den Arend
PAC Harland
EMG Hewitt
JLB Larkins
PR Lees
DHB Newson-Smith
RJW Perryman
M Sands
MCM Smith
JB Snow RAN
PM Stanford*
AF Tilley

1957
JGB Armstrong
RAJT Arundel RAN
MPH Bryan
TW Clowes
HDY Faulkner*
I Fergie-Woods
JM Findlay
JS George
IF Grant
M St J Thomson SAN
PPL Wells
RJE Wooley

1958
HP Boys-Stones
HF Campbell
RT Clarke
RL Copp
RG Franklin RNZN
RW Keogh
LJ Kelaher RAN
CA Laurence
MF Parry
MJ Rivett-Carnac
DG Sears
AR Wood*

1959
RM Allen
HM Balfour
TFR Crozier
JMS Ekins
M Fulford-Dobson
DT Hunt RAN
NIC Kettlewell
WH Kelly SAN
JT Lord*†
J Penny†
TJW Sergeant
MA Stockton

1960
JC Appleyard-List†
RM Baird RAN
JM Beattie
G Brits SAN
CK Callins RAN
JB Gallagher
WLRE Gilchrist
MC Gwinner
KH Jay*†
CRL Patten RAN
JA Sanderson
BD Salwey
MDM Sellar
AA Waugh
PN Wright RNZN

1961-62
MFP Arcedeckne-Butler
KPD Bruce-Gardyne
JPG Bryans
MEH Earlam RAN
MGMW Ellis*†
DW Fryer
D Gunn
BE Lemonde
AH Lorimer

ANA MacDonald
WE Rothwell RAN
PJV Tuke
BH Todd
D Whitehead†

1962
RM Banks RAN
JC Dreyer
GC Clark†
DA Gunn
CR Holland
WR Joubert SAN
C Maitland-Dougall
PH de Merindol
TE Reeder
CA Reid RAN
EL Roberts RNZN
JW Roskill
LM Saunders-Watson*
CG Traill†
GM Tullis

1963
DC Allen
A Banham*†
MA Broomfield
RH Carr
EYC Goring
C Grobbelaar SAN
HPH O'Brien
JP de H Saumarez
GM Timpson
CW Williams
PK Wigram
JB Wells RAN

1964-65
JM Brink SAN
VSV Duke
DA Harries RAN
RAG Herron RAN
SE Hughes
ORH Maitland
WE Redmond*
EGL Sclater
SF Teagle RNZN

1965
DJ Carver*†
J Davies
CH Layman
RA Shelton-Agar
LG Terry RAN
JJ Watson

1966
RK Dibble*
JE Dykes
DJ Freemantle
NJ Hill-Norton
IE Pfennigwerth RAN
RH Scott RAN

1967-68
JM Benson
CDS Brown
CKD Cobley
JC Hornsby RAN

PD Luce,
CJ McMullen
AGMA Provest
OD Somerville-Jones
SS Wilson RAN*

1968-69
BJ Adams
RF Cave
S Drake-Wilkes
J McN Ferguson
GDR Hammer RAN
CW Hunter
AB Richardson*
JK Williamson
TB Wise RAN

1969-70
B Burns
WM Caswell
CJ Campbell
DT Frost
RD Griffiths RAN
DE Hiron RAN
DMA Howard
PJ King
KR Moen RNZN*
CJ Pink
A Robinson
RK Ryall RAN
JT Sanders
PR Sutermeister
GASC Wilson

1970
PC Abbott*
RAP Cossins
CW Crichton
BA Davies
MJD Farrow
MGA Knapp
TB Mitford
JT Murphy RAN
HA Robertson
CEK Roe
PAC Wheen

1971
RMH Bawtree
NRH Cartwright
WJ Christie
JB Drake-Wilkes
FM Emmett
CFB Hamilton
R Howell
IB Hughes
AL Lang*
AJC Morrow
WR Overton RAN
CS Samuel
P Withers

Advanced Warfare Officer (C) (AWO(C))

1975
DJM Mowlam
IW Peel†
RJ Talbot

1977 (1)
BTJ Behets
DB Fitzpatrick RAN
CSH Harrington RAN
MA James†

1977 (2)
DB Cotsell RAN
WFG Griffin*
HMA Richardson
R Ward
MC Webster RAN

1978 (1)
RV Harding
AC Lyddon
AJ Peck RNZN
RD Sanderson

1978 (2)
JEK Ellis
PL Mole RAN
BB Perowne*
PWH Swan

1978 (3)
RJ Everett RAN
ARW Hulley
AW Pomphrey

1979 (1)
GE Hearnden
NB Humphreys*
AJ Lanigan RAN
WVJ Smith

1979 (2)
FB Breeze RAN
GP Ewins
JE Langsford RAN
DJM Lynch

1979 (3)
T Morton
C Mundy
O Rogers RAN

1979 (4)
C Craven
R Eams
GD Piggott
P Torrens

1980 (1)
R Grimsey
CD Stanford*
BD Robertson RAN

1980 (2)
J Butt
M Franklin RNZN
W Whelan

1981 (1)
JPJ Blansjaar RAN*
TJ Boulton
JL Vear

1981 (2)
NGH Bray
AK Dymock
PR Engeham

1981-82
KS Brimley
MW Stenning

1982
J Bycroft
M Jackman RNZN
GR Johnson
G Walpole RAN

Principal Warfare Officer (C) (PWO(C))

1980-81
RP Steele
TA Williams

1983 (1)
M Bell RAN
GR Bent*
MR D'Cruz
PJF Eberle
A Paterson
R Smith RAN
HN Watson

1983 (2)
F Biddle RAN
GP Brocklebank
R Cameron-Tucker RAN
MJ Dale*
RW Easton
JW Evans
AC Gwilliam
PJ Hatchard
RN Lucey
J Pickel RAN

1984-85
RJ Adams
D Burnett RNZN
MC Butcher
GM Davenport
A Gale RAN
M Melvin RAN
I Moncrieff*
G Richardson
RJ Searle

1985-86
G Churton
RW Flower
E Fraser*
DC Simmonds
PK Walpole

1987
PM Daykin
RD Evans
SM Gillespie
MP Mansergh
NF Taylor*
NC Wade

1988
GC Corner*
AW Knight
PF Payne

1989
MW Ewence
AW Jackman*
PA Jones
KF Robertson
AC Stewart
DC Tarrant

1990
JJ Conway
R Farrington
M Rimmer
SA Ross
WB Welton
SP Williams*

1991
RL Hall*
L Jones

1992
AJ Adams
RG Marshall
FW Smyth*

1993
PM Birdman
K Fincher
JLR Foreman
SJA Gurmin
I Smart

Appendix 2

RM Signal Officers

(By Seniority as Lieutenant)

1895
R ff Willis

1896
N Burge

1897
FBA Lawrie
GL Raikes

1898
BC Gardiner
AF Salkeld

1899
CGG Crawley
W Sinclair
RCS Waller

1900
AA Cordner
G Harrison

1901
AM Deakin
ADB Godfray

1902
EG Cheesman
FW Home
SC Wace

1903
DL Aman
E Gillespie
CA Lambert
CH Malden

1904
AGW Grierson
RDH Hough
GM Kendle
AJ Mellor
EH Ward

1905
J Geldard
WGH Miles

1906
CG Fothergill
HM Franks
HS Walker

1914
CH Congdon

1915
RCG Mackenzie

1917
HA Bass
ECL Bearcroft
JHG Wills

1918
BGB Mitchell

1921
RD Hale

1922
JK Cordeaux
JG Hume

1924
JFM Moulton
HA Tracey

1928
EA Brown

1929
AGC Langford

1930
I Riches

1931
HW Sanders

1933
GT Haines

1937
JN Congdon
PF Knight
AL Laxton
JHN Lloyd
RA Pigot

1938
GJ Bower

1939
IS Harrison
ED Stroud

1940
WJG Acton
L de W Lyons-Montgomery
LCS Spray
RB Stacey

1941
J Bolingbroke
BE Darby
JJ Day
TP Furlonge

KE Light

1942
D Fraser
GJC Smith

1943
FCE Bye
DI Goodchild
C Oldham
HM Tyndall

1945
PH Darling
JA Good
AGH Jukes
JC Luxmoore
MP Roche-Kelly

1946
RBK Kelso
WJ Stanbury

1949
DG Alexander
IA McDougall
SR Pringle

1951
FC Darwall
JR Moon
PM Reed
LH Williams

1952
ACJ Sharland

1953
R Frost

1954
E St V Troubridge

1955
DV Child

1956
HJ Flamank
PNM Jennings
GJH Mackie

1957
RW Perkins

1958
S Pope

1959
JF Murphy

PAC Howgill

1960
EJ Oatley
GEF Thurston

1961
JH Fisher

1962
CI Hickinbotham
EJ Sim
RM Wheeler
JPG Wiseman

1963
AG Gowen

1964
MA Taffinder

1965
AP Grant

1966
IIF Binnie
BL Carter
JS Chester
DAS Pennefather

1967
JR Bright
SB Cusack
PMH Dunn
PS Robinson

1968
JE Haycock
MJ Samuelson

1970
I Ballantyne
WR de W Lash
AA Milton
AJ Pickett

1971
JGM Downton
RHG Fulton
G Langford
MA Stevens

1972
SC Bailey

1974
SA Cutler
GJ Ebbutt
PDT Irvine

1975	1980	1982	1986
MY Cooke	SA Conway	CK Bunting	TN Daniels
JB Dutton	PJ Martin	NJ Cusack	DMM Evans
JW Rye	JMF Robbins	A MacDonald	IR MacDonald
	E Shutt		RAW Spencer
1976		1984	R Watts
AW MacCormick	1981	NP Brown	
	CJ Eggar	GN McBain	1989
1978	RN Kendall-Carpenter	RE Walker	NM Bennett
JB McCubbin	SG Shadbolt	TJC Webster	BR Curry
	DJ Stewart		GSC Manger
1979	MK Taylor	1985	
TM Gregory	MV Townsend	DA Hook	*Note:* Burge (1896) and Cheesman (1902) also did the RN Long Signal Course in 1906 and 1907 respectively.

Appendix 3

Directors of the Signal Division

The Signal Section of the Operations Division became a separate Directorate on 18 August 1917, the first Director (DSD) being Commander (Acting Captain) R L Nicholson, who had been Jellicoe's Fleet W/T Officer at Jutland. In 1920 it became a Department under the Controller, though with operational responsibilities to VCNS, and in 1943 it became a Division of the Naval Staff. In 1964 with the reorganisation of the Ministry of Defence and the institution of the post of Assistant Chief of Defence Staff (Signals), the title was changed to Director of Naval Signals (DNS), and in 1977 to Chief Naval Signal Officer. The first ACDS (Signals) was Rear Admiral Edward Ashmore.

Director of the Signal Division or Signal Department (DSD)		Director of Naval Signals (DNS)	Chief Naval Signal Officer (CNSO)
1917 RL Nicholson	1942 CS Holland	1964 JRG Trechman	1977 WTT Pakenham
1919 RM Burmester	(as Rear Admiral)	1965 NEF Dalrymple-Hamilton	1977 MJL Freeman
1920 JK im Thurn	1943 LV Morgan	1966 CBH Wake-Walker	1979 HM Balfour
1921 HK Kitson	(as Rear Admiral)	1968 JE Pope	1981 AR Wood
1923 R Fitzmaurice	1945 JRS Haines	1969 DA Poynter	1983 NIC Kettlewell
1925 JF Somerville	1947 GR Waymouth	1972 HR Keate	1986 JC Appleyard-List
1927 CE Kennedy-Purvis	1949 RG Swallow	1974 RD Franklin	1989 JT Sanders
1930 JWS Dorling	1951 RS Foster-Brown	1975 WTT Pakenham	1990 BB Perowne
1932 AJL Murray	1954 AD Lenox-Conyngham		1992 WM Caswell
1934 GW Halifax	1955 RFT Stannard		
1935 WT Makeig-Jones	1957 CA James		
1937 PF Glover	1958 ETL Dunsterville		
1941 AJL Murray	1960 WJ Parker		
(as Rear Admiral)	1961 JRG Trechman		

Appendix 4

Captains of the Signal School

The Officer in Command of the Signal School was known as the Superintendent of Signal Schools until 1920, then as Captain, HM Signal School. From 1941 he became the Captain, HMS *Mercury*, but was still generally referred to as the Captain of the Signal School, or CSS.

The term 'HM Signal School' was used for many years, probably because, being housed in the Barracks as part of HMS *Victory*, it had no ship's name of its own, so instead of being HMS ..... it became known colloquially as HM Signal School. It became HMS *Mercury* when commissioned as an independent command on 16 August 1941. The Experimental Department became separated from the Signal School as a result of the move from Portsmouth, and was commissioned at Lythe Hill House, Haslemere, as HMS *Mercury II* under Captain Basil Willett on 27 August 1941.

1895 LG Tufnell	1912 FL Field	1937 AJL Murray	1960 PN Howes
(as Commander)	1915 CE Collins	1939 AEMB Cunninghame	1961 D Bromley-Martin
1898 H Evan-Thomas	(as Commander)	Graham	1963 DV Morgan
(as Commander)	1916 JD Allen	1941 GH Warner	1966 JR McKaig
1900 AF Everett	1918 AK Macrorie	1943 AK Scott-Moncrieff	1968 Sir P Anson
(as Commander)	1920 LG Preston	1946 CL Firth	1970 BH Kent
1904 DRL Nicholson	1922 C Seymour	1948 JHF Crombie	1972 RC Morgan
(as Commander)	1925 JK im Thurn	1950 JGT Inglis	1975 DP O'Reilly
1905 HGG Sandeman	1928 JSC Salmond	1952 P Dawnay	1977 SDS Bailey
(as Commander)	1930 WB Mackenzie	1954 JRB Longden	1981 GA Plumer
1906 AF Everett	1932 H Fitzherbert	1955 AHC Gordon-Lennox	1983 WF Chatterton-Dixon
1908 HMcI Edwards	1934 RHC Bevan	1957 CB Brooke	1985 FD Lowe
1911 EM Philpotts	1935 JWS Dorling	1959 JAC Henley	1988 AC Morrow
			1991 PR Sutermeister

Appendix 5

Experimental Commanders

HMS *Vernon*		HM Signal School	
1903	FCA Ogilvy	1917	JF Somerville
1906	CR Payne	1920	CE Kennedy-Purvis
1909	THM Maurice	1922	GC Candy
1911	RM Groves	1924	AJL Murray
1913	JK im Thurn	1927	JWS Dorling
1916	CE Kennedy-Purvis	1928	CS Daniel
		1930	LV Morgan
		1933	Hon JB Bruce
		1935	FJ Wylie
		1937	BR Willett

Note: In 1941 the Experimental Department split from the Signal School and became the Admiralty Signal Establishment. Basil Willett, promoted Captain in 1940, then became ASE's first Captain Superintendent.

Appendix 6

SD Officers who have reached the rank of Commander

1915 CE Collins (Act)	1973 RA Thompson	1982 M Goacher	1989 RW Talma
1944 WR Paris	1976 K Wollan	1985 J Bywater	1990 F Morris
1959 PM Swiney (Act)	1977 LW Orchard	1987 DL Palmer	1991 MJ Bee †
1966 CH Cox	1979 MDY Phillips	1988 AA Colmer	1992 WR Root
1971 J Pearce	1981 WJ Burling	1989 JC Mundy	1993 MJ Dale

Appendix 7

Sub-Lieutenants SD Course - Top Qualifiers

(Amalgamated with WRNS (C) Course in 1981)

1965 BA Davies	1973 MAD Muggeridge	1980 MJ Dale	1987 L Richmond
1966 FME Emmett	1974 DL Palmer	1981 DC Simmonds	1988 AL Nolan
1967 CC Smith	1975 MJ Bee	1982 GE Alexander	1989 RM Moreland
1968 P Withers	1976 MI Parks	1982 S Pearce WRNS	1990 KM Cowie
1969 RC Styles	1976 CH Clark	1983 L Oakes	1991 L Thomas
1970 BP Beckwith RAN	1977 F Morris	1984 K Silver WRNS	1992 GGH Hughes
1971 AA Colmer	1978 D Chettle	1985 G Thompson	
1972 PG Gadsden	1979 IA Sullivan	1986 KE Daniels WRNS	

Appendix 8

Presidents of the Warrant Officers' and Senior Rates' Mess, HMS *Mercury*

1958 CRS(S) JJ Maye	1965 CRS G Laws	1974 FCCY TCW Hankey	1984 FCCY TE Hatherley
1959 CCY F Rainsbury	1966 CCY AF Markins	1974 FCCY NP Underwood	1985 FCRS JE Sanderson
1961 CRS AF Ryder	1967 CCY ED Palfrey	1976 FCRS MJ Challinor	1986 WO(CY) D Boyes
1962 CRS JWE Kelson	1968 CRS JHD Buchanan	1977 FCRS AD Shuker	1987 WO(CY) HI Axton
1964 CRS R Taylor	1969 CRS DL Alderson	1977 FCCY L Murrell	1988 WO(CT) A Zawada
1964 CRS J Petchey	1971 FCRS WG Bernard	1982 FCCY AD Parkinson	1989 WO(CY) AJ Murphy
1964 CRS R Gray	1973 FCRS JE Eilbeck	1982 FCCY DS Morris	1993 WO(CT) A Zawada
1965 CCY GP Mayers			

Appendix 9

The Semaphore Code

A

B

C
Answering Sign

D

E

F

G

H

I

J
Direction Sign

K

L

M

N

O

P

Q

R

S

T

U

V

W

X

Y

Z

Attention Sign

Error Sign

Separative Sign

Numeral Sign

Appendix 10

Morse and Phonetic Alphabets

Morse	RN - 1917	RN - 1945	NATO
• —	Apples	Able	Alfa
— • • •	Butter	Baker	Bravo
— • — •	Charlie	Charlie	Charlie
— • •	Duff	Dog	Delta
•	Edward	Easy	Echo
• • — •	Freddy	Fox	Foxtrot
— — •	George	George	Golf
• • • •	Harry	How	Hotel
• •	Ink	Item	India
• — — —	Johnnie	Jig	Juliett
— • —	King	King	Kilo
• — • •	London	Love	Lima
— —	Monkey	Mike	Mike
— •	Nuts	Nan	November
— — —	Orange	Oboe	Oscar
• — — •	Pudding	Peter	Papa
— — • —	Queenie	Queen	Quebec
• — •	Robert	Roger	Romeo
• • •	Sugar	Sugar	Sierra
—	Tommy	Tare	Tango
• • —	Uncle	Uncle	Uniform
• • • —	Vinegar	Victor	Victor
• — —	William	William	Whiskey
— • • —	Xerxes	Xray	Xray
— • — —	Yellow	Yoke	Yankee
— — • •	Zebra	Zebra	Zulu

Notes:

1. The need for a phonetic alphabet developed with the introduction of the telephone, but these tended to be made up at random. The first official alphabets were used by the Army, generally a variant of the one introduced in the Navy during the first world war.

2. In the 1917 instructions, accented letters were to be preceded by the word 'Curly', thus 'Curly A for Apples'.

3. The need for an agreed alphabet for air traffic control purposes led to the adoption of an international standard, similar to the present NATO one.

Bibliography

For permission to quote from the following I am grateful to the authors, publishers and copyright holders:

Ashmore, Admiral of the Fleet Sir Edward, GCB, DSC, *Naval Reminiscences.*
Briggs, Ted, MBE, & Alan Cole, *Flagship Hood*, Robert Hale.
Broome, Captain J E, *Make Another Signal*, HarperCollins/A M Heath;
          Convoy is to Scatter, HarperCollins/A M Heath.
Chalmers, W S, *Full Cycle*, Hodder & Stoughton.
Fremantle, Admiral Sir Sydney, *My Naval Career 1880-1928*, Hutchinson.
Harker, Jack S, *Well Done Leander*, Collins.
Humble, Richard, *Fraser of North Cape*, Routledge.
James, Admiral Sir William, *The Sky was Always Blue*, Methuen.
Keegan, John, *The Price of Admiralty*, Hutchinson.
Kennedy, Ludovic, *On My Way to the Club*, HarperCollins.
Kiely, Dr David, *Naval Electronic Warfare*, Brassey's.
Macintyre, Donald, *Fighting Admiral*, Evans Bros.
Navy Records Society.
Phillips, C E Lucas, *The Greatest Raid of All*, William Heinmann.
Pope, Dudley, *73 North*, William Heinmann.
Popham, Hugh, *A Damned Cunning Fellow*, The Old Ferry Press, Cornwall.
Roskill, Captain S W, *Admiral of the Fleet Earl Beatty*, HarperCollins.
Stephens, Dr Martin, *The Fighting Admirals*, Leo Cooper.
Vian, Admiral of the Fleet, Sir Philip, GCB, KBE, DSO**, *Action This Day*, Frederick Muller.
Woodward, Admiral Sir John, KCB, *One Hundred Days*, HarperCollins.

Other publications which have been consulted and contain useful background material relevant to Signalling and the Communications Branch:

Hezlet, Vice Admiral Sir Arthur, *The Electron and Sea Power*, P Davies.
Hill-Norton, Lord, *Sea Power*, Faber & Faber
Holmes, Tom, *The Semaphore*, Stockwell, Ilfracombe.
Howse, Commander H D, MBE, DSC, *Radar at Sea*, Macmillan.
Mead, Commander H P, *Sea Flags*, Brown, Son & Ferguson, 1938.
Pack, Captain S W C, *The Battle of Matapan*, Batsford, 1961.
Pakenham, Captain W T T, *Naval Command & Control*, Brassey's.
Perrin, W G, *British Flags*, Cambridge University Press, 1922;
          Nelson's Signals, H.M.S.0., 1908.
Roskill, Captain S W, *The Secret Capture*, Collins.
Winton, John, *Ultra at Sea*, Leo Cooper.

Additional sources are annotated in the margin throughout the book.

Illustration Acknowledgements

Beken of Cowes Ltd: 182

The Communicator: 21, 22, 23, 38, 48 (bottom), 71, 100, 123, 124, 125, 126, 133, 140, 144, 162, 163, 166, 170, 178, 181, 202, 204, 208, 218, 219, 273, 293, 306, 311, 318, 320, 325, 328, 340, 348, 351, Plate III (top)

© Crown Copyright 1993/MOD; Reproduced with the permission of the Controller of HMSO: 195, 209, 213, 214, 219, Plate III (centre), Plate VI (top left and bottom), Plate VII, Plate VIII (centre)

Defence Research Agency: 82, 86

Fleet Air Arm Museum: Plate VIII (bottom right)

Imperial War Museum: 26 (Q80194), 73 (Q22656), 97 (HAM25956), 116 (A23440), 132 (A13363T), 151 (A23597), 235 (Q19549), 258 (Q20643), 277 (Q22614), 312 (A14944)

National Maritime Museum: 3, 4, 5, 7, 9 (top and bottom), 17

Navy & Army Illustrated: 11, 48 (top), 240, 343

Private Collections: 20, 34, 45, 70, 75, 79, 81, 84 (top and bottom), 88, 91, 95, 96, 129, 131, 142, 148, 153, 167, 174, 175, 200, 206, 231, 238, 241, 247, 264, 265, 267, 280, 283, 285, 302, 319, 322, 330, 347, PlateIII (bottom), Plate VI (top right), Plate VIII (top left and right, bottom left)

Sotherby's: Plate IV

Royal Australian Navy: 205

Royal Marines Museum: 37

Royal Naval Museum: 60

Submarine Museum: 255

Trustees of the Broadlands Archives: 77

INDEX

Note: Ranks shown are generally those finally held